A History of the

Thermometer

and Its Use in Meteorology

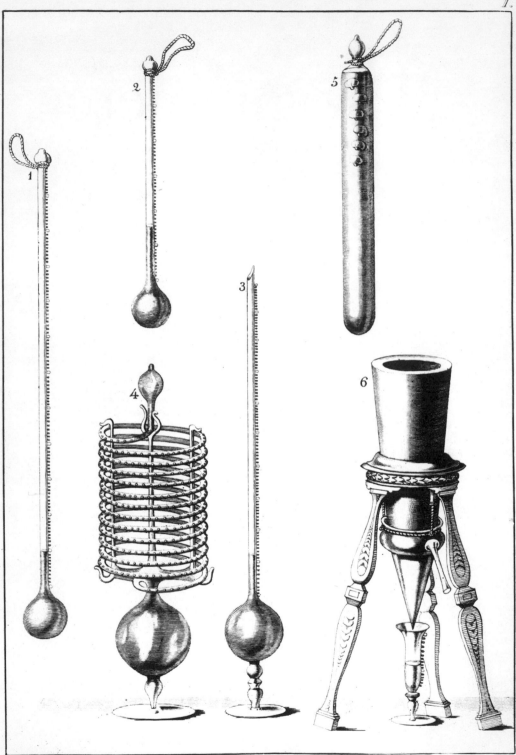

Thermometers and a hygrometer of the **Accademia del Cimento.**

A History of the

Thermometer

and Its Use in Meteorology

by W. E. Knowles Middleton

The Johns Hopkins Press
Baltimore, Maryland

Preface

After finishing *The History of the Barometer,* I began to study with a view to writing a short history of all the ordinary meteorological instruments, but I soon came to the conclusion that the thermometer deserved a book to itself, and this volume is the result.

Readers of the earlier work will find a rather different emphasis in this one. This was necessary, for while the principles underlying the measurement of atmospheric pressure were discovered and accepted in a few decades of the seventeenth century, so that the history of the barometer for the succeeding three centuries is largely a record of technical progress, that of the thermometer is quite different. The instrument itself—at least the liquid-in-glass thermometer, its most important form—is relatively simple and structurally almost invariable. The interest in its history lies mainly in the controversies about its discovery and about the establishment of the various scales of temperature that have been in favor from time to time and in different places. Part of the difficulty of the subject is based on the circumstance that temperature is a concept of a rather special sort, quite different from such concepts as length, mass, and time, so that it was about 1800 before the people interested in thermometers began to see clearly what it was that they were measuring.

The impulse to improve thermometry came largely from the study of the weather. The liquid-in-glass thermometer was the meteorologist's instrument before it was the chemist's or the physicist's, and it held the field during the long search for rational scales. For that reason its history forms the major portion of this book, which is conceived as the history of a *meteorological* instrument. The improved air thermometer has a place because of its great theoretical importance. Electrical thermometers and metallic thermometers are briefly treated, and also the recording instruments in so far as they are of meteorological application.

v

In the final chapter I have dealt with the attempts to find a satisfactory way of exposing thermometers out of doors.

I cannot hope to have said the last word on the controversy about "the invention of the thermometer," or on those that concern the origin of the Fahrenheit and centigrade scales. All that I have done is to read as many of the documents as possible and then make up my mind. Many of the arguments in the literature have distinct national overtones, and I may at least plead that, as no one has ascribed any of these discoveries to a Canadian, nothing that I have written about them can possibly be twisted by a misplaced patriotism. Some attempt at a serious study of these problems is overdue. Even in the last few years "historical" articles have been published in some technical journals, repeating old textbook errors and adding new statements that will not bear confrontation with the primary sources.

Readers familiar with *The History of the Barometer* may be disappointed at the comparative paucity of references to museums in this book. I have looked at the thermometers in almost all the museums mentioned in the earlier work, and a few more; these contain far more thermometers than barometers; but most of these specimens differ only in ways of little importance, and I have mentioned only those of unusual interest. The patent literature is also much less illuminating than in the study of the barometer, except of course in connection with the elaborate devices used in modern industry to measure temperature, the adequate history of which would demand another book at least as large as this one. No attempt has been made to deal with them. I have also left medical thermometry to the historians of medicine.

Primary sources have been used as far as possible in writing this book. In transcribing from printed works I have followed my custom of neglecting the meaningless capitals and italics affected by printers in past centuries, while preserving the spelling. Manuscripts have been copied as exactly as possible. Translations from other languages are my own, unless otherwise noted.

References in text and footnotes to a number of museums, libraries, and national meteorological services will, I trust, be interpreted by the directors and staff of these institutions as an expression of my thanks for their unfailing kindness. I have tried to acknowledge numerous special favors in footnotes.

I am also much obliged to Mr. J. A. Chaldecott of the Science Museum, London, for reading the draft of Chapter 4, and to Mr. Nicholas Goodison and Mr. Stephen K. Marshall for looking critically at some passages translated from the Latin. I wish to thank the Director of the Biblioteca Nazionale at Florence, the

Trustees of the British Museum, the Council of the Royal Society, and the Académie des Sciences for permission to reproduce passages from manuscripts in their archives. Credits for certain illustrations are given in their captions.

Most of the research that had to be conducted on the Continent of Europe was made possible by a grant from the Leverhulme Trustees, which is gratefully acknowledged.

No words can express my obligation to my wife, who not only typed the entire manuscript twice but has assisted with proofs and index and given me infinite encouragement.

Finally I wish to thank the officers and staff of The Johns Hopkins Press for their habitual expertness and courtesy.

London, 1966

Table of Contents

List of Figures

xi

A History of the

Thermometer

and Its Use in Meteorology

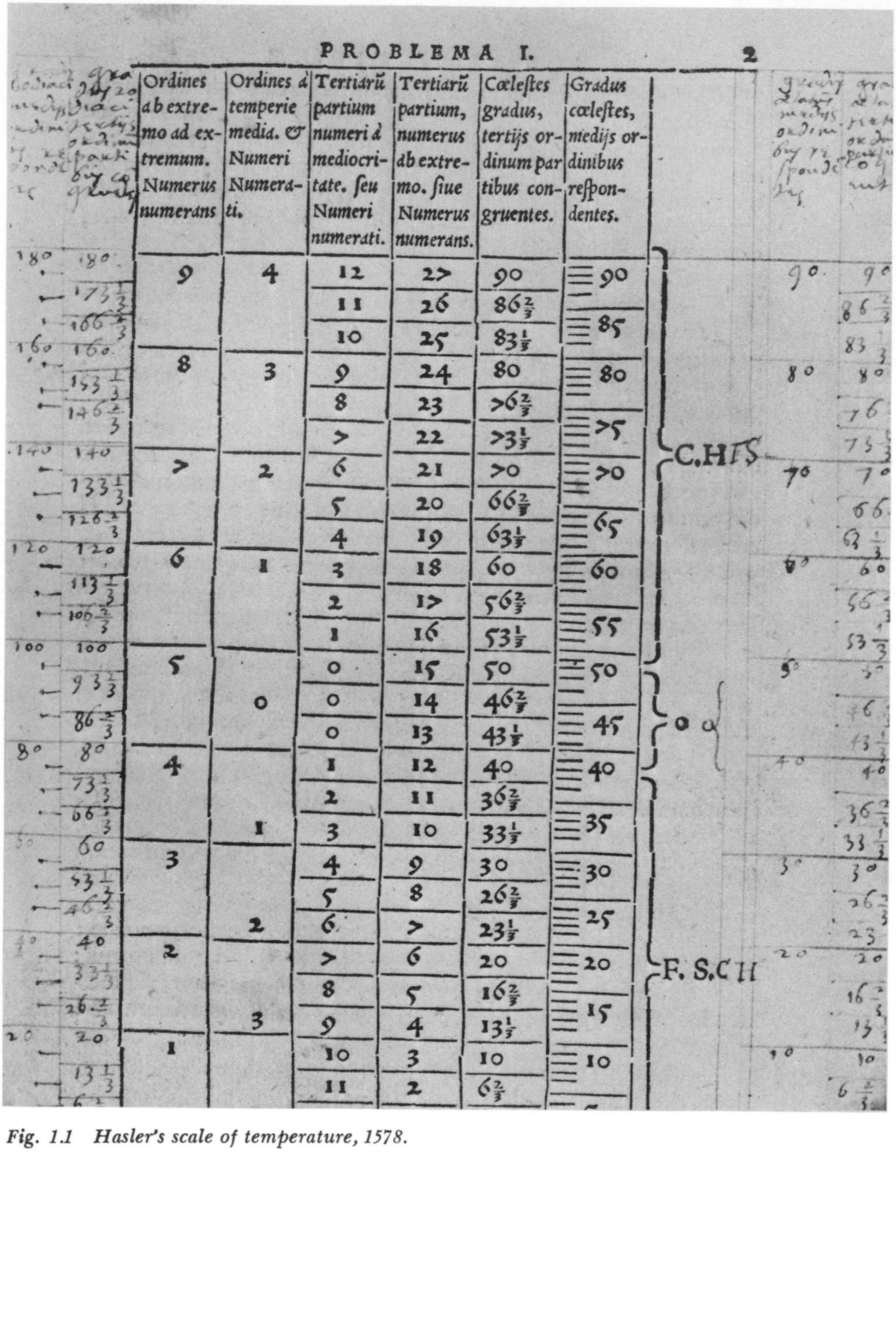

Ordines ab extremo ad extremum. Numerus numerans.	Ordines à temperie media. & Numeri Numerati.	Tertiarū partium numeri d mediocritate. seu Numeri numerati.	Tertiarū partium, numerus ab extremo. siue Numerus numerans.	Cœlestes gradus, tertijs ordinum partibus congruentes.	Gradus cœlestes, medijs ordinibus respondentes.
9	4	12	27	90	90
		11	26	$86\frac{2}{3}$	
		10	25	$83\frac{1}{3}$	85
8	3	9	24	80	80
		8	23	$76\frac{2}{3}$	
		7	22	$73\frac{1}{3}$	75
7	2	6	21	70	70
		5	20	$66\frac{2}{3}$	
		4	19	$63\frac{1}{3}$	65
6	1	3	18	60	60
		2	17	$56\frac{2}{3}$	
		1	16	$53\frac{1}{3}$	55
5		0	15	50	50
	0	0	14	$46\frac{2}{3}$	
		0	13	$43\frac{1}{3}$	45
4		1	12	40	40
		2	11	$36\frac{2}{3}$	
	1	3	10	$33\frac{1}{3}$	35
3		4	9	30	30
		5	8	$26\frac{2}{3}$	
	2	6	7	$23\frac{1}{3}$	25
2		7	6	20	20
		8	5	$16\frac{2}{3}$	
	3	9	4	$13\frac{1}{3}$	15
1		10	3	10	10
		11	2	$6\frac{2}{3}$	

Fig. 1.1   *Hasler's scale of temperature, 1578.*

I

Air Thermoscope and Air Thermometer

1. Introduction. The opposition of "hot" and "cold," like that of "dry" and "moist," is an inevitable by-product of our sense of touch. These antitheses, noted by the pre-Socratic philosophers of Greek antiquity, were used by Aristotle in the formation of his doctrine of opposites, while from their combinations the four elements—earth, water, air, and fire—were built up.[1] In doing this, Aristotle made no attempt to assign numbers to these qualities. The great physician Galen seems to have introduced the idea of "degrees of heat and cold," four in number each way from a neutral point in the middle. The neutral point was to be a mixture of equal quantities of ice and boiling water, substances that Galen seems to have thought of as the hottest and coldest of materials. Whether the quantities were weights or volumes is not certain, and we may wonder whether Galen ever made such an experiment;[2] but it is the earliest notion of a fixed point or standard of temperature.

Strange as it may seem, the idea of a scale of temperature was familiar to physicians before they had any instrument to measure it with. This is illustrated by the *De logistica medica* of Johannis Hasler of Berne. Hasler's very first "Problem" is entitled "To find the natural degree of temperature of each man, as determined by his age, the time of year, the elevation of the pole [i.e., the latitude] and other influences."[3] It was believed that the body temperature of dwellers in the tropics was higher than those living in higher latitudes. Hasler showed this supposed relationship by an elaborate table[4] (Fig. 1.1), in which the nine degrees

[1] Cf. S. Sambursky, *The Physical World of the Greeks* (London, 1956; paperback edition, London, 1963), p. 91.

[2] See F. Sherwood Taylor, *Ann. Sci.*, Vol. 5 (1942), p. 129. Note that equal weights (with the ice at its melting point) would result in a temperature of about 10°C.

[3] Hasler, *De logistica medica* (Augustae, 1578), fol. B1r.

[4] *Ibid.*, fol. B2r.

of heat in the first column and the Galenic degrees of heat and cold in the second (divided into three parts in the fourth and third columns respectively) are set opposite the latitude. From this table the physician could read the normal degree of heat or cold to be expected in an inhabitant of any place and thus decide how to mix his medicines.

This was the medical scale. There was also a "philosophical scale" with eight degrees of heat and eight of cold. As we shall see, the first thermometer of which we have a description and illustration has a scale of "degrees of cold" that goes from one to eight.[5]

Questions of priority are loaded with embarrassment for the historian of science and technology, even if they are of great interest to the general reader. The thermometer provides a particularly acute example, at least partly because more than a piece of apparatus is involved. Its "invention" cannot be considered apart from its use and calibration. According to the point of view adopted in this chapter a distinction must be made between the terms *thermoscope* and *thermometer,* in which a thermometer is simply a thermoscope provided with a scale. This may seem too elementary to be worth notice; but if it had been kept in mind, many gallons of ink might have been saved in the attempt to establish when, where, and by whom "the thermometer was invented." I propose to regard it as axiomatic that a "meter" must have a scale or something equivalent. If this is admitted, the problem of the invention of the thermometer becomes more straightforward; that of the invention of the thermoscope remains as obscure as ever.

As to the thermoscope, a further preliminary question must be answered: when does a pneumatic experiment, of whatever sort, become a thermoscope? I take it as essential that the experimenter should have had clearly in view the construction of an instrument intended to give some visible indication of changes in its condition with respect to heat.[6] It is not enough that the behavior of some instrument should be *interpretable* in this way.

Pneumatic experiments that could form the basis of a thermoscope were made in antiquity by Philo of Byzantium, who probably flourished about the end of the second century B.C.,[7] and also by Hero of Alexandria, possibly in the first half of the first

[5] See p. 12 below.

[6] This circumlocution is gathered together in the German compound *Wärmezustand.* See E. Mach, *Die Prinzipien der Wärmelehre* (Leipzig, 1896), p. 39, and *passim.*

[7] George Sarton, *Introduction to the History of Science* (3 vols. in 5; Washington, 1927–48), I, 195, puts a question mark after this statement.

century B.C., but perhaps much later.[8] Philo's work, lost in the original Greek, remained in Latin and Arabic manuscripts, unpublished, until the end of the nineteenth century.[9] Hero's *Pneumatics* fared better, having been published in Latin in 1575,[10] in an Italian translation in 1589,[11] and again in Italian in 1592,[12] the year in which Galileo took up his post at Padua. Hero's work was studied a great deal in Italy toward the end of the sixteenth century, as Hellmann has found.[13] Galileo is known to have read it by 1594.[14] Meanwhile Giambattista della Porta had read about Hero's experiment, of a "fountain that drips in the sun," and described an apparatus that could have been used as an air thermoscope but was in fact intended only to show that water could be raised by the action of heat.[15] Even in 1606 it is plain that a similar experiment described by Della Porta merely shows the expansion of air by heat and its contraction by cold, but that he had no idea of making a measuring instrument.[16] Like many others, he was repeating some of Hero's experiments, with variations.

The serious candidates for the honor of having "invented the thermometer" are usually considered to be four in number: Galileo, Santorio (or Sanctorius), Drebbel, and Fludd. The first two lived in Italy, the other two lived north of the Alps. As interaction across the Alps is very unlikely in this case, we may profitably consider the two pairs separately.

2. *Galileo and Santorio*. Like the British idolators of Newton, the Italian partisans of Galileo have done their best to magnify the achievements of their hero, often with scant regard for historical method, or

[8] *Ibid.*, p. 202.

[9] Albert de Rochas, *La science des philosophes et l'art des thaumaturges dans l'antiquité* (Paris, 1882), in which Philo's *Pneumatics* is translated into French on pp. 205–18.

[10] *Hieronis Alexandrini spiritalium liber. A Federico Commandino Urbinate, ex graeco nuper in latinum conversus* [etc.] (Urbino, 1575).

[11] *Gli artificiosi et curiosi moti spiritali, tradotti da Gio. Battista Aleotti* [etc.] (Ferrara, 1589). Bennet Woodcroft, in *Hero of Alexandria. Pneumatics,* trans. J. G. Greenwood (London, 1851), p. xii, gives the date as 1547. It is probable that Woodcroft confused this with an edition of Aleotti's translation printed in Bologna in 1647.

[12] *Spiritali di Herone Alessandrino, ridotti in lingua volgare da Alessandro Giorgi* [etc.] (Urbino, 1592).

[13] Gustav Hellmann, "Beiträge zur Erfindungsgeschichte meteorologischer Instrumente," *Abh. preuss. Akad. Wiss., phys.-math. Kl.* (1920), pp. 1–60.

[14] *Ibid.*, p. 7.

[15] Della Porta, *Magia naturalis libri XX* (Naples, 1589), p. 289. "Possumus etiam solo calore aquam ascendere facere."

[16] Della Porta, *I tre libri de spiritali* (Naples, 1606), pp. 76–77.

even for probability. It may now, I think, be maintained categorically that Santorio applied a measuring device to the air thermoscope, at least as early as 1612, thus making an air thermometer; although he was not the only one to have done this, as we shall see. Whether he or Galileo, or someone else, first made an air thermoscope is much less clear. I suspect that if the great name of Galileo were not involved it would not really be of much importance, in view of the very small utility of the thermoscope.

Three pieces of documentary evidence are usually cited in support of Galileo's claim to the invention. The first consists of a series of letters from Giovanfrancesco Sagredo to Galileo in the period June, 1612, to April, 1615. The second is a letter from Benedetto Castelli to Ferdinando Cesarini, written in 1638. The third is Vincenzio Viviani's biography of Galileo, written in 1654.

On June 30, 1612, Sagredo wrote a letter to Galileo in which the following passage occurs:

Signor Mula . . . told me about an instrument of Santorio's, with with which cold and heat were measured by means of compasses;[17] and finally let me know that this is a large glass bulb[18] with a long neck. I immediately devoted myself to making some very fine and elegant ones.[19]

Sagredo was apparently much taken with this new invention, for he goes on:

I make the ordinary ones at a cost of four lire each, for a wine glass with a foot, a small ampoule, and a glass tube; and I work so fast that in an hour I finish as many as ten of them. The finest that I have made was worked at the lamp, and it is in all its parts as in the enclosed scale drawing.[20]

It may be supposed that the ordinary ones were assembled with mastic and perhaps a cork, in view of the reference to glass blowing in the description of the finest one.

Galileo's reply to this has not been preserved, but within the next few months Sagredo had been told that this was an invention made by the great philosopher, for on May 9, 1613, we find him writing again:[21]

The instrument for measuring heat, invented by your excellent self, has been reduced by me to various very elegant and convenient

17 See below, p. 9.
18 *Una gran bozza di vetro;* literally a swelling.
19 *Le opere di Galileo Galilei,* ediz. naz. (20 vols.; Florence, 1890–1909), XI, 350–51.
20 The drawing has not survived.
21 *Ibid.,* p. 506.

forms,[22] so that the difference in temperature between one room and another is seen to be as much as 100 degrees. With these I have found various marvellous things, as, for example, that in winter the air may be colder than ice or snow; that the water just now appears colder than the air; that small bodies of water are colder than large ones, and similar subtle matters.

He goes on to say that the Aristotelian philosopher Bernardino Gaio cannot understand how it works, thinking that the "attractive virtue" of heat should make the liquid rise farther in the tube when the bulb is hotter.

By July 27 of the same year the really hot weather had arrived, and Sagredo wrote a charming letter that deserves a special place in the history of meteorology, because of the following paragraph:

With the arrival of your most precious wine, and with this heat, my meditation is about measuring the aforesaid heat and cooling the wine. The measurement of the heat is already reduced almost to perfection, and I have made records of it for the last 15 days; I shall send a copy of these by the next post, not having had time to copy them. I have also found a funnel that quickly cools wine when it is passed through it. . . .[23]

These records must be by far the earliest systematic records of temperature. Like all Sagredo's letters that I have read, it shows him as a man of great charm, and one can believe the editors of Galileo's works when they say that Sagredo "was Galileo's dearest friend."[24] He certainly was one of the most fervent admirers of the great man. Apart from these letters we know little about him except that he held various diplomatic and other posts in the Venetian government service. In his spare time he was a devotee of the new science.

On February 7, 1615, Sagredo returned to the subject again, finding that well water is actually colder in winter than in summer, "though our senses judge differently."[25]

On March 15 the thermometer appears again:

I have been making additions and changes every day to the instrument for measuring temperatures, so that if I were able to discuss it with you by word of mouth, in your presence, I could, beginning *ab ovo*, easily recount to you the whole story of my inventions, or more correctly my improvements. But because, as you wrote to me and as I certainly believe, you were the first author and inventor [of it], I am therefore sure that the instruments you made with your exquisite skill very greatly surpass mine. . . .[26]

[22] Sagredo had the co-operation of the glassworks at Murano, near Venice, as appears, e.g., in *Le opere,* XII, 168.

[23] *Ibid.,* XI, 545.

[24] *Ibid.,* XX, 528.

[25] *Ibid.,* XII, 139.

[26] *Ibid.,* p. 157. This shows that Galileo had actually claimed the invention.

It would be interesting to know what Galileo had written to inspire this self-negation. The mystery is not lessened by a later passage in the same letter:

> The man who supposes himself the inventor of these instruments is not very able, indeed entirely unfit to instruct me according to my wish and desire, for I have striven vainly to make him understand the cause of the effects that seem composite and multiple in some of my instruments (if I may so call them).[27]

If we are to assume that this sentence refers to Santorio, it is very hard not to believe that Sagredo was not simply trying to flatter Galileo.

Let us now consider Castelli's letter, written on September 20, 1638, to Mgr. Ferdinando Cesarini. "I remember," he writes,

> an experiment shown me by our Signor Galileo more than thirty-five years ago.[28] He took a small glass flask, about as large as a small hen's egg, with a neck about two spans long and as fine as a wheat straw, and warmed the flask well in his hands, then turned its mouth upside down into a vessel placed underneath, in which there was a little water. When he took away the heat of his hands from the flask, the water at once began to rise in the neck, and mounted to more than a span above the level of the water in the vessel. The same Sig. Galileo had then made use of this effect in order to construct an instrument for examining the degrees of heat and cold.[29]

There follows a long discussion of the phenomenon.

Finally, there is Viviani, whose biography of his great teacher is infinitely laudatory. Writing about the events of Galileo's early days at Padua, that is to say between 1592 and about 1597, Viviani asserts that, "In these same years[30] he discovered thermometers, that is to say those instruments of glass, with water and air, for discerning the changes of heat and cold, and the changeableness of the temperature of places. . . ."[31]

We must now turn to Santorio Santorre, often called Sanctorius. Born in 1561 at Capodistria, he studied medicine at Padua and after practicing at Padua, in Poland, and elsewhere, he went to Venice in 1601. He was elected Professor of Medicine at Padua on October 6, 1611, the year after Galileo left that famous university for Florence. He died at Venice in 1636. He is famous as the first to apply the quantitative methods of physi-

---

[27] *Ibid.*
[28] *Già più di trentacinque anni sono.* Taylor, *Ann. Sci.,* Vol. 5 (1942), p. 142, translates this as "about thirty-five years ago"—a very different matter. Hoppe, *Geschicte der Physik* (Brunswick, 1926), p. 172, interprets it as "vor 35 Jahren, also 1603."
[29] Galileo, *Le Opere,* XVII, 377.
[30] *In questi medesimi tempi.*
[31] *Le opere,* XIX, 607.

cal science systematically to medicine, and his interest in the air thermometer grew out of his clinical and physiological studies. Fortunately, Santorio's work on the thermometer is much better documented than that of Galileo. Apart from the reference in Sagredo's letter of June 30, 1612, mentioned above, Santorio himself published a reference to it in the same year. This is in the *Commentaria in artem medicinalem Galeni,* Part III:[32]

> I wish to tell you about a marvellous way in which I am accustomed to measure, with a certain glass instrument, the cold and hot temperature of the air of all regions and places, and of all parts of the body; and so exactly, that we can measure with the compass the degrees and ultimate limits of heat and cold at any time of day. It is in our house at Padua and we show it very freely to all. We promise that a book about medical instruments that are not well known will shortly appear, in which we shall give an illustration of this instrument and describe its construction and uses.[33]

Later on he makes an interesting addition which makes it even clearer that his thermometer was a meteorological as well as a medical instrument:

> the temperature of the air can be observed not only in so far as it belongs to the body, but also as a thing in itself; so that the mean between very hot and cold temperatures of the air can be exactly perceived. For we have an instrument with which not only the heat and cold of the air is measured, but all the degrees of heat and cold of all the parts of the body, as we show to our students at Padua, teaching them its uses; and they have heard about this novelty with no little astonishment.[34]

A new edition of the *Commentaries on Galen* was published in Venice in 1630, which differs somewhat from the 1612 edition. For my present purpose it is important to note one or two differences. In Part II we find an added paragraph, as follows:

> By means of the glass instrument with which we observe temperaments,[35] we learn the extremes and the mean thus: we apply snow to the sphere of the glass instrument so that the water may ascend to its upper limit. Then with the flame of a candle we make the water descend as far as it will go. Knowing the extremes we shall at once find the mean and temperate, and it will be easy to determine how far any part [of the body?] departs from this.[36]

---

[32] (Venice, 1612). Part III of this book, which has a separate title page, is very rare. I am obliged to Dr. John B. Blake of the National Library of Medicine, Bethesda, Maryland, for photocopies of the relevant passages.

[33] *Ibid.,* col. 62 (Cap. LXXXV, Particula X).

[34] *Ibid.,* col. 105 (Cap. LXXXVI, Particula III).

[35] *Temperamenta.* Sanctorius generally wrote of *temperaturae* in writing about his instrument.

[36] Sanctorius, *Commentaria in artem medicinalem Galeni* (Venice, 1630), col. 762.

On the evidence of this passage, but incorrectly supposing that it is in the first edition, Dorsey has claimed for Santorio that he was the first to attempt to define a scale of temperature by means of two fixed points,[37] even if the upper one would not be very well fixed. In point of fact the honor seems to belong to Sagredo, who tried an experiment of this kind in 1615. Near the end of his letter of February 7, 1615, to Galileo, Sagredo wrote:

> two days ago it snowed. Here in the room my instrument showed 130 degrees of heat more than there was two years ago at the time of the very rigorous and extraordinary cold; which instrument, immersed and buried in snow, showed 30 degrees fewer, that is to say only 100. But then, immersed in snow mixed with salt, it showed another 100 fewer; and I believe that it might have showed fewer still, but this could not be seen for lack of snow and salt. Thus, as the instrument had gone up to 360 degrees in the greatest heat of summer, it appears that salt combined with snow increases the cold by as much as amounts to a third of the difference between the excessive heat of summer and the excessive cold of winter—a thing so wonderful, that I can provide no credible reason for it.[38]

If we might take the extreme summer and winter temperatures at Venice in those years to be about 34°C. and −5°C., this would bring his mixture of ice and salt to −18°C., a very likely value.

While Sagredo's lower fixed point was not much more stable than Santorio's upper one, it is evident that he did a great deal of experimenting with these air thermometers. In 1615 he made one using a short column of liquid as an indicator and noted that it works better if the tube is bent twice so that most of the tube is horizontal.[39]

From the reference to the compass it would appear that in 1612 Santorio's instrument did not have a scale.[40] This is confirmed by the first published figure of a thermoscope (Fig. 1.2), contained in the *Sphaera mundi* of Giuseppe Biancani, apparently written by 1617.[41] Biancani describes the instrument, noting that the water was colored in order to make it visible enough, and explains its action. He goes on:

[37] N. Ernest Dorsey, *J. Washington Acad. Sci.*, Vol. 36 (1946), p. 364, Table I. M. D. Grmek, *L'introduction de l'expérience quantitative dans les sciences biologiques* (Paris, Palais de la Découverte, 1962), p. 23, makes the same assertion.

[38] In Galileo, *Le Opere*, XII, 140.

[39] Sagredo, letter to Galileo, April 11, 1615, in Galileo, *Le Opere*, XII, 168.

[40] Did Sagredo's instruments have scales? From the large numbers of "degrees" (gradi) to which he refers, it seems likely.

[41] Biancani [Blancanus], *Sphaera mundi, seu cosmographia demonstrativa* [etc.] (Bologna, 1620), p. 111. The dedication to P. F. Malaspina ends "Vale Parmae Idibus Febr. M.DC.XVII" (Feb. 13, 1617).

Fig. 1.2 The first published figure of a thermoscope.

Fig. 1.3 *The first known drawing of a ther-mometer, 1611.* (Courtesy of the Bibliothèque de l'Arsenal [Paris].)

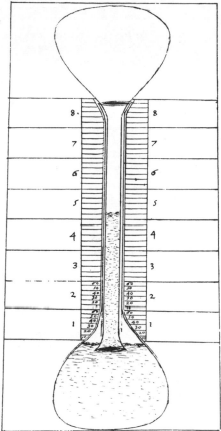

With the help of this instrument, which I might well call the thermo-scope (*thermoscopium*), many things may be found out about the nature of the air. I have heard that the inventor of this is a certain Doctor of Medicine called Santorius, who lives at Padua.

As far as I know, this is the first appearance of the word "ther-moscope."

But an air thermometer with a scale is described and figured, though not very clearly, in an unpublished manuscript bearing the date 1611. This manuscript[42] has been comprehensively dealt with, as far as the thermometer is concerned, by J. A. Chalde-cott,[43] whose paper I have used.

The figure of the thermometer in the manuscript by Telioux is reproduced in Fig. 1.3. It is quite clear from the accompanying text that Telioux did not understand how the instrument worked.

[42] Paris, Bibliothèque de l'Arsenal, ms. 8525, *Mathematica maravigliosa* [etc.], by Bartolomeo Telioux. The date 1611 is clearly lettered on the elabo-rate title page.
[43] Chaldecott, *Ann. Sci.,* Vol. 8 (1952), pp. 195–201.

11

Take two flasks with necks at least a foot in length, one flask being slightly larger to enable them to be inserted one into the other. Then fill the larger until a quarter of its volume remains empty, and insert the smaller into it until the opening of the neck is far enough into the water so that it cannot take in air. I might explain that the water will rise or fall according to how hot or cold it is. Because, heat causing expansion, the water needs more room and thus, confined by the narrowness of the neck, rises. Then when the cold comes, the expanded water condenses and, desiring less room, descends. The various changes are estimated by means of the degrees and minutes placed at the side for that purpose.[44]

There are two difficulties about this description considered together with the figure. The first is that if the smaller flask had had a flared mouth as shown, the apparatus could not have been assembled. But this is a minor matter; the important thing is that the action of the instrument is quite wrongly described by Telioux. This discrepancy between the figure and the text led the historian G. Libri to state that Telioux was the first to make a sealed thermometer, free from the influence of atmospheric pressure.[45] Telioux nowhere states that the instrument is sealed and rather makes a point of the immersion of the end of the neck of the inverted flask into the water. Nor would anyone intending to make a thermometer with a liquid as the thermometric substance have left a quarter of the lower flask empty. Finally, if the expansion of the water had been used, and the proportions of the instrument had been anything like those shown in the figure, the total motion of the liquid with meteorological temperature changes would have been scarcely perceptible. We can conclude, with Chaldecott, only that "Telioux was setting down something that he had heard about, but did not fully understand."[46]

At any rate, there was a thermometer—a thermoscope with a scale—in 1611. The scale, as will be seen from the figure, has eight "degrees," each divided into "minutes," numbered 10, 20, 30, 40, 50, and 60, as might well seem obligatory to an engineer.[47] If we are to believe the drawing, these are "degrees of cold," the highest temperature being at zero. If Telioux's explanation could be right, they would of course be degrees of heat.

Apart from its early date, the instrument is of special interest

[44] Telioux, *Mathematica*, pp. 44–45.

[45] G. Libri, *Histoire des sciences mathématiques en Italie, depuis la renaissance des lettres jusqu'à la fin du XVII siècle* (4 Vols.; Paris, 1838–41), Vol. 4, pp. 471–72.

[46] Chaldecott, *Ann. Sci.*, Vol. 8 (1952), p. 200.

[47] Libri, *Histoire des sciences*, calls Telioux "un ingénieur romain," with what justification I do not know.

D

O

because of the fact that the manuscript is dated from **Rome**, a city with which none of the candidates for the honor of having invented the thermoscope or the thermometer are especially associated. It seems strange, if either Santorio or Galileo is the inventor, that the instrument should have been known in Rome before it was known in Padua or Venice.

Santorio took a long time to redeem his promise to describe his instrument; thirteen years, in fact.[48] For good measure, he then described several, some of which are shown in Figs. 1.4 and 1.5. The first of these (Fig. 1.4)[49] still has no scale but has two threads tied around the stem, presumably to be shifted to mark a change in temperature, which would then be measured with the compasses, as before. We are told that for clinical purposes the rate of change of the temperature was measured by observing the change in the reading during ten beats of a small pendulum, called a *pulsilogium,* after the thermometer had been put in the patient's mouth, or into his hand. As the peripheral circulation is much more rapid in fever, this apparently strange method was probably excellent.

Later in the book other types of thermometer are illustrated (Fig. 1.5);[50] these have scales. While they are of various shapes, they all have a bulb at the top, and a tube dipping into an open vessel.

It is noteworthy that Santorio says that the instrument is derived from "a vessel proposed by Hero for another purpose,"[51] and the question thereby arises whether his original invention was inspired by Hero's "sun fountain," as seems to be generally conceded, or was quite independent. Apart from the very slight resemblance between Hero's apparatus and his, I think that a comparison of the 1612 and 1630 editions of the *Commentaries on Galen* throws some light on the matter. Let us compare the last sentence of the passage quoted above from column 62 of the 1612 edition[52] with the corresponding passage from the later one: "We promise that a book about medical instruments will shortly appear, in which we shall give an illustration of *this very*

[48] *Sanctorii Sanctorii Iustinopolitani . . . commentaria in primam fen primi libri canonis Avicennae* [etc.] (Venice, 1625). There was a second edition in 1626, apparently identical except for the title page and the provision of an index. Both are in the Bibliothèque Nationale, Paris.

[49] *Ibid.,* col. 22.

[50] *Ibid.,* col. 220.

[51] *Ibid.,* col. 23.

[52] See p. 9 above. The Latin reads: "Nos pollicemur vel breui in lucem daturos, librum de instrumentis medicis non amplius visis, in quo iconem, constructionem, & usus huius instrumenti proponemus."

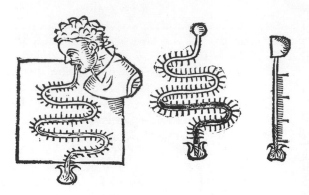

old instrument and describe its construction and uses."[53] The phrase that I have italicized is absent from the 1612 edition. It seems probable that at some time between 1612 and 1625 (when he published his commentaries on Avicenna) Santorio had had Hero's book pointed out to him, and, not wishing to claim more than his due, mentioned Hero. Or indeed the *Spiritalium liber* may have remained in his unconscious since his student days at Padua. It is of course taken for granted by the partisans of Galileo that Santorio saw him demonstrate a thermoscope at Padua; but on the other hand there is no reason why Santorio could not have shown the experiment to Galileo, who was three years his junior. Whatever may be the source of his inspiration, Santorio not only invented a thermometer but made good use of it.

3. *Fludd and Drebbel.* Let us now cross the Alps. After considering the two famous Italians, innovators in their respective fields of science, we have now to do with a Welsh Rosicrucian mystic and a Dutch inventor of mechanical devices.

Robert Fludd, or Flud, was of Welsh origin. Born in 1574, he took a medical degree at Oxford in 1605 after having traveled on the Continent for several years around the turn of the century. For the rest of his life he practiced medicine in London, at least when he was not engaged in writing strange and elaborate books in support of his peculiar view of the universe. If any brief statement of his position could be useful at all, it might be said that he thought that all true science is rooted in revelation.

[53] *Commentaria in artem medicinalem Galeni* (Venice, 1630), col. 1152. "Nos pollicemur vel breui in lucem daturos librum de instrumentis medicis in quo iconem, constructionem, & usus huius instrumenti antiquissimi proponemus."

14

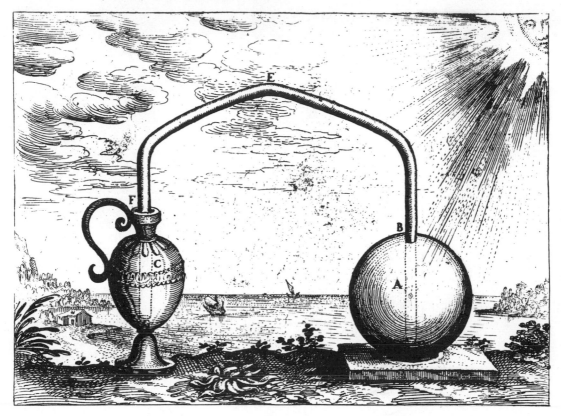

Certainly he took no part in the scientific revolution of the
seventeenth century, which would not have interested him in
the least.[54]

Fludd's claim to have invented the air thermometer was
brilliantly examined by Sherwood Taylor in the paper to which
I have already referred.[55] In the first place, Taylor shows the
textual parallelism between a passage in Fludd's *Utriusque cosmi
historia* (Oppenheim, 1617, p. 30) and a passage in the *De ingeniis
spiritalibus* of Philo of Byzantium.[56] He also showed that Fludd
almost certainly had access to a twelfth- or thirteenth-century
manuscript of Philo's work, now in the Bodleian Library (ms.
Digby 40). The parallelism extends to the figure (1.6) in Fludd's
book, obviously an elaboration of the rough sketch in the manuscript in question. As Taylor points out, Fludd at this time had

[54] For a sympathetic biography, see J. B. Craven, *Doctor Robert Fludd . . .
Life and Writings* (Kirkwall, 1902).

[55] *Ann. Sci.*, Vol. 5 (1942), pp. 129–56.

[56] This parallelism was pointed out by G. Hellman in 1920. See *Abh.
Preuss. Akad. Wiss., phys.-math. Klasse* (1920), p. 8.

15

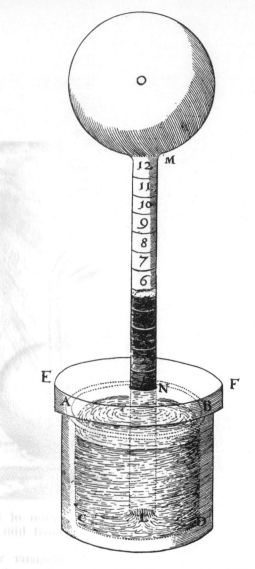

Fig. 1.7 *Fludd's air thermometer, 1626.* (Courtesy of the Wellcome Trustees.)

no idea that he was describing an instrument for measuring temperature.[57] But in his *Meteorologica Cosmica* (Frankfurt, 1626, p. 287) we have the instrument shown in Fig. 1.7, clearly an air thermometer. He also reproduces the earlier figure and discusses it in such a way that he appears to be claiming the invention of the later instrument, or at any rate its development from the earlier one. In a still later book (*Philosophica Moysaica* [Gouda, 1638], fol. 1ᵛ–2ʳ) he shows the two forms together (Fig. 1.8) and discusses the instrument in the following passage:

[57] See Taylor, *Ann. Sci.*, Vol. 5 (1942), p. 147, where he translates a long passage to show that Fludd was interested merely in supporting his cosmic theory.

16

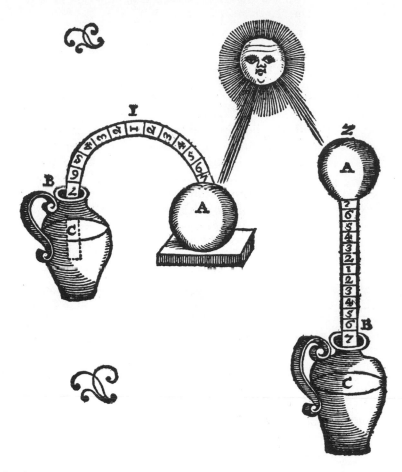

the instrument, commonly termed the Calender, or Weather-Glasse, hath many counterfeit masters or patrons, in this our age, who, because that they have a little altered the shape of the modell, do vainly glory and give out, that it is a master-piece of their own finding out. As for my self, I must acknowledge, and willingly ascribe unto each man his due, and therefore will not blush or be ashamed, to attribute justly my philosophical principles unto my master Moses, who also received them, figured or framed out by the finger of God; neither can I rightly arrogate, or assume unto my self, the primary fabrick of this instrument, although I have made use of it in my Naturall History of the great World, and elsewhere (but in another form), to demonstrate the verity of my philosophicall argument; for I confesse, that I found it graphically specified, and geometrically delineated, in a manuscript of five hundred years antiquity at the least. I will therefore set down unto you first, the shape, in which I found it in that antient monument, *and afterwards made use of it for demonstration's cause:* And secondly, I will describe the figure and position of, as it is commonly known and used among us.

17

Where you see, that there is no difference betwixt them, but onely in their forms or shapes. . . .[58]

In interpreting this passage it must be made clear that the air thermometer, "weather glass," or *vitrum calendarium* was a common and well-known instrument in England by 1638, and indeed in 1620 Francis Bacon had given lucid directions for its construction.[59] In 1634 a scarcely literate artisan called John Bate described and illustrated various shapes of "weather glass," with detailed instructions for making them so that the water either ascends or descends with heat, as desired.[60] One gets the impression that by this time the "weather glass" was an article of commerce; and in the preface (fol. Al, recto) Bate says that the work "hath lien by mee a long time penned."

There is, in fact, further evidence that the principle and the possibility of making such an instrument were known north of the Alps by 1615. Salomon de Caus, "Engineer and Architect to the Elector Palatine," is not usually numbered among the inventors of the thermometer, but in that year such an instrument was described and illustrated in his book about machines.[61] The title of his "problem XII" is "To make a machine that will move by itself," but in the text he states clearly that he knows that perpetual motion in the usual sense is impossible; he means only to imply that this machine is always being moved by changes in the "four elements" of which it is composed. It had a copper tank, cubical and about 1½ feet on a side, entirely closed except for a tube soldered into a hole in the top and descending nearly to the bottom, dipping into water that partly filled the tank. The expansion and contraction of the air in the tank would vary the level of the water in the tube, in which floated a hollow copper ball attached to a cord going over a pulley to a counterweight. On the shaft of the pulley was a hand moving over an ordinary clock face numbered from I to XII. The mechanism, in fact, was exactly like that of the well-known wheel barometer devised by Hooke half a century later.

He knew he was making (or describing) a thermometer, for he says:

[58] From the translation published as *Mosaicall Philosophy* (London, 1659), p. 3. The phrase that I have italicized does not seem to be represented in the original Latin.

[59] *Novum Organum*, Book II, Aphorism XIII, para. 38.

[60] [John Bate], *The Mysteryes of Nature and Art: Conteined in Foure Severall Treatises . . . by J. B.* (London, 1634). I am indebted to Mr. D. Chilton for this reference.

[61] De Caus, *Les raisons des forces mouvantes* [etc.] (Frankfurt, 1615), pp. 18–19. I have to thank Dr. A. G. Keller for this reference.

As to the use of the said machine, it may be used to mark the coldest or hottest days; for if the said machine is in some part of the room that the sun never shines on, the copper ball will rise according to the temperature of the day.[62]

Reading the passage from Fludd in the light of all this, can we interpret it as a claim to have invented the air thermometer? I do not think so. He acknowledges his debt to the old manuscript, whose age he overestimates. Then he says that the weather glass "commonly known and used among us" is really the old instrument in another form. What he is objecting to is that anyone should claim to have invented it just because they have altered its shape.

Whatever may be the truth of this interpretation, it is worth noticing that in the figure dating from 1626 the scale runs from bottom to top, so that the numbers are "degrees of cold"; but in the later figure the numbers increase both ways from the digit 1 in the middle of the tube.[63]

We now come to the claims of Cornelius Drebbel, born in 1572 at Alkmaar in Holland, in "a family of good position." Trained as an engraver, he turned to mechanical invention and in 1598 took out a patent for a "watch or time-piece, which may be used for fifty, sixty, yea, one hundred years without being wound up or having anything done to it, as long as the wheels and other works are not worn out."[64] In, or about, 1604 he came to England and so greatly impressed James I that the king gave him an annuity and, apparently, lodgings in Eltham Palace. Here he made the "perpetual motion machine" described and figured by Thomas Tymme in 1612.[65] Tymme gives a full-page woodcut of what looks like a large clock, elaborately decorated. Part of it is "a ring of cristall glasse, which being hollow, hath in it water, representing the sea, which water riseth and falleth . . . twice in 24 houres, according to the course of the tides in those parts, where the instrument shall be placed." Drebbel "extracted a fierie spirit, out of the mineral matter, ioyning the same with his proper aire, which encluded in the axletree, being hollow, carrieth the wheeles . . ."[66] There is no doubt that what Drebbel made for James I was an astronomical clock, for Tymme says that it shows the times of sunrise and sunset from day to

62 *Ibid.*, p. 19.

63 In the 1659 translation the scale has reverted to the earlier type.

64 *Register Acten States General*, 1589–1602, no. 3328, quoted by G. Tierie, *Cornelius Drebbel* (Amsterdam, 1932), p. 41. Pages 37–42 of this work are very valuable in this connection.

65 Thomas Tymme, *A Dialogue Philosophicall* [etc.] (London, 1612), pp. 60–61.

66 *Ibid.*

19

day, what sign of the zodiac the moon is in, and so forth. A similar instrument was made for Rudolf II, emperor of the Holy Roman Empire.

The reference to the tides was a piece of mystification that satisfied the pious Tymme, but Tierie marshals an impressive list of people who were quite well aware that the motive power was the expansion and contraction of the air contained in the instrument.[67] These included Pieresc, Constantyn Huygens, Mersenne, and Daniello Antonini. We shall return to Antonini later. Thus, there seems to be no doubt that the clocks made by Drebbel were those referred to in the patent of 1598.

However, while it is clear that Drebbel understood the principle, this instrument is not an air thermometer. Can Drebbel be credited with the independent invention of such a device?

The problem is made more interesting by the fact that a distinctive type of air thermometer came into use in the Low Countries before 1625 at the latest; it consisted of a J-shaped tube with a closed bulb at the end of the long leg and an open bulb at the end of the short one. The first illustration of this seems to have been published by a Jesuit, Jean Leurechon, who under the pseudonym H. Van Etten wrote a work entitled *Récréation mathématique*. This first appeared in 1626 or earlier[68] and is noteworthy in that it contains the first use of the word "thermometer." The illustration (Fig. 1.9) shows the Italian type of thermoscope, probably derived from Biancani, and also the two-bulbed, or "Dutch" thermometer with a scale.[69] Taylor[70] shows that this type of thermometer was familiar to J. B. Van Helmont in 1624 and mentions references to it throughout the seventeenth century.

This sort of thermometer was devised in the Low Countries, as I have said. Can it be ascribed to Drebbel, as has often been done? In 1628 Gaspar Ens of Cologne published a *pastiche* called *Thaumaturgus mathematicus*,[71] in which the ascription is casually made in a chapter heading, as follows: "De thermometra, sive instrumento Drebiliano, quo gradus caloris frigorisque aëra

[67] Tierie, *Cornelius Drebbel,* pp. 38–42.

[68] Numerous authors refer to an edition published at Pont-à-Mousson in 1624, but I have been unable to find a copy of this, or to meet anyone who has seen it. In the Bibliothèque Nationale, Paris, an edition from "Pont à Mousson, par J. Appier Hauzalet, 1626" (V. 18321) is treated as the first edition; there is a "2e ed.," Paris, 1626 (V. 29303). The Lyon edition of 1627 is somewhat enlarged.

[69] By analogy with the barometer, these forms might be referred to as the "cistern" and "siphon" types.

[70] *Ann. Sci.,* Vol. 5 (1942), pp. 152–53.

[71] I have seen only a 1651 edition which Taylor ([1942], p. 154, note) says is the third.

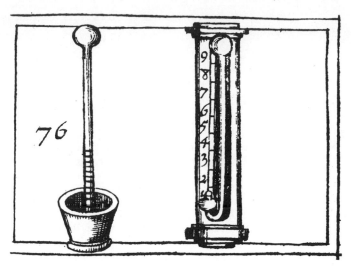

occupantis explorantur."[72] The casualness of the reference could indicate that Drebbel was widely thought of as the inventor of the thermometer. According to Taylor, "at least half a dozen seventeenth-century authors supported Drebbel."[73] Nevertheless, it is fair to say that none of them was in a position to have positive knowledge, and when we consider the general level of scholarship in the seventeenth century the evidence does not seem very strong. But it can certainly be said that Drebbel knew more than enough about the behavior of air to have made an air thermometer if it had occurred to him to do so. He is at all events a more likely candidate than Fludd.

4. The Italian Puzzle. So we must leave the northern countries with our curiosity far from satisfied and cross the Alps again to find a situation in Italy even more complicated, I believe, than most authors have felt it to be.

It was noted on page 19 that Antonini was aware of the mechanism of Drebbel's self-winding clock. I have deferred consideration of his letters on the subject, because they shed more light on Galileo than on Drebbel as far as this chapter is concerned. On February 1, 1612—five months before the first of Sagredo's letters mentioned above—Daniello Antonini, who had

[72] P. 132 (1651 ed.) "On the thermometer or Drebbel's instrument, with which the degrees of heat and cold in the air are explored." The Latin gender of the new words *barometer* and *thermometer* took some time to settle down, finally becoming neuter.

[73] Taylor, *Ann. Sci.*, Vol. 5 (1942), p. 154.

been a student of Galileo's at Padua, wrote from Brussels to Galileo:

> Some time ago I learned that the King of England has a perpetual motion, in which some liquid moves inside a glass tube, now rising, now falling, after the manner of the tides, it is said. Pondering this, I came to think that this might not really be like the tides, but that it might be said to be so in order to cover up the real cause. I thought that the truth might be that this motion came from a change in the air, namely that which might be caused by heat and cold; deriving this from a consideration of *those experiments with the big drinking glass that you know about*.[74] So I did my best to make one of these motions myself. I did not do it the way the one in England was described to me, which has the tube round, like a ring, but with a straight tube . . .[75]

Eleven days later Antonini gave Galileo a sketch with details of the motive power of Drebbel's self-winding clock.[76]

Now it seems to me that the italicized passage in Antonini's first letter is very good evidence that Galileo had made at Padua the experiment that could lead to a thermoscope. The letter adds nothing whatever to the probability that Galileo had ever added a scale to the instrument; yet we know that someone had done so by 1611 or Telioux could not have described it. Furthermore, the device described by Telioux resembles neither the Paduan thermometer nor the Dutch one. There are three types, not two, appearing almost simultaneously.

Some of those who wished to cast doubt on Galileo's supposed experiment have made much of the different dates suggested by Castelli's letter and Viviani's biography. In fact there is no necessary difference in the dates; for Castelli, in his sixties, merely said "more than thirty-five years ago." It could have been forty, or even more.

What are we to conclude? Certainly, that Santorio was the first to make use of the thermometer as a scientific instrument. Galileo may well have made an experiment before his students, even in the 1590's, but on the available evidence it is impossible to argue that he invented an instrument. The provenance of the Roman thermometer remains entirely unknown, but its very existence suggests that the instrument was more widely distributed in the years near 1610 than would be guessed from the printed literature; and indeed De Caus had described a thermometer with a dial by 1615, though it is not entirely certain that he fully under-

[74] *Quelle isperienze del bellicone che V.S. sa.* A *bellicone* appears to be a specially large glass used for drinking healths, etc. The italics are mine.
[75] Galileo, *Le Opere*, XI, 269–70.
[76] *Ibid.*, p. 275.

stood its working. There is some doubt that Santorio derived his instrument from Hero, even though he quoted Hero's book. Only Fludd seems to have read Philo in manuscript.

5. *Other Early Air Thermometers.* The air thermometer became very common in the second quarter of the seventeenth century. By 1644 Mersenne refers to it as "thermoscopium vulgare," or the common thermoscope, and incidentally describes and figures it in a form that could not possibly work.[77] That energetic Jesuit, Athanasius Kircher, made one with mercury as the liquid, perhaps in the 1620's, for he wrote in 1641: "I remember having myself made other machines of this kind, working with quicksilver, and with these all the differences between the winds were recognized nearly correctly."[78]

A famous air thermometer[79] (Fig. 1.10) was made about 1660 by Otto Guericke, mayor of Magdeburg, the inventor of the air pump. The figure on the left shows the mechanism, that on the right the completed instrument. It was about ten feet tall and was made entirely of copper and brass, so that it speaks well for the workmanship that it seems to have operated for a long time. We are told that it was made in order to see which was the coldest and which the warmest day of the whole year, and that Guericke "suspended this globe for a whole year out of doors, from the wall of his house, at a place which the sun never reaches. It was painted blue, and sprinkled with golden stars, with this inscription, MOBILE PERPETUUM."[80] The working liquid was "brandy or spirits of wine," which would not freeze, and the level, which could be adjusted by pumping a little air in or out through a tap at *H*, was indicated by a float. A waxed cord passed from this over a pulley to an index "in the form of an angel or a little naked baby." There is a large model of Guericke's thermometer in the Science Museum, London.[81] It is interesting that what seems to have impressed Guericke, and many of his contemporaries, was more the ceaseless motion of the index than

[77] Marin Mersenne, *Cogitata physico-mathematica* (3 vols.; Paris, 1644–47), Vol. 2, pp. 140–44.

[78] Kircher, *Magnes, sive de arte magnetica* (Rome, 1641), p. 587.

[79] First described by Gaspar Schott in *Technica curiosa, sive miriabilia artis* [etc.] (Nuremberg, 1664), p. 871; later by Guericke in *Ottonis de Guericke experimenta nova (ut vocantur) Magdeburgica de vacuo spatio* [etc.] (Amsterdam, 1672), pp. 122–24.

[80] *Ibid.*, p. 124.

[81] Inventory no. 1926–473.

Fig. 1.10   Guericke's air thermometer.

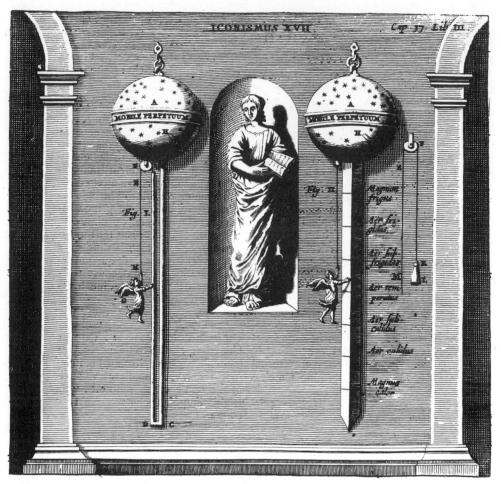

the use of the instrument as a thermometer. We find that his water barometer was called *semper vivum* by Schott.[82]

The mystification about the tides, introduced by Drebbel, was kept going by his son-in-law, Kufler, who was visited by the French globe-trotter Balthasar de Monconys at "Stratford-bou" on June 2, 1663;[83] but even the rather credulous Monconys had his doubts. Nevertheless, Samuel Reyher quoted Monconys' visit seven years later and seemed to accept the story about the tides, referring to

[82] *Technica curiosa*, p. 52; quoted by Guericke, *Nova experimenta* (1672), p. 100.

[83] Monconys, *Journal des voyages de M. de Monconys*, (2 vols.; Lyon, 1665–66), Vol. 2, p. 40.

Fig. 1.11 Differential thermometer, after Reyher, 1670.

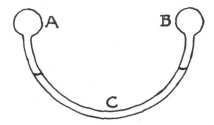

the instrument for examining the ebb and flow of the sea, which Drebbel invented. It consists of two bulbs, connected by a little semi-circular siphon, into which some liquid is introduced, and sometimes approaches one bulb, sometimes the other.[84]

He shows a figure (Fig. 1.11). If both bulbs were closed this would be a differential air thermometer—an instrument that was independently invented several times. Another form is clearly described by Reyher; this is like the "Dutch" thermometer with the two bulbs at different levels. He tells us that the lower bulb is to be hermetically sealed after the liquid is introduced and that this bulb is then enclosed in a wooden box to keep it at a constant temperature.[85] Reyher makes no claim to this device but says it is "much used" in the Low Countries. It would show, not the temperature of the upper bulb but some function of the rate of change of the ambient temperature.

Also in the Low Countries arose that peculiar and characteristic form of air thermoscope called by Henri Michel "le baromètre liégeois"[86] and used as a domestic weather glass for about three centuries. It consists of a pear-shaped glass flask—frequently the shape of a pear cut in half axially, so as to hang against a wall— with a spout rather like that of a teapot but rising nearly vertically from near the bottom of the flask. The spout is roughly graduated by means of glass beads or ridges, and the instrument is partly filled with colored water. In the comparatively constant temperature of a heated room the changes in water level in the spout would mainly express the variations in barometric pressure.

I shall end this chapter by referring to another thermometer that may have been derived from Drebbel's astronomical clock.

[84] *Samuelis Reyheri Dissertatio de aere* (Kiel, 1670), fol. D1r.

[85] The invention of this form of differential thermometer is commonly ascribed to Johann Christoph Sturm (*Collegium experimentale sive curiosum* [etc.] [2 vols.; Nuremberg, 1676 and 1685], Vol. 1, p. 54).

[86] H. Michel, *Physis* (Florence), Vol. 3 (1961), pp. 205–12. Some of the more general statements in this paper are open to question.

25

On June 12, 1663, Monconys visited "M. Renes," who turns out to be none other than Sir Christopher Wren—almost as good a natural philosopher as he was an architect. Wren showed him how to make

> a thermometer with a drum, around which is a glass tube, having a hole in it that communicates with the drum, and another that communicates with, or receives, the ambient air; then, putting water into this tube, it makes the tube, which is suspended by its centre, turn. This happens when the air that is in the drum expands, comes out through the hole into the tube, and presses on the water, which, changing its position, moves the wheel. . . . And this may well be Drebbel's ebb-and-flow machine, or perpetual motion.[87]

Antonini's second letter to Galileo, referred to above, puts this beyond doubt, but I cannot discover where Wren found the idea if not in his own acute mind.

[87] Monconys, *Journal*, Vol. 2, pp. 53–54.

II

The Invention of the Liquid-in-Glass Thermometer

In 1630 a physician named Jean Rey, who lived in the small town of Le Bugue, in the Dordogne, published a book describing some chemical researches that were, in some ways, far ahead of their time.[1] Rey believed that the increase in weight when tin and lead are heated in air is due to air condensing and adhering to these substances. This idea brought him a long letter from Marin Mersenne in Paris, dated September 1, 1631,[2] in which Mersenne very naturally objected that air is not condensed by heat, but rarefied. As an example he adduced the air thermoscope: "Then the thermoscope, making the liquid descend by the rarefaction of its air, bears witness that heat makes air more subtle, unless denser air comes down to take its place."[3]

Rey wrote an answer on January 1, 1732, at even greater length.[4] As to the thermoscope, it seems evident that he had never even heard of the ones commonly in use, for on page 244 he writes:

> there are a variety of thermoscopes or thermometers, or so it appears. What you say cannot agree with mine, which is nothing more than a little round phial with a very long and slender neck. To use it I put it in the sun, and sometimes in the hand of a feverish patient, after first filling all but the neck with water. The heat, expanding the water, makes it rise more or less according to whether the heat is great or small. If I knew the construction and use of the one you speak of, I believe that the difficulty would be easy to resolve.

Thus, with no help from outside, Jean Rey had invented a liquid-in-glass thermoscope. But Mersenne does not seem to have

[1] Jean Rey, *Essays . . . sur la recherche de la cause pour laquelle l'estain et le plomb augmentent de poids quand on les calcine* (Bazas, 1630).

[2] *Correspondance du P. Marin Mersenne, religieux minime. Commencée par Mme. Paul Tannery, publiée & annotée par Cornelis de Waard* (7 vols.; Paris, 1933–65), Vol. 3 (1946), pp. 185–92.

[3] *Ibid.*, p. 191.

[4] *Ibid.*, pp. 232–49.

Fig. 2.1 Sealed thermometer with immersed glass balls.

5

recognized the importance of this, and it was forgotten. Apparently, Rey's thermoscope was not sealed up so as to make a permanent instrument.

When the variability of the pressure of the air became known in the years following 1644,[5] a capital defect of the air thermometer at once showed itself; namely, that it responds to changes of pressure as well as of temperature. Pascal mentioned this when he was describing the celebrated barometric experiment on the Puy-de-Dôme:

> From [this experiment] there follow many consequences, such as . . . the lack of certainty that is in the thermometer for indicating the degrees of heat (contrary to common sentiment). Its water sometimes rises when the heat increases, and sometimes falls when the heat diminishes, even though the thermometer has remained in the same place.[6]

This consequence does not really follow from the Puy-de-Dôme experiment but rather from the variability of atmospheric pressure. However, the times were plainly right for the invention of a thermometer of a quite different sort. It is universally believed —and I have found nothing to cast doubt on this belief—that the sealed liquid-in-glass thermometer was invented by a man of a very different station from Dr. Rey, none less than the Grand Duke of Tuscany, Ferdinand II, one of the great family of the Medici. Even after a very great allowance has been made for the desire of courtiers to flatter, the scientific ability of Ferdinand, and of his brother Leopold, shines brightly in the learned manuscripts of the period.[7] Unfortunately, Ferdinand's grasp of politics was far inferior to his scientific acumen, and the prestige of Tuscany declined sadly during his reign.

Ferdinand, we may believe, invented the sealed thermometer and it remains to assign a date to this invention. A good deal of the difficulty of doing this vanishes when we recognize that two quite different sorts of thermometer were invented in Florence before 1660. These are shown in Figs. 2.1 and 2.2 respectively, taken from Plate I of the famous *Saggi* of the Accademia del Cimento, which will come into our story later in this chapter. The first of these consists of a tube of liquid (spirits of wine) containing a number of glass balls or similar objects in which the ratio of weight to volume varies. If the temperature is very low

[5] See my *The History of the Barometer* (Baltimore, 1964), Chaps. 3 and 4.

[6] Blaise Pascal, *Récit de la grande expérience de l'equilibre des liqueurs* [etc.] (Paris, 1648), p. 17. *Oeuvres,* ed. Leon Brunschwicg *et al.* (14 vols.; Paris, 1904–14), Vol. 2, p. 368.

[7] For an interesting example of their acuteness, see W. E. K. Middleton, *Weather,* Vol. 20 (1965), pp. 255–56.

Fig. 2.2 The "100-degree" Florentine thermometer.

and the density of the spirit correspondingly high these will all float; but as the temperature rises they will sink one after another, so that the temperature of the spirit can be estimated from the number that have sunk.[8] The other thermometer will be immediately clear to the twentieth-century reader.

Various authors have stated that the sealed thermometer was invented in Florence not later than 1641. This statement almost certainly stems from an entry in the original diary of the Accademia del Cimento, dated June 20, 1657, which reads, "A thermometer made 16 years ago was cut open with a diamond."[9] The object was presumably to see whether the spirit had altered.

This would seem to bring the date to 1641 without any question; but what kind of thermometer was this? To find the most probable answer we have to turn to the travel diary of Balthasar de Monconys, who went around Europe at intervals between about 1645 and 1665, buttonholing whatever celebrities he could—especially the *virtuosi*—and making notes, often obscure but always copious, on what he heard and saw. On November 7, 1646, he was in Florence and saw Torricelli,

> who told me that the Grand Duke had various thermometers for determining heat and cold, all with *eau de vie* and glass balls full of air, but one in which there are two balls, one at the top and the other at the bottom; when it is hot the lower one rises, and when it is cold the one at the top descends. He told me of another which has a ball half full of air and half full of water, with a hole in the bottom, and prevented from rising by a glass chain; when the air condenses, more water goes in, and so the chain shortens and the bottle descends; on the contrary, when the air expands, the water goes out, the bottle rises and the chain is longer.[10]

The first and second of these are clearly the thermometers with the glass balls, and there is no sign of the more familiar form. The third kind is of interest in that it must be one of the earliest applications of a chain as a weighing machine, antedating by at least a year or two Pascal's suggestion for measuring atmospheric pressure in this way.[11]

We may, therefore, be fairly certain that the *termometro*

---

[8] There are a number of these in the Museo di Storia della Scienza in Florence. They are referred to as *Termometri infingardi* (slow to respond). In some the balls are of various colors.

[9] "Si tagliò col Diamante un Termometro fatto di sedici anni." Quoted in G. Targioni-Tozzetti, *Notizie degli aggrandimenti delle scienze fisiche accaduti in Toscana nel corso di anni LX del secolo XVII* (3 vols. in 4; Florence. 1780), Vol. 1, p. 150.

[10] Balthasar de Monconys, *Journal des voyages de M. de Monconys* (3 vols.; Lyon 1665–66), Vol. 1, p. 130.

[11] See my *The History of the Barometer*, pp. 396–97.

Fig. 2.3 *The thermometer illustrated by Berigardus in 1643.*

infingardo was invented in or before 1641. What about the Florentine thermometer of the more familiar sort?

One red herring must be helped to evaporate from the trail. In 1929 Giuseppe Boffito wrote[12] that in 1643 Claude Guillermet de Berigard, who used the pen name Berigardus, gave the first illustration of a liquid-in-glass thermometer, calling it "a rather common glass instrument for measuring the degrees of heat and cold." But when we examine Berigardus' book[13] we find (*pace* Boffito) an illustration (Fig. 2.3) and description of what is most certainly an air thermometer. The solution to the mystery is very simple; in 1661 there was a second edition, published at Padua, in which the illustration was changed to a spirit-in-glass thermometer on a base, destroying the correspondence between text and figure. This had been noticed in 1909 by Galli.[14] It would seem that Boffito must have seen the edition of 1661.

As far as I have been able to determine, the earliest date for the invention of the "Florentine" spirit-in-glass thermometer, that can be fully documented, is sometime in 1654. What is quite certain is that by December of that year a number of comparable thermometers with a scale having fifty degrees had been made and sent to observers at Parma, Milan, and Bologna, at least. For on December 22, 1654, Antonio Terillo wrote from Parma to Luigi Antinori in Florence a letter (Fig. 2.4) that has been preserved,[15] which begins,

> I have received the letter from your Reverence, with the box, in which were the two ampoules for measuring the variation of heat and cold; and keeping them for some time in the same place in a room I reflected that they both moved at the same rate without any considerable difference occurring. I made the liquid unite by getting out the air that was mixed with it; and I have fastened them outside two windows, one facing south, the other north, and I am observing them three times a day.

A few sample observations follow, which make it evident that these were the so-called "50-degree" thermometers. Antinori also prints letters from the observers at Milan (December 29, 1654) and Bologna (January 2, 1655)[16] acknowledging the receipt of similar instruments.

[12] G. Boffito, *Gli strumenti della scienza e la scienza degli strumenti* [etc.] (Florence, 1929), p. 108.

[13] Berigardus, *Circulus Pisanus* [etc.] (Utini [Oldenburg], 1643), pp. 88–89. The book is dedicated to Ferdinand II.

[14] Ignazio Galli, *Mem. Accad. Nuovi Lincei*, Vol. 27 (1909), pp. 214–15.

[15] In Florence, Bibl. Naz., ms. Gal. 307, fol. 87. Printed by V. Antinori, *Archivio meteorologico centrale Italiano, prima pubblicazione* (Florence, 1858), pp. XXVIII–XXIX.

[16] *Ibid.*, pp. XXX–XXXI.

Fig. 2.4 *The letter of 22 December 1654 from Terillo to Antinori.* (Courtesy of the Biblioteca Nazionale, Florence.)

R.^do P.re in Xpo

C

Fù riceuuta la littera di V.R. colla scatola, nella quale erano
le due ampolle per misurare la diuersità del caldo et freddo; et tenendole
alquanto in camera all'istesso luogho hò fatto riflessione che tutte due bat-
tino all'istesso grado senza che conesse senso diuersità considerabile, ho fatto
che s'unisca l'acqua facendo uscire l'aria che era mellata, et l'hò attaccate
fuori di due fenestre l'una delle quali riguarda il mello di l'altra a tramontana, e l'osseruo 3 uolte il dì. la prima lunga colonna mostrarà
sempre l'osseruationi della mattina, la seconda quelle di mello dì, et la terza
quelle della sera, quella della mattina fù uerso le le quatordici. parimente
si deue osseruare che li numeri sinistri di tutte le colonne mostrano il

	La mattina	il mello dì	la sera
19 Decemb: e fù sereno	14 · 14 1/2	18 · 17 1/2	16 · 16 1/2
20 Decemb: e fù nuuolo	15 · 15 1/2	16 3/4 · 17	16 · 16 1/2
21 Decemb: e fù pioggia	15 3/4 · 16	16 1/4 · 16 3/4	16 1/5 · 16 3/4
22 Decemb: e fù pioggia	16 · 16 1/2	17 · 17 2/5	17 · 17 1/2

sommo della acqua di quella ampolla che fù et è esposta a mello dì, et
li numeri destri mostrano l'altezza della acqua nell'ampolla esposta alla
tramontana, e parrà forse merauiglioso come l'ampolla esposta a mello dì
mostri il freddo maggiore di quella ch'è esposta dritta alla tramontana;
io ho paura che ciò nasca da qualche camino benchè molto lontano, e
penso di mutare il luogho, aspettarò nondimeno la sua risposta et
per tanto seguitarò a osseruare medesimamente nelli stessi posti. conto li numerò
dalla sphera del uetro al in sù. et questo stesso sarà l'ordine col quale farò
l'altre osseruationi, per tanto se fosse necess.^o potrà V.R. conseruare questa lettera
per chiarire ogni dubbio che potesse nascere circa l'intendere delle colonne et
numeri dell'osseruationi. il tempo qui è assai mite. saluto singulos et mi raccom
mando alli santi sagr: di V.R. il P.re Giacomo Micaglia è morto, et il P.re
Pietro Camillo Camigi legge casi al collegio delli Schiauoni. in Inghilterra molti si

Roma 22 Decemb: 1654.

D. V. R.

Seruo nel sig.re

Of all the observations in this, the first meteorological network, organized by Luigi Antinori at the orders of Ferdinand II, only those made at the Monastery of the Angels in Florence have survived. V. Antinori was able to publish the complete series from December 15, 1654 to March 31, 1670, with short interruptions.[17] We are given the temperatures of the northward-facing and southward-facing thermometers and the state of the sky almost every hour during the day.

Thus, the spirit-in-glass thermometer certainly belongs to 1654, and probably earlier; at any rate many were available by December of that year. It is quite likely that a search through the enormous mass of manuscripts at Florence might establish a date a year or two earlier.

The Florentine thermometer is universally associated with the Academy of Experiments (Accademia del Cimento) founded in 1657 by the Grand Duke, and a few words about this remarkable institution may not come amiss. In the ten years of its existence it made an extensive series of experiments which may fairly be said to have laid the foundations of experimental physics, and in 1666 published at Florence a corporate account of these as *Saggi di Naturali esperienze fatte nell' Accademia del Cimento*. The printing was apparently continued into 1667, most copies having this date. There were further editions published at Florence in 1691 and 1841 and a facsimile of the first edition in 1957. An English translation by Richard Waller appeared in 1634 and a Latin version, with much commentary by the translator Petrus Van Musschenbroek, at Leiden in 1731. The most useful edition is the third Florentine edition of 1841, for it ends with a long account by G. Gazzeri of the surviving diaries of the Academy and is prefaced by 130 pages of the most resounding Italian by Vincenzio Antinori. While this introduction is intended to celebrate the glories of Italian, and especially Tuscan science—after all, the edition was being paid for by the then Grand Duke—it nevertheless contains a good deal of the history of the Academy and the lives of the members.

The Academy was disbanded in 1667. It is probable that this was due mainly to the opposition of the Church. The Medici family wanted a Cardinal's hat for Prince Leopold, and this arrived in 1667, presumably with conditions attached. But according to Antinori the dissolution of the Academy began earlier and was largely the work of the Neapolitan member Gianalfonso Borelli,[18] whose hatred of Vincenzio Viviani is notorious. How-

[17] *Ibid.*, pp. 2–233.
[18] In one sentence we are told that Borelli was "difficult, exacting, envious," and—Neapolitan. Some allowance must be made, no doubt, for the fact that Antinori was a Florentine.

ever this may be, the end of the Accademia del Cimento marked the end of Italian predominance in the new sciences of the seventeenth century.

While there is no doubt whatever that the Florentine thermometer was invented before the Academy came into being, they made it the subject of the very first chapter of the *Saggi,* entitled "Explanation of some instruments for finding out the changes of the air resulting from heat and cold," and beginning with the interesting sentence, "It is a very useful thing, and indeed necessary for the purpose of scientific experiments,[19] to have exact knowledge of the changes of the air."[20] This is how the making of a thermometer is described:

Let us first deal with the instrument shown in the first figure [Fig. 2.2]. This serves, as do the others, for finding out the changes of the heat and cold of the air, and is commonly called a thermometer. It is made entirely of the finest glass by those artisans who, using their own cheeks as bellows, blow through a glass mouthpiece into the flame of a lamp, either all one or divided into various wicks one after another, as their work requires; and blowing into this, finally make the most delicate and marvellous objects of glass. Such an artisan we call the glass-blower.[21] It will be his task to form the bulb of the instrument of such a size and capacity, and to attach a tube of such a bore, that when it is filled with spirit of wine to a certain mark on its neck, the ordinary cold of snow or ice will not suffice to bring it below 20 degrees in the tube, while on the other hand the greatest activity of the rays of the sun, even in the middle of summer, will not have the power to dilate it beyond 80 degrees.

The way to fill it is to heat the bulb red-hot, and then to plunge the open end of the tube into spirit of wine at once, so that it gradually begins to suck it up little by little. But as it is difficult, if not entirely impossible, to get out all the air by means of rarefaction, and because if even a little remains, the bulb will not be quite full, the filling can be finished with a glass funnel having its neck reduced to an extreme thinness. This can be done when the glass is red-hot, for then it may be drawn out into a very fine hollow thread or tube, as is clear to anyone who has a knowledge of glass-working.

So with such a funnel the filling of the thermometer may be completed, introducing its extremely narrow neck into the tube, and driving the liquid in by the force of the breath, or sucking some out again if too much has been put in. One must also be careful that the degrees are marked accurately on the tube, and therefore it must all be divided carefully with a pair of compasses into ten equal parts, marking the divisions with a tiny button of white enamel. Next the other degrees are marked by means of little buttons of black glass or enamel; and this division may be done by eye, in as much as the

[19] *Nell' uso delle naturali esperienze.* I am aware that the word "scientific" is an anachronism, but the usual translation "natural experiments" makes no sense. Experiments are artificial.

[20] *Saggi* (1841, ed.), p. 11.

[21] According to V. Antinori, *Archivio meteorologico,* p. XXXVIII, note 2, the name of the Grand Duke's glass-blower was Mariani.

33

practice, care, and skill of the art teaches one to regulate the spaces, and adjust the divisions well, by it alone; and those who have experience are usually but little in error. When these things have been done, and the amount of spirit adjusted by experiments in the sun and in ice, the end of the tube is closed with the seal commonly called Hermetic, that is to say with the flame, and the thermometer is finished.[22]

This is very clear, and it is interesting that the Academy—or rather Lorenzo Magalotti its secretary—thought it necessary to explain just what a glass blower is and does, and that a tube can be drawn out very fine. On the other hand, it is difficult to believe that the glass beads to mark the degrees can have been put on after the instrument had been filled, for surely this operation would involve heating the tube to the point of softening.

This thermometer has been called the 100-degree thermometer. There was also a 50-degree thermometer (Fig. 2.5) and one with 300 degrees. The 50-degree instrument, "nothing but a small copy of the first," was made in large numbers; several dozen still survive, mainly in Florence. We are told that in winter the 100-degree thermometer went down ordinarily to about 17° or 16°, the 50-degree one to 12° or 11°, but one year, exceptionally, to 8° and in another even to 6°. In the heat of summer the former never exceeded 80° and the latter 40°, or if so only by a little.[23]

It is not justifiable to consider the Florentine scale of temperature as being based on fixed points.[24] It is evident that the sun and the ice were used merely to adjust the amount of spirit as the very last operation before sealing. Nevertheless, the 50-degree thermometers, at least, were remarkably uniform. In 1828 there was discovered in Florence a chest containing a great number of these, besides other thermometers and various glass instruments that had belonged to the Accademia del Cimento.[25] Most of these are now among the treasures of the Museo di Storia della Scienza in Florence.[26] Libri made more than 200 comparisons between the 50-degree thermometers and found a really astonishing agreement. In melting ice they stood very near 13½°; their zero corresponded to −15°R. (−18.75°C.), and their 50° mark to 44°R. (55°C.).

How was it done? The *Saggi* provides the only possible answer:

an artisan, very famous in this trade, who served the Most Serene Grand Duke, was accustomed to say that if the 50-degree thermom-

[22] *Saggi, ed. cit.*, pp. 12–13.
[23] *Ibid.*, p. 14.
[24] Cf., for example, N. E. Dorsey, *J. Washington Acad. Sci.*, Vol. 36 (1946), p. 364.
[25] G. Libri, *Ann. de Chim.*, Vol. 45 (1830), pp. 354–61.
[26] See its *Catalogo degli strumenti* (Florence, 1954), pp. 27–33.

2

Fig. 2.5   The "50-degree" Florentine thermometer.

Fig. 2.6 *The thermometer with a helical scale.*

eters were desired he could very well manage to make two or three
or any number which, surrounded by the same atmosphere, would
always move equally; but certainly not the 100-degree ones, much
less those of 300 degrees, inasmuch as inequalities could more easily
occur in the larger bulb and the longer tube, and since every little
error made in working them is able to produce very great disturb-
ances, and alter the equality that there ought to be between them.[27]

The Duke's glass blower, Mariani, was apparently a consummate
workman. According to Antinori, the Abbé Nollet saw some of
the things he left behind and declared that they were of un-
imaginable perfection.[28] We can concur when we look at the
beautiful instrument with a helical scale (Fig. 2.6), still preserved at Florence and used so many times as the subject of an
illustration that it begins to seem like the symbol of the Academy.
I make no apology for following the fashion although it is
scarcely a meteorological instrument, as the Academy well knew,
saying that it was made rather "for a caprice (*per una bizzarria*)
. . . than to deduce the just and infallible proportions of heat
and cold."[29]

There is a further piece of evidence that the temperature of
melting ice was not considered as a fundamental point. Among
the manuscripts left by the Academy there is one dealing with
experiments on these thermometers. The 50-degree one put in
snow or ice, "comes down regularly to 13½ degrees, although the
coldest air in Florence has reduced it to seven.[30] It is most unlikely that a number such as 13½ would have been picked for
the ice point if it had been felt to be of fundamental importance.
It is perhaps even more significant that the reading at the ice
point is not mentioned in the description given in the *Saggi*.

Spirit of wine was chosen as a thermometric liquid because,
they said, it is more sensitive than water, and also because water
eventually spoils the transparency of the tube, while alcohol does
not. At first they colored the spirit with kermes, or dragon's
blood, but found that this dirtied the glass, so that the tinting
of the spirit was abandoned. Most of the surviving examples have
uncolored spirit in them, but there is a group of five 50-degree
thermometers in the Museo Copernicano at Rome, in which the
liquid is red.

That the change had been made by 1658 is shown by a letter
from the French diplomat Des Noyers to Ismael Boulliau dated

[27] *Saggi, ed. cit.,* pp. 14–15.

[28] V. Antinori, *Archivio meteorologico,* p. XXXVIII, note 2.

[29] *Saggi, ed. cit.,* p. 15. A beautifully illustrated account of the Academy's
glassware has been published by Dr. Maria Luisa Bonelli in *Die BASF*
(Ludwigshafen), Vol. 13 (1963), pp. 155–62.

[30] Florence, *Bibl. Naz.,* ms. Gal. 269, fol. 230r.

35

on the 12th of May in that year.[31] Advising Boulliau about the construction of thermometers, Des Noyers warns him not to use colored spirit "because after a time it makes the glass dirty, and remaining attached to the tube beyond the liquid, diminishes its apparent quantity."[32] And there is a letter written in 1660 from one of the members of the Academy, Francesco Redi, to Carlo de' Dottori, dated on the 6th of December of that year. Redi asks his correspondent not to be surprised that the thermometers he has obtained for him have uncolored spirit in them. He had requested this on purpose, "because those that have the spirit colored red, so often let the tube get dirty as they get older," making them hard to read.[33]

When a spirit-in-glass thermometer gets a bubble in the column, it is common practice to dispose of the bubble by holding the instrument in one hand and tapping it against the palm of the other, as every meteorological observer is taught. This trick too was known about 1660.[34]

But the academicians experimented with other liquids. Putting water into a bulb attached to a tube divided into 200 degrees, they found, among other things, that water has a minimum volume at some temperature above freezing.[35] They also discovered that when the bulb was suddenly put into the crushed ice the level of the water in the tube made a little jump upward (un balzetto in su) before starting to go down as one would expect.[36] Similarly, they found a fall when the bulb was first put in hot water, and one of the academicians suspected that these effects proceeded from the sudden enlargement of the bulb when it was first placed in the hot water, and the sudden contraction when it was first placed in ice.[37]

Naturally they tried mercury. Some time in November, 1657, they took two similar bulbs and tubes, and filled one with mercury and the other with spirit of wine. They were disappointed to find that the mercury did not rise nearly as far as the spirit when both were put in the same vessel of hot water, although it "received the heat first."[38] On November 10, 1657, they found that mercury cooled down more quickly than water when glasses

31 Bibliothèque Nationale (hereafter BN), fonds français 13020, fol. 39r–40v. See also page 37 below.
32 Ibid., fol. 40v.
33 Redi, Opere (5 vols.; Florence, 1712–27), Vol. 5, p. 30.
34 Florence, Bibl. Naz., ms. Gal. 269, fol. 230r.
35 Ibid., ms. Gal. 263, fol. 50r.
36 Ibid., fol. 52v. In another hand there is a note that "L'autore fu il S.mo P. Leop."
37 Ibid., fol. 55r.
38 Targioni-Tozzetti, Notizie, Vol. 2, p. 179.

of both were placed in the same bowl of crushed ice, and on December 3 they found that the mercury heated more quickly in hot water.[39] But in spite of this, "not having paid attention to proportioning the bore of the tube to the capacity of the bulb, the academicians judged [the mercury thermometer] less suitable than that of spirit-of-wine."[40] Which was a pity.

The Grand Duke, obviously proud of his invention, did his best to spread it far and wide. As far as I know, the first published descriptions of the spirit-in-glass thermometer came not from Florence, but from Rome in 1656[41] and from Perugia in 1658.[42] In the Roman book there is a chapter on "finding the increase or decrease of heat and cold in air, water, or other liquids," in which the experiments of the Grand Duke Ferdinand are praised. After describing the air thermometer very clearly, the author goes on, "But not content with this invention alone, His Serene Highness sought to perfect it in a manner that leaves nothing to be desired."[43] He then described the spirit thermometer, and enlarges on its many uses. Finally, he tells us that

> in the winter this most Serene Grand Duke looks at the said instrument on rising in the morning, and by the observations that have been made he knows quite well whether the cold is greater or less in this or that other place than in Florence, or wherever His Most Serene Highness may be, and to what degree.[44]

His Highness has also found, we are told, that the water of wells and springs, and the air of caves and cellars, is not warmer in winter, as our senses would lead us to believe.

The phrase "by the observations that have been made" (*per l'osservationi fatte*) can only refer to the meteorological network mentioned above.

The Florentine thermometer got much farther than Rome and Perugia—and very quickly—to be used for the first systematic observations of temperature in Paris. In the library of the Observatoire de Paris there is a manuscript[45] table of observations

39 *Ibid.*, Vol. 2, p. 625, where the original documents are reproduced.

40 Galli, *Mem. Acad. Nuovi Lincei*, Vol. 27 (1909), p. 226.

41 *Trattato della sfera di Galileo Galilei, con alcune prattiche intorno à quella . . . di Buonardo Savi* [pseudonym of Urbano Daviso] (Rome, 1656). The dedication to Cardinal Giovanni Carlo de' Medici is dated March 20, 1656. The *imprimatur* is not dated.

42 Anon., *Microcosmi physicomathematici, seu compendii, in quo clare, & breuiter tractantur praecipuae mundi partes, coelum, aer, aqua, terra, eorumque praecipua accidentia. Tomus primus* (Perusiae, 1658). Both the BM catalog and the *Biographie Universelle* ascribe this to Francesco Eschinardi, whom we shall meet again in Chapter 3.

43 *Trattato della sfera*, p. 191.

44 *Ibid.*, p. 193.

45 Paris, Observatoire, ms. B.5.12, item 3.

made by the astronomer Ismael Boulliau, headed "Ad Thermomentrum observationes anno 1658 Parisiis. Thermometru Florentiae fabricatum." The first observation is dated May 25, 1658, and the last August 19, 1660. From March 25 to May 10, 1659, there is a parallel series of observations in a column headed "Ad mercurio plenum thermometron"; these show little variation, a fact that Boulliau was quick to report to Prince Leopold in a letter dated April 4, 1659,[46] from which we learn that the bulbs and tubes of the two thermometers had been similar, and that the mercury only expanded two degrees while the spirit was expanding fifteen. So he abandoned the mercury thermometer.

We know how Boulliau got his Florentine thermometer, for there exist letters written to him by P. Des Noyers, a Frenchman attached to the court of Poland.[47] It appears that the Queen of Poland sent T. L. Burattini to Italy and that he came back in 1657 with various instruments, including several thermometers, gifts of the Grand Duke. Des Noyers sent one of these to Boulliau, together wth a description and a full-size sketch.[48]

The Florentine thermometer reached England in 1661, when one was shown to Robert Boyle by a young man called Robert Southwell, just back from the Grand Tour. A hopeful examination of his rather juvenile notebook[49] reveals nothing of scientific interest, but only a taste for trivia and a liking for rather off-color, and not very funny, stories. It does show that he was in Florence on April 3, 1661. At a more solemn age, as Sir Robert, he was President of the Royal Society (1690–95), and this is how we know that it was he who showed Boyle the thermometer.[50] Boyle had a good deal to say about the instrument a year or two later in his *New Experiments and Observations Touching Cold* [etc.]:[51]

> Weather glasses . . . that are hermetically sealed . . . are in some things so much more convenient than the others, that (if I be not mistaken) it has already prov'd somewhat serviceable to the inquisitive, that I have directed the making of the first of them, that have

[46] Florence, Bibl. Naz., ms., Gal. 275, fol. 143r–145r.

[47] These are in BN, fonds fr. 13019 and 13020, and have been partly reproduced by A. Favaro, *Mem. Reale Ist. Veneto,* Vol. 25 (1896), No. 8.

[48] Maze (*Compt. Rend.,* Vol. 120 [1895], pp. 230–31, 731–32; Vol. 121 [1895], pp. 732–33) described the entire episode, but was in error in his belief that Boulliau made the first mercury thermometer.

[49] British Museum (hereafter BM), ms. Egerton 1632.

[50] It was disclosed by Hooke in a paper read on Dec. 12, 1694, and printed in *The Posthumous Works* [etc.], ed. Richard Waller (London, 1705), p. 556. It is confirmed by Halley in *Phil. Trans.,* Vol. 22 (1701), pp. 791–94.

[51] London, 1665 (*Works* [1772 ed.], Vol. II, pp. 462–734). It is known that this was written not later than 1663 (see my *The History of the Barometer,* p. 71).

been blown in England. At the beginning indeed I had difficulty to bring men to believe, there would be rarefaction and condensation of a liquor hermetically seal'd up, because of the school doctrine touching the impossibility of a vacuum . . . I found my work much facilitated by the sight of a small seal'd weather-glass newly brought by an ingenious traveller from Florence, where it seems some of the eminent virtuosi, that enobled that fair city, had got the start of us in reducing seal'd glasses into a convenient shape for thermoscopes. But since that, the invention has in England by a dexterous hand, that uses to make them for me, been improv'd, and the glasses we now use are more conveniently shap'd, and more exact than the pattern, I caused the first to be made by.[52]

It would be interesting to know the nature of these improvements and to identify the "dexterous hand." It may well have been Robert Hooke, whose work on the thermometer we shall examine shortly.

We see that by about 1660 the spirit-in-glass thermometer had been brought to a technically satisfactory state and that the mercury-in-glass thermometer had been tried and temporarily abandoned. But whatever comparability had been achieved depended on the extraordinary skill of a workman. The history of thermometry for the succeeding century and more is largely a record of attempts to make thermometers universally comparable.

[52] *New Experiments*, pp. 54–55 (*Works, ed. cit.*, Vol. II, p. 494).

III

Seventeenth-Century Developments

1. Early Experiments at the Royal Society. The thermometer was naturally of interest to the Fellows of the new Royal Society, and there are references to it at about the time that Robert Boyle was writing his *New Experiments and Observations Touching Cold.* From one of the earliest of their records we learn that their ideas were not very highly developed. On October 7, 1663, they were discussing the provision of four thermometers, to be kept in cellars, and we read that, "For the adjusting of these thermometers it was thought sufficient to know what mark they stood at then; and for the making of observations, to take notice, how they should afterwards differ from this mark."[1] Five days later Hooke was instructed to "make ready the two thermometers of Dr. [Christopher] Wren's invention, one of tin, the other of glass,"[2] and on October 14 there is another mention of "Dr. Wren's new kind of thermometer with two round glasses and quicksilver in them."[3]

One of these thermometers is clearly shown in a drawing bound in a copy of the *Parentalia*[4] belonging to the Royal Institute of British Architects.[5] It forms part of a meteorograph or "weather clock," certainly the first such instrument which recorded wind direction and temperature, as well as attempting to indicate hourly amounts of rainfall. The thermometer consisted of a large bulb connected by a narrow tube to a vertical cylinder partly full of mercury. A float in the latter is connected to a

[1] Thomas Birch, *The History of the Royal Society of London* (4 vols.; London, 1756), Vol. 1, p. 311. This work is mainly transcribed, with changes in spelling, from the *Journal Books* of the Society.

[2] *Ibid.*, Vol. 1, p. 313.

[3] *Ibid.*, Vol. 1, p. 315.

[4] Christopher Wren [the grandson of the famous architect], *Parentalia: or, Memoirs of the Family of the Wrens [etc.]* (London, 1750).

[5] Reproduced by H. E. Hoff and L. A. Geddes in *Isis*, Vol. 53 (1962), p. 320.

cord passing over a pulley, then horizontally over another pulley to a counterweight. A pencil is attached to the horizontal portion of the cord and records on a rectangular chart moved sideways by a clock. A close examination of Wren's drawing would suggest that this is an air thermometer, and indeed if the drawing is even approximately to scale, this must be so.

This meteorograph was seen by Balthasar de Monconys on June 10, 1663.[6] Wren's second thermometer "with two round glasses and quicksilver in them" was also intended for a meteorograph.[7] The only clue I have found to its construction is contained in a famous letter written on July 30, 1663, to Lord Brouncker, the President of the Royal Society,[8] suggesting experiments for the entertainment of Charles II on the occasion of a proposed visit that the King never made. The relevant passage is as follows:

> I have pleased myself not a little with the play of the weather wheele (the Onely true way to measure Expansions of the Ayre) & I fancy it must needs give others satisfaction if it were once firmly made which I suppose may be donne if the circular pipe which cannot be truly blown in glasse were made of Brasse by those who make Trumpets & Sackbuts (who wire draw their pipes through a hole & equal them, & then filling them with melted Lead turne them round into what flexures they please) but the inside of the pipe must be vernished with China vernish (which Gratorex hath) to preserve it from the quicksilver, & the glasses must be fixed to the Pipe with Varnishe, which I take to be the best cement in the world, for thus the Chinese fix glasse & mother of Pearle in their workes.[9]

If we consider the instrument illustrated in Fig. 2.6, this passage leaves us with a poor impression of the state of glassworking in England in the seventeenth century.

Hooke and Wren were very good friends and exchanged ideas freely,[10] and Hooke was also interested in constructing a meteorograph, finishing an elaborate one about fifteen years later.[11] He had a scheme for a thermograph on January 4, 1664/5, for we

[6] Balthasar de Monconys, *Journal des Voyages de M. de Monconys* (3 vols.; Lyon, 1665–66), Vol. 2, p. 53.

[7] See W. E. K. Middleton, *Physis*, Vol. 3 (1961), pp. 215–16.

[8] BM, Sloane Ms. 2903, fol. 104r–105v.

[9] *Ibid.*, fol. 105r. "Gratorex" refers to Ralph Greatorex, a well-known instrument maker who had his shop on the Strand (see E. G. R. Taylor, *The Mathematical Practitioners of Tudor and Stuart England* [Cambridge, 1954], p. 229). "China vernish" is presumably shellac.

[10] This is clear from many entries in Hooke's diary. See H. W. Robinson and Walter Adams, eds., *The Diary of Robert Hooke, M.A., M.D., F.R.S., 1672–1680* (London, 1935), *passim*.

[11] Middleton, *Physis*, Vol. 3 (1961), pp. 218–20. Hooke acknowledged that the idea had originated with Wren.

read that on that day

> Mr. Hooke shewed the way of applying a thermometer to a weather-cock [*sic*], by sealing up spirit of wine in a glass cane, with two pretty large heads, one of which was filled with spirit of wine, as was also the intermediate stem; the other not quite full, a space of air being left to give liberty for the expanding liquor. The cane thus filled was poised in the manner of the beam of a balance, and [its operation was described].
>
> It was moved to consider, whether this instrument were sensible and nice enough.[12]

The same doubts seem to have arisen about another somewhat different instrument, for on the twenty-seventh of the same month we find Sir Robert Moray writing to Christiaan Huygens at The Hague: "Nous avons des Thermometres faits en spiral qui tournent autour dun Essieu, dont le moindre Mouvement marque sur un grand cercle un grande espace. Mais il n'est pas assez delicat."[13] The mention of a "spiral" reminds one of Drebbel's "perpetual motion" as described by Antonini,[14] but if it had been an air thermometer the question of sensitivity would have been less likely to arise. It is of some interest that in 1878 and 1879 patents[15] were awarded to Friedrich Kuntze of Leipzig for a "Drehthermometer" of this general sort, but more highly developed technically.

These mechanical schemes, however interesting, are not our main concern. The Royal Society soon recognized the importance of making comparable thermometers; and when, on October 21, 1663, Hooke brought out a number of spirit thermometers and said they all agreed "at the figure 8," it was decided "that one of them should be kept by the Society as a standard, and all the rest so adjusted, as to agree therewith."[16] And on December 2 of the same year, Dr. Jonathan Goddard was asked to "draw the air out of" rectified spirit of wine and see how it worked in a thermometer.[17] We shall see that for another century people tried this without realizing that they were drawing a good deal of the alcohol out at the same time.

It must have been at about this period that Robert Hooke devised the earliest method of preparing comparable thermometers from first principles, without the necessity of making their dimensions exactly similar as the Florentines had tried to do.

[12] Birch, *The History* . . . , Vol. 2, pp. 1–2.
[13] *Oeuvres complètes de Christiaan Huygens* (22 vols.; 1888–1950), Vol. 5 (1893), p. 228.
[14] See p. 21 above.
[15] Deutsches Reichspatent (hereafter D.R.P.) 4752 (1878) and 7473 (1879).
[16] Birch, *The History* . . . , Vol. 1, p. 320.
[17] *Ibid.*, Vol. 1, p. 338.

Indeed, the thermometers just referred to may well have been made by Hooke's new method, which was first published two years later in his remarkable *Micrographia,*[18] a book chiefly devoted to the microscope and the things that can be seen with its aid.

Hooke first describes the construction of a large thermometer —as much as four feet long—and its filling with "the best recti- fied spirit of wine highly ting'd with the lovely colour of co- cheneel." He chose spirit of wine for three reasons: because it is easily colored; because it responds quickly to heat; and because "it is not subject to be frozen by any cold yet known." He then deals with the graduation of his thermometer, and we shall quote his own words:

Then, for graduating the stem, I fix that for the beginning of my division where the surface of the liquor in the stem remains when the ball is placed in common distilled water, that is so cold that it just begins to freeze and shoot into flakes; and that mark I fix at a convenient place of the stem, to make it capable of exhibiting very many degrees of cold, below that which is requisite to freeze water: the rest of my divisions, both above and below this (which I mark with a [0][19] or nought) I place according to the degrees of expansion, or contraction of the liquor in proportion to the bulk it had when it indur'd the newly mention'd freezing cold. And this may be very easily and accurately enough done by this following way; prepare a cylindrical vessel of very thin plate brass or silver, *ABCD* of [Fig. 3.1]; the diameter *AB* of whose cavity let be about two inches, and the depth *BC* the same; let each end be cover'd with a flat and smooth plate of the same substance, closely soder'd on, and in the midst of the upper cover make a pretty large hole *EF,* about the bigness of a fifth part of the diameter of the other; into this fasten very well with cement a straight and even cylindrical pipe of glass, *EFGH,* the diameter of whose cavity let be exactly one tenth of the diameter of the greater cylinder. Let this pipe be mark'd at *GH* with a diamant, so that *G* from *E* may be distant just two inches, or the same height with that of the cavity of the greater cylinder, then divide the length *EG* exactly into 10 parts, so the capacity of the hollow of each of these divisions will be $\frac{1}{1000}$ part of the capacity of the greater cylinder. This vessel being thus prepared, the way of marking and graduating the thermometers may be very easily thus performed:

Fill this cylindrical vessel with the same liquor wherewith the thermometers are fill'd, then place both it and the thermometer you are to graduate, in water that is ready to be frozen, and bring the surface of the liquor in the thermometer to the first marke or [0]; then so proportion the liquor in the cylindrical vessel, that the sur- face of it may just be at the lower end of the small glass-cylinder;

[18] Robert Hooke, *Micrographia: or some physiological descriptions of minute bodies made by magnifying glasses with observations and inquiries thereon* (London, 1665).
[19] The square brackets are in the original.

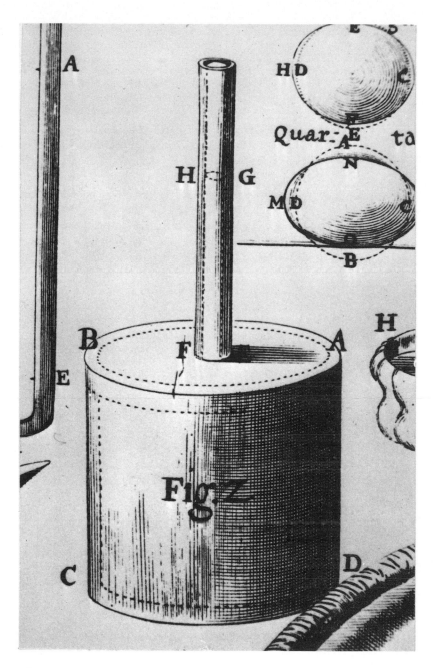

Fig. 3.1 Hooke's apparatus for measuring the dilatation of spirit of wine.

then very gently and gradually warm the water in which both the thermometer and this cylindrical vessel stand, and as you perceive the ting'd liquor to rise in both stems, with the point of a diamond give several marks on the stem of the thermometer at those places, which by comparing the expansion in both stems, are found to correspond to the divisions of the cylindrical vessel, and having by this means marked some few of these divisions on the stem, it will be very easie by these to mark all the rest of the stem, and accordingly to assign to every division a proper character.[20]

This is the earliest serious attempt at a scale of temperature that could really be standardized. As usual, Hooke's efforts in this field were forgotten, and Réaumur could describe his rather similar method in the next century with no reference to them at all. While it was an excellent attempt, it suffered from several disabilities: spirit of wine is not a well-defined substance, its properties varying rapidly with the amount of water in it; Hooke's choice of the freezing point of water, rather than the melting point of ice, was unfortunate; and he did not make any allowance for the difference in expansion of brass—or silver— and glass. It may be noted that Réaumur inherited the first two of these sources of error.[21]

At any rate, here we have an example of one of the two ways of establishing the scale of a liquid-in-glass thermometer. The other, using two fixed points, was finally recognized as being far superior.

Hooke's thermometer is the subject of an interesting study by Louise Diehl Patterson,[22] who lists a number of celebrated users of this scale between 1668 and 1708—Boyle, Derham, Halley, Hauksbee, Hunt, and Locke. From the dimensions of Hooke's apparatus and the coefficient of expansion of alcohol solutions, she deduces that in 1664 a degree of Hooke's scale was about 1.1 or 1.2°C. But from a consideration of the scales in Hooke's "marine barometer," a combination of an air thermometer and a spirit thermometer,[23] she concludes that he must soon have doubled the value of his degrees to about 2.38°C.[24] Papin, Hunt, Derham, Hauksbee, and Halley used a unit ⅒ as large as Hooke's revised degree.

[20] *Ibid.*, pp. 38–39.
[21] See p. 79 below.
[22] Patterson, *Amer. J. Phys.*, Vol. 19 (1951), pp. 523–35; *Isis*, Vol. 44 (1953), pp. 51–64.
[23] Cf. Middleton, *The History of the Barometer* (Baltimore, 1964), pp. 375–76.
[24] Patterson derives this figure from a paper by Halley (*Phil. Trans.*, Vol. 22 (1701), pp. 791–94) which is the first *published* description of Hooke's "marine barometer," invented in 1667. The change in the degree could have been made by Richard Shortgrave or Harry Hunt, who made and sold these instruments.

These results of Patterson's have been used by Professor Gordon Manley in a valiant attempt to correlate several seventeenth-century records of London temperature with modern measurements.[25]

Robert Boyle seems to have doubted whether spirit of wine is the best thermometric liquid, wondering whether "well-refined quicksilver" might not be superior.[26] In this he was to some extent supported by Edmond Halley, who measured the dilatation of mercury from room temperature to the boiling point of water, and thought that "Mercury may possibly serve as well for a thermometer as most other liquors."[27] But the small expansion of mercury was a difficulty, and in 1693 Halley wrote that it "might most properly be applied to the construction of thermometers were its expansion more considerable."[28] But even though the expansion of mercury is small it is enough to cause an error in the readings of the barometer. Spirit of wine would be a good thermometric liquid, except that it is variable in quality, and he suggests that the boiling point might be as good a test as any of the strength of spirit or spirituous liquors. After some discussion Halley concludes that air is very much the best fluid for thermometers.

None of this seems very important; but we are immediately brought up short by the following passage:

> Now the thermometers hitherto in use are of two sorts; the one shewing the differing temper of heat and cold by the expansion of spirit of wine, the other by the air; but I cannot learn that any of them of either sort were ever made or adjusted, so as it might be concluded, what the degrees or divisions of the said instruments did mean; neither were they ever otherwise graduated, but by standards kept by each particular workman, without any agreement or reference to one another: so that . . . observations . . . cannot be understood, unless by those who have with them thermometers of the same make and adjustment. Much less has the way been shewn how to make this instrument without a standard, or to make two of them to agree artificially without comparing them together.[29]

The work of poor Hooke (who had still fifteen years to live) appears to have been quite unknown to Halley, and nobody in the Royal Society seems to have set him right. He announced his intention of showing "a method of constructing and regulat-

[25] Manley, *Weather,* Vol. 18 (1963), pp. 98–105.
[26] Boyle, *The General History of the Air* [etc.] (London, 1692) (posthumous), p. 80. (*Works,* ed. Birch [London, 1772], Vol. 5, p. 643.)
[27] Halley, *Royal Soc., Classified Papers,* xxi, item 20 (fol. 53). On the verso it is stated that this was "Read March 14, 1687/8."
[28] *Phil. Trans.,* Vol. 17 (1693), p. 652. This was read in 1688.
[29] *Ibid.,* pp. 655–56.

ing thermometers to the best advantage,"[30] but he wished to make more experiments first. This method does not seem to have been published; but there is a draft in manuscript in the Royal Society's library,[31] which shows that it was the air thermometer that he had in mind.

2. *Temperature and Temperature Scales.* While I have no intention of dealing with the history of the theories of heat in this book,[32] it will be well to examine briefly the notion of temperature and the attributes of temperature scales. We must first notice that temperature is one of a class of quantities that are not additive, in contrast to such things as length, mass, and time, which are. If we pour 40 grams of water into a beaker on one pan of a balance, and then 60 grams more, we shall find that all the added water weighs 100 (=40+60) grams. But if the temperatures of two samples of water are 40° and 60°, we shall of course not expect to obtain a temperature of 100°. There are many other quantities, such as refractive index and magnetic permeability, that cannot be added, but these are of a different sort because they are constant for the same kind of material under the same conditions. Two lumps of the same optical glass, even of different sizes, will have the same index of refraction. But temperature is not a numerical property of any given material, and indeed we expect a number of pieces of different materials to come eventually to the same temperature if they are in a closed space together. It seems that temperature is a quantity of a very special sort.

It is fundamentally a quantification of the sensations "hot" and "cold," but it was realized long ago that such sensations are often difficult to interpret; for example, if we pick up a piece of iron and a piece of wood on a winter day the iron will feel colder, but if they have been lying in the summer sun the iron will feel warmer. Observations of this kind show us that we cannot hope to quantify our sensations directly.

When a given body gets hotter or colder many of its properties change. One of these properties is its volume, and the change in the volume of the body is commonly measured and interpreted as an indication of the change in its temperature. The choice of

[30] *Ibid.*, p. 656.
[31] *Classified Papers,* xxi, item 23.
[32] The reader may be referred to Ernst Mach, *Die Prinzipien der Wärmelehre* (Leipzig, 1896), especially to Mach's valuable discussion of the concept of temperature.

the volume for this purpose is considered by Mach as entirely arbitrary.[33] It might equally well be considered a historical accident, for at the time of Sagredo, Santorio, and the Grand Duke Ferdinand this was the property whose changes with temperature were most easily observable.

The volume of a body is a function of the temperature of the body itself; but we observe that bodies in contact tend to become equally warm, and so we assume that a thermometer shows the temperature of its surroundings. This is far from being axiomatic, and indeed—especially in meteorological thermometry— is often only a rough approximation to the truth, as we shall see. But to the extent that it is true it is an experimental result, not a logical necessity.

Another such experimental finding is that if a body, originally at a temperature A, attains a temperature B, its temperature must at some time have assumed every value between A and B. It is quite possible to *imagine* it doing otherwise, but in fact it does not.

Now, having arbitrarily, or for historical reasons, adopted volume as an indication of temperature, we must make two further choices: the choice of a thermometric substance, and the choice of a way of numbering—or naming—each point on the scale. The history of the thermometer is largely an account of attempts to make and justify choices of these two kinds.

The first thermometric substance was air, for the simple and excellent reason that its change of volume is large and easily observed. Only when it was recognized in the 1640's that the pressure of the atmosphere varies was there any impulse toward the use of liquids, and the almost immediate rejection of mercury was simply due to its relatively small change of volume with temperature. The use of the expansion of solids for the measurement of temperature was a much later development and, as far as meteorological temperatures are concerned, depended on the introduction of technical tricks to make the very small dilatation of metals useful.

Considering the volume of a substance as a function of the temperature, it is clearly essential that the function should be single-valued in the range of temperature to be measured. This disposed of water as a thermometric substance, for it passes through a minimum of volume at a temperature above its freezing point, as the Accademia del Cimento quickly found.[34] It is interesting that Robert Hooke flatly refused to believe in this

[33] *Ibid.*, p. 39.
[34] See p. 36 above.

49

property of water, interpreting the experiments that seemed to show it as being due to the properties of glass.[35]

Having chosen a substance, how do we make a scale of temperature? To do this we must make some further choices—of one or more fixed points, and of a way of numbering the scale.

We have seen that Sagredo and later Santorio attempted, not very successfully, to use two fixed points; Hooke, on the other hand, used only one. Using two, it is natural to divide the scale between them into some convenient round number of degrees. Using one, it is equally natural to make the size of a degree correspond to some convenient fractional increment in the volume of the thermometric substance at the fixed point, for instance $\frac{1}{1000}$, as Hooke did. What the two methods have in common is important. It is the tacit assumption that equal increments of volume correspond to equal changes in temperature; or to put it in another way, that the volume of the thermometric substance bears a linear relationship to its temperature. Apart from the special case of water it was recognized only much later, and rigorously proved much later still, that different substances behave differently in this respect, so that if the volume of one substance is taken as the basis of a linear scale of temperature, the volume of another need not vary uniformly with temperature as measured on this scale.

I shall return to this subject in later chapters. Here I shall remark only that the early experimenters were happily unaware of the extreme arbitrariness of their thermometer scales, even those with fixed points.

3. *Experiments in France and Italy.* In 1663 the great Dutch physicist Christiaan Huygens had been in London and had become acquainted with many of the Fellows of the Royal Society. A correspondence developed with Sir Robert Moray, and on December 19, 1664, Moray told him rather vaguely how Hooke made his thermometers, but nothing about standardization.[36] Huygens replied on January 2, 1664–65, that

> It would be a good thing to think about a certain and universal measure of cold and of heat; first making the capacity of the bulb have a certain proportion to that of the tube, and taking as a start-

[35] W. Derham, ed., *Philosophical Experiments and Observations of . . . Dr. Robert Hooke* [etc.] (London, 1726), pp. 132–33.

[36] In *Oeuvres complètes de Christiaan Huygens publiées par la Société Hollandaise des Sciences* (22 vols., The Hague, 1888–1950), Vol. 5 (1893), pp. 168–69.

ing point the degree of cold at which water begins to freeze, or else [*ou bien*] the degree of heat of boiling water, so that without sending any thermometers, the degrees of heat and cold found in experiments can be communicated and consigned to posterity.[37]

It should be noted that Huygens was not proposing that two fixed points should be used, but only one: either the freezing point or the boiling point of water. On January 27 Moray replied: "As to the universal measure of cold, Mr. Hook believes he has succeeded, unless it happens that the same degree of cold is not always capable of producing ice."[38] As we shall see, the constancy of the freezing point was a subject of debate for decades.

In France, meanwhile, the interests of standardization were very poorly served by what was going on at the Paris Observatory. The thermometers used at this new institution were made by an instrumentmaker called Hubin,[39] who seems to have been an Englishman,[40] and became *émailleur ordinaire du Roi*. The most likely date for the construction of these thermometers is 1676,[41] and one at least, with a bulb about 2 inches in diameter and a tube about 4 feet long, was still in good order in 1774.[42] This may well be the thermometer used by Edme Mariotte some time before 1679, in a set of experiments that had far-reaching results.[43] It is unfortunate that we are still in doubt about the scale of this thermometer, for various chance comparisons with others give discordant figures. The document that might have solved the problem cannot be found. On May 8, 1776, the retiring Secretary of the Academy, Jean Paul Grandjean de Fouchy, noted in the *Registres:* "I have given to the Academy some papers containing the comparison that I had made a long time ago between the thermometers of Messrs De la Hire and Réaumur."[44] But I have found no trace of these papers.

The Observatory, built for his new Academy in the 1660's by Louis XIV, was and is a remarkable building. Under it was sunk a shaft 28 meters deep with horizontal tunnels extending from the bottom. It had been accepted since ancient times that caves

[37] *Ibid.*, p. 188.

[38] *Ibid.*, p. 228.

[39] I have found no trace of his given name.

[40] According to Maurice Daumas, *Les instruments scientifiques aux XVIIe et XVIIIe siècles* (Paris, 1953), p. 81.

[41] Observatoire de Paris, ms. A.7.4, item 22, unsigned and undated, but almost certainly by J. N. Delisle, and probably dating from about 1750.

[42] Louis Cotte, *Traité de météorologie* (Paris, 1774), p. 111, note. Cotte refers to this as a "Florentine" thermometer.

[43] Mariotte, *Essay du chaud et du froid* (Paris, 1679), pp. 38–44.

[44] Acad. r. Sci. Paris, *Registres des procès-verbaux des séances*, t. 95, fol. 136.

51

were warmer in winter than in summer though, as we saw in Chapter 2, Grand Duke Ferdinand had not found this to be true.[45] Mariotte, who probably was not aware of the Grand Duke's experiments, decided to settle the matter and had a spirit thermometer by Hubin taken into one of the tunnels. This thermometer was about 3½ feet long, and was not calibrated in any way, but had an arbitrary scale divided into spaces of four lines (=⅓ inch) each,[46] which Mariotte calls degrees. We are told that "in a room" the spirit rose about 3 feet above the bulb in summer, but descended to near the bulb in winter, so that one of these degrees might have been about 0.2 or 0.3°C. The temperature in the Observatory cellar was higher at the end of summer than in January and February, but the total variation was only about one of Mariotte's degrees.

The effect of these experiments was felt for decades, resulting in the wide adoption of the temperature of the Observatory cellars as a fixed point in preference to the freezing point of water. Halley, in the paper already mentioned, refers to Mariotte's experiments and recommends the temperature of "places deep underground."[47]

Hubin's thermometer with its arbitrary scale was used at the Observatory of Paris until about 1730 when Réaumur replaced it. Various other arbitrary thermometers were being used at the end of the seventeenth century, and authorities on historical climatology are obliged to use a great deal of ingenuity in relating the results to more recent observations.[48]

Nevertheless, the last three decades of the seventeenth century saw attempts to base thermometer scales on two fixed points. The first suggestion for the use of snow and boiling water for this purpose was published in 1679 by a professor at Naples, Sebastiano Bartolo, in a posthumous book on hot springs,[49] in which the dedication of Volume 2 to P. V. Diazio is dated October 9, 1672. This rather peculiar document is not made clearer by a complete lack of correspondence between the figure, which is of a liquid-in-glass thermometer, and the text, which refers to an air thermometer. Nevertheless, after describing the way of

[45] See p. 37 above.

[46] The Paris foot = 12.785 English inches = 0.32474 meter.

[47] Halley, *Phil. Trans.*, Vol. 17 (1693), p. 656.

[48] See for example Walter Lenke, *Berichte des deutschen Wetterdienstes*, Vol. 10 (1961), no. 75, and other papers.

[49] Bartolo, *Thermologia Aragonia, sive historia naturalis thermarum* [etc.] (2 vols.; Naples, 1679). The passage about the thermometer is on some unnumbered pages (sig. L2r–L4r) near the end of Volume 2. Bartolo died in 1676.

Fig. 3.2 Illustrating Bartolo's scale.

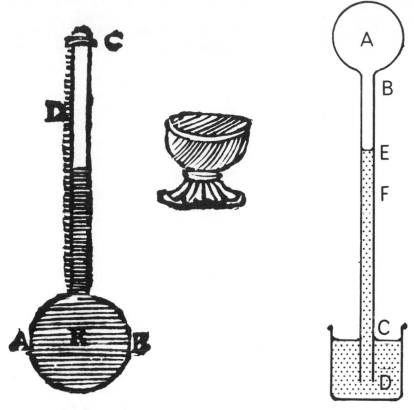

getting the liquid to come up the stem to E[50] by warming the bulb A and letting some of the air escape at D, Bartolo goes on:

> When this has been done, the bulb A is covered with snow, and now, because of the condensation of the air in it, the liquid rises of its own accord from E to B. Then when it is taken out of the snow and restored to its former ordinary surroundings, and the air again rarefied, the liquid at B gives place to it and descends once more to E. Next the bulb A is immersed[51] in boiling water, and because of the rarefaction of the air the liquid descends headlong to C. It returns to E again if the bulb A is removed from the boiling water and returned to the ordinary temperature. In this way you will get to know three points: B the greatest cold, C the greatest heat, E the ordinary temperature (*communis ambiens*).[52]

He also marked body temperature, F. Finally, he divided the distance between B and C into 18 degrees. Thus there seems to

[50] I have thought it well to reproduce in Fig. 3.2 both Bartolo's irrelevant illustration and the one certainly demanded by his text.

[51] It is far from clear how this is to be done, and the discrepancy in the illustration suggests some tampering with the text after Bartolo's death, especially as his thermometer was intended specifically for measuring the temperatures of hot springs.

[52] *Thermologia*, Vol. 2, sig. L3r.

be no doubt that he used snow and boiling water as fixed points. If there could be any question about this, it would be dispelled by the following passage:

> It must also be noted that the points marked on the thermometer, *B* for cold, and *C* for heat, are fixed, and everywhere immutable (*fixa sunt. & ubique immutabilia*), for they depend on fixed causes, such as snow and boiling water; but the points *E* and *F*, of ordinary temperature and body heat, are subject to change. . . .[53]

Bartolo's connection with the thermometer has not been given enough attention.[54]

In 1680 another Italian, Francesco Eschinardi, published an account of an attempt to graduate thermometers on scientific principles.[55] To do this

> at least two vessels are taken, a thermometer being suspended in each at the center of its upper part. In one vessel is placed one little light;[56] in another, two, exactly equal to the first. Put them in at the same time. Then observe to what degree the spirit rises in each thermometer, and note it down on the scale; it will necessarily rise higher in the vessel with two lights. Now watch carefully to see when that in the vase with one light rises to this same height and then note immediately the height of the other thermometer in the vessel with two lights; and so on, obtaining in this way always the double ratio. From this geometrical ratio you will then obtain each arithmetical division. All this is to be done in as cool a place as possible, and with exactly similar thermometers.
>
> But for the said graduation you will need to know the two extremes and the mean. Now to find out the greatest heat, the thermometer may be immersed in a glass vessel full of water, and then the water heated to the highest degree.[57] In this way we shall have the height for the greatest heat. For the greatest cold, it will already have been put in ice, when the thermometer was first filled. Then from this the tepid point will be obtained.[58] The spirit ought to be tinted with red ink, so that it can be seen inside the other vessel full of water; and all the thermometer should be immersed right up to the top, or otherwise it will burst.[59]

Shortly after this was published the Royal Society was given an

[53] *Ibid.*, sig. L4r–L4v.
[54] Ignazio Galli, *Mem. Accad. nuovi Lincei,* Vol. 27 (1909), pp. 237–38, dismissed him in a few lines.
[55] Eschinardi, *Raguagli . . . sopra alcuni pensieri sperimentabili* [etc.] (Rome, 1680).
[56] *Un solo lumicino.* A *lumicino* is "a small light, either from a natural object that shines in the dark, or made artificially for man's use" (Tommaseo and Bellini, *Dizionario della lingua italiana* [Turin, 1929]). Eschinardi probably means a small candle.
[57] *E poi scaldar l'acqua in sommo grado.* I suppose he meant until it boils as fast as possible.
[58] *Quindi poi si hauera il Tiepido.* I do not understand this, unless he proposes to mix the ice and the boiling water.
[59] Eschinardi, *Raguagli,* pp. 62–63.

account of it by Sir John Hoskyns,[60] whereupon Robert Hooke referred to his own method, and no more attention was paid to Eschinardi.

For all the doubtful experimental method and confused thinking, Eschinardi does seem to have used melting ice and boiling water as fixed points. Nearly all the textbooks assign this idea to Carlo Renaldini and date it 1694.[61] Renaldini was one of the original Florentine academicians[62] and in 1694 was seventy-nine years old.

After describing the air thermometer he dismisses it with the complaint that it "shows only the increase and decrease of heat, but not the proportion of one amount of heat to another." So he will describe a thermometer that gives indications proportional to the heat. Take a bulb with a long, slender neck, and fill it with just enough spirit of wine to come to the top of the bulb when this is surrounded by ice. Next, seal the tube hermetically at the end.

Then take, say, six vessels, each able to hold a pound of water. Provide a dipper holding one ounce and fitted with a long handle "so that it can be dipped into boiling water to take some out without scalding the hand."

Take one of the six vessels, pour in eleven ounces of ice-cold water (*gelida aqua*), put the bulb of the thermometer in this, and add one ounce of boiling water.[63] Observe how far the spirit ascends, and mark the tube. Repeat this with ten ounces of ice-cold water and two ounces of boiling water, and so on, until it is all boiling water. In this way we get twelve degrees of heat (*caloris termini*) between ice-cold and boiling. The idea of using six vessels is so that we can start with a cold one for each experiment.

It becomes evident that Renaldini thought that ice-cold water had no heat in it at all, for we read:

> If we are in some place where the air has enough heat to make the spirits of wine in the instrument rise to the second mark, and in another where it ascends to the third, we say that the heat in the second place is to that in the first as 3 to 2, and similarly for the rest of the marks.[64]

However, because of the resistance of the air included in the tube, Renaldini thinks, the spirit will not rise "secundum arith-

[60] On March 2, 1680–81. See Birch, *The History* . . . , Vol. 4, p. 72.
[61] *Carlo Renaldini . . . naturalis philosophia . . . corrigente J. B. Sanctio auctoris amanuensi* (3 vols.; Patavii, 1693, 1694), Vol. 3, pp. 275–76.
[62] Antinori, in his introduction to the 1841 edition of the *Saggi*, spells the name Rinaldini.
[63] His pound was 12 ounces, as in our Troy weight.
[64] *Carlo Renaldini*, p. 275.

meticam progressionem," i.e., in a linear relationship with the amount of heat. This, and the possibility that the tube may not be uniform, is the reason for the elaborate procedure he has described. We may make the general remark that the supposed effect of pressure in hindering the thermal expansion of liquids was greatly overestimated throughout most of the succeeding century. It had been emphasized in 1686 by Francesco Lana-Terzi in the second volume of a somewhat old-fashioned work[65] containing numerous strange ideas about instruments. He introduced the further philosophical difficulty that the spirit—like air and water, he says—resists rarefaction more and more as it gets away from its "natural state." At any rate, Renaldini clearly used the two fixed points and used them in a better way than Eschinardi had done.

Other fixed points were suggested. In 1688 a little duodecimo volume was published anonymously at Amsterdam by one Joachim Dalencé[66] which, though its style and engraved illustrations reveal it as intended for rich amateurs, is our only source of information regarding two pairs of fixed points: (1) the temperature at which water freezes, and the melting point of butter. At the mid-point was marked *temperé*, each half of the interval was divided into 10 equal degrees, and the scale extrapolated 4° at each end. (2) A mixture of ice and salt ("ce fera le plus-grand froid qu'il peut faire"),[67] and the temperature of a very deep cellar. The interval was divided into fifteen divisions and extrapolated upward. It was marked 0 at the temperature of the cellar and numbered in both directions. Dalencé suggests that the freezing point may be marked on this, but does not say where it will come.

Philippe de la Hire, who at the end of the century was responsible for the meteorological observations at the Paris Observatory, suggested two fixed points: "l'eau glacée" and the temperature of the Observatory cellars.[68] As the latter is only about 12°C., these were rather close together. The thermometer by Hubin that he actually used marked "the commencement of frost" at 30° and stayed at 48° in the cellars.[69]

La Hire's son Gabriel Philippe made experiments with ther-

<hr>

65 Lana-Terzi, *Magisterium naturae et artis* [etc.] (3 vols.; Brixiae, [Brixen], 1684, 1686, 1692), Vol. 2, p. 381.
66 *Traittez des baromètres, thermomètres, et notiomètres, ou hygromètres. Par M^r. D**** (Amsterdam, 1688). Another edition was published in 1691 at Liège, with the identical engraved half-title showing the date 1688, and it was republished in Paris in 1713 as *Curieux traité de mathematique* [etc.].
67 *Ibid.*, p. 74.
68 *Mém. Acad. r. des Sci., Paris* (1708), p. 288.
69 *Ibid.* (1702), p. 5.

mometers; in 1710 he reported that blowing air against the bulb of a thermometer with a bellows that had been left with the thermometer for some hours did not change the reading.[70] In the following year he placed a thermometer in water in freezing weather and hung another in the air nearby. During the freezing of the water, which lasted more than five hours, the reading of the immersed thermometer stayed steady at 24½ "parts." When the water was all frozen, it began to go down.[71] But the conclusions that De la Hire drew from this are really surprising. Instead of recognizing that in the constancy of the temperature during the freezing he had an excellent fixed point, he says that

> It does not seem to me that one can say that the coldness of ice is always the same; for we have seen . . . that the greater or lesser cold of the air is felt fairly quickly on the bulb of the thermometer that is enclosed in the ice. If the spirit is susceptible to alteration through solid ice, will it not be so when the ice is only crushed, or mixed with water?[72]

It seems that the idea that the temperature of ice is always the same (whether it is melting or not) was held by some people in Paris at the time, and De la Hire was so greatly concerned to refute this that he missed the wider implications of his experiments.

4. Newton's Thermometer. The great Newton had a go at thermometry, which must be recorded even though the results were scarcely worthy of him. His experiments were communicated to the Royal Society on May 28, 1701. Their author's name was not mentioned in the *Journal Book,* nor in the resulting paper in the *Philosophical Transactions,*[73] but Roger Cotes records that he guessed that Newton was the author and confirmed his guess by asking him about it.[74] Newton chose linseed oil as the thermometric liquid, and for the lower fixed point (0°) "the heat of the air in winter when water begins to freeze." But, he notes, "this heat can be found by putting the thermometer in compressed snow as it is melting." The second fixed point, 12°, was blood heat, "the maximum heat that the thermometer can attain by contact with the human body." On this scale, rapidly boiling water

---

[70] *Ibid.* (1710), pp. 546–52.
[71] *Ibid.* (1711), pp. 144–50.
[72] *Ibid.,* pp. 149–50.
[73] Anon., "Scala graduum caloris," *Phil. Trans.,* Vol. 22 (1701), pp. 824–29.
[74] Roger Cotes, *Hydrostatical and Pneumatical Lectures, Published with Notes by Robert Smith* (London, 1738), p. 222.

turns out to be 34°, and Newton notes that if the volume of the oil in melting snow is 10,000 parts, it will be 10,256 at body heat and 10,705 at the boiling point.

For meteorological temperatures 0, 1, 2 correspond to "the heat of the air in winter," 2, 3, 4 to that in spring and autumn, 4, 5, 6 in summer, and 6 "the heat of the air near mid-day in the month of July." He also extrapolated widely to give the melting points of various alloys, etc., up to the temperature of a small coal fire (192°). For these high temperatures he suggested a logarithmic scale according to the formula

$$y = 12(2^{x-1})$$

where x is the logarithmic temperature and y the arithmetic scale previously noted.

Newton's thermometer seems to have been used for no serious meteorological observations, and it is likely that some time elapsed before it was generally known that Newton had written the paper, although this was common knowledge in the 1740's,[75] by which time there were better thermometers.

5. *The So-called "Royal Society" Thermometer.* As Dr. Louise Patterson has pointed out,[76] the thermometer developed by Hooke and described in the first section of this chapter ought to be considered the Royal Society's thermometer. Yet there was an entirely different scale which came to be known as the Royal Society scale in the 1720's or 1730's and has continued to bear that appellation. I do not think that there is any mystery about this, but before explaining this statement I had better describe the scale itself.

It is inverted; that is to say the zero represents the greatest heat, the numbers increasing as the temperature decreases. The hottest weather—probably in the sun—showed about −5°, "temperate" +45°, and the freezing point 65°.[77] The temperature that was supposed to correspond to the zero can only be guessed at; Van Swinden, who made an exhaustive study of thermometer scales,[78] could reach no firm conclusion.

Nevertheless, there was some excuse for calling it the Royal Society scale, for in 1723 a secretary of the Society, James Jurin,

[75] Cf. J. Castillon, in the preface to his edition of Newton's *Opuscula mathematica* [etc.] (3 vols.; Lausanne and Geneva, 1744), Vol. 1, pp. XI–XII.

[76] *Isis,* Vol. 44 (1953), p. 63.

[77] William Derham, *Phil. Trans.,* Vol. 38 (1734), p. 407.

[78] J. H. van Swinden, *Dissertation sur la comparaison des thermomètres* (Leiden, 1792), pp. 224–38.

issued a general invitation to the learned in all parts of the world to make meteorological observations and send them to London.[79] Desiring uniformity, he went into a good deal of detail about instruments. He recommended barometers by Francis Hauksbee of Crane Court, who "will also supply exact thermometers with that scale or marking of the degrees which, accurately engraved on his thermometers, has been known for many years to the learned."[80]

It is necessary to say a little about Francis Hauksbee, especially as there were two instrumentmakers of that name, the younger, with whom we are concerned at the moment, being either the son[81] or the nephew[82] of the older. The elder Hauksbee became an F.R.S. (Fellow of the Royal Society) and made celebrated experiments in static electricity. Both men were successively employed by the Society to make instruments and perform experiments. The younger man had his shop in Crane Court, where the Royal Society also had their house after 1710. In view of this, and of Jurin's words, there is no wonder that his thermometers became associated with the Society in the minds of the learned.

A number of observers responded to Jurin's invitation, and for a time sent the results to London. But alas! Hauksbee's thermometers were not as good as Jurin thought. After a detailed examination of all the evidence he could find, Van Swinden had to say that "It seems abundantly clear, from all we have just said, that it is impossible to make an exact comparison between Hauksbee's thermometer and other thermometers, because those made by Hauksbee do not agree among themselves."[83]

A look at the data adduced by Van Swinden shows that the differences were not small, reaching 10°F. or more at low temperatures. It seems that even the freezing point was a long way from 65° in some of these thermometers.

A few of these old thermometers still exist, usually attached to barometers. There is an independent one at the National Maritime Museum, Greenwich,[84] "Made by P.[atrick] Sullivan at yᵉ. South back of Sᵗ. Clements Church in Temple Barr london."

[79] James Jurin, *Phil. Trans.*, Vol. 32 (1723), pp. 422–27.

[80] *Ibid.*, p. 424.

[81] As is considered possible by the *Dictionary of National Biography* (hereafter D.N.B.).

[82] According to E. G. R. Taylor, *The Mathematical Practitioners of Tudor and Stuart England* (Cambridge, 1953), p. 302; but see note 90. Professor Taylor thinks that Francis Jr. may also have been apprenticed to the older man.

[83] Van Swinden, *Dissertation*, p. 230. George Martine (*Essays Medical and Philosophical* [London, 1740], pp. 226–27) had reached the same conclusion.

[84] Inventory no. 0–47. This was in the storeroom in 1964.

The scale is marked "Extreme hot," at 0°, "Temperate air" at 45°, and "Extreme cold" at 90°.

Now how did this peculiar scale arise? This question has not received a satisfactory answer, but we may make some conjectures.

Just at the end of the seventeenth century there was an instrumentmaker called John Patrick living in the Old Bailey,[85] a barometermaker of some celebrity. There exists a rare broadsheet of his[86] which, though undated, refers to "Capt. Halley, in his late southern voyage." Edmund Halley's voyage as captain of the "Paramour Pink" ended in 1700, so that the broadsheet was probably printed soon after that date. Describing his diagonal barometer, Patrick writes, "It has a thermometer on the same frame, showing 90 degrees of variation between the greatest heat and the greatest cold." About thirty-five years later, Captain Christopher Middleton took with him on a voyage to Hudson's Bay a thermometer

> made by Mr. John Patrick, together with the baroscope; in his thermoscope he places [0] at the top, supposing it to be the heat under the line, and so the figures increase downwards, with the increase of cold. Temperate is placed at 25.[87]

It is tempting to suppose that the "25" is a misprint, for "45" would bring this thermometer into accord with that of Francis Hauksbee the younger. It appears that we cannot take this easy way out, for by using some observations of Derham's, Van Swinden shows that 25° on Patrick's thermometers of the later period corresponded to about 47°F., while their zero was at about 96°F., which, Van Swinden believes, represents blood heat.[88]

But the thermometer referred to in the broadsheet cannot have been similar to these, for if it had, its 90° mark would have corresponded to about −80°F., far colder than the greatest cold anyone had observed, or even imagined as possible, in 1700. Fortunately, we may examine a few barometers by John Patrick, such as the one in the storeroom of the National Maritime Museum,[89] which has a thermometer filled with red spirit and a

[85] See Taylor, *The Mathematical Practitioners*, p. 297. Datable references to him occur in 1695 and 1704. See also my *The History of the Barometer*, pp. 120 and 151.

[86] *A New Improvement of the Quicksilver Barometer, Made by John Patrick, in Ship-Court in the Old-Baily, London.* n.d., 1 page.

[87] *Phil. Trans.*, Vol. 39 (1736), p. 280. The square brackets are in the original.

[88] Van Swinden, *Dissertation*, pp. 209–11.

[89] Inventory no. 0–1. The mounting of this instrument is in a sad state but the thermometer is intact.

scale graduated from 90° at the bottom to 0° at the top, with the following notations at the figures indicated:

90°	Extream Cold	55°	Cold Air	15°	Sultry
85°	Great Frost	45°	Temperate Air	5°	Very Hott.
75°	Hard Frost	35°	Warm Air	0°	Extream Hott
65°	Frost	25°	Hott		

The thermometer by Sullivan referred to above has precisely the same notations, apart from spelling. The mounting of the barometer would suggest a date a little earlier than 1700 rather than later. There is a diagonal barometer at the History of Science Museum, Oxford, with this scale, and another barometer by "T. Heath, London."

What, then, may we conclude? I will make the following suggestion: John Patrick made thermometers with this scale some time before 1700, and Francis Hauksbee the younger, going into business for himself at some time after 1710,[90] simply took Patrick's scale as a conveniently available one and copied it, not very successfully. This interpretation is supported to some extent by the fact that the elder Hauksbee had a thermometer with an entirely different scale, with the freezing point at zero, which may have been a submultiple of Hooke's, and which he used in his physical experiments.[91] Thus it is improbable that the scale was transmitted through him. John Harris, who knew the elder Hauksbee well and in 1704 gave an illustration of Hauksbee's barometer in his *Lexicon technicum*, refers only to Hooke's scheme in discussing the graduation of thermometers.[92] It is most unlikely, in view of this, that the Royal Society had anything to do with the establishment of the scale that bore its name. I have searched the *Journal Books* of the Society for the years between 1685 and 1702 and found no indication that it did; what I did find was an entry dated November 27, 1700, which reads, "Capt. Halley read an account of Mr. Patrick's new Barometres and Thermometers." This is one more indication that John Patrick may have introduced this "Royal Society"

90 A German traveller, Zacharias Conrad von Uffenbach, visited the elder Hauksbee in 1710, finding him away from home; but "sein Vetter, ein junger Mensch" (i.e., his cousin—was it Francis the younger?) showed some experiments (Uffenbach, *Merkwürdige Reisen durch Niedersachsen, Holland und Engelland* [Ulm & Memmingen, 1753], Vol. 2, p. 518.) The elder Hauksbee is thought to have died in 1713.

91 Hauksbee, *Physico-mechanical Experiments on Various Subjects* [etc.] (London, 1709), pp. 171–73.

92 John Harris, *Lexicon technicum: or, An Universal English Dictionary of Arts and Sciences* [etc.] (London, 1704), s.v. "Thermoscope, or thermometer."

scale in the last years of the seventeenth century; and for this reason I have included it in this chapter, but also because it belongs to the period in which the capital importance of making thermometers universally comparable had not been recognized—except, of course, by Robert Hooke and by Huygens. More stress was put on making thermometers decorative, as indicated in Dalencé's illustrations; or spectacular, like the huge thermometer of which the much-damaged scale and tube remain in a storeroom at Kassel.[93] It is 3.60 meters high, and the bulb must have been a sphere about 20 cm. in diameter.[94] The scale, graduated from −1 to 26, was probably quite arbitrary.

6. *Further Development of the Air Thermometer.* The air thermometer had gone entirely out of favor after the variability of the atmospheric pressure became known in the 1640's. It is true that textbooks of natural philosophy and the like continued to describe the instrument, and new and ingenious forms of it were invented.[95] But by 1678 it had given place to the spirit thermometer wherever temperatures had to be measured with serious intent.

It was quite natural that people should think of protecting the air thermometer from the pressure of the atmosphere. A simple and clever way of doing this was devised in December, 1672, by the instrumentmaker Hubin whom we have already mentioned. In order to explain this, it must first be noted that Hooke in 1668 and Huygens independently in 1672 had invented a two-liquid barometer with the intention of magnifying the fluctuation of the ordinary instrument. This barometer is shown in Fig. 3.3. The column of mercury of height *AB* balances the pressure of the air plus that of the column of a lighter liquid—Hooke and Huygens used water—*BD*. A small change of atmospheric pressure produces a much greater change in the level *D*.[96]

It occurred to Hubin that if the air pressing on the liquid at *D* were in a closed vessel, its pressure, and thus the indications of the instrument, would depend on the temperature and not on the atmospheric pressure. So he added the bulb shown by broken

93 Inventory no. 446/F106.

94 Dr. Paul Kirchvogel, the Curator of the *Astronomisch-physikalisches Kabinett,* who kindly showed me this old thermometer, dates it about 1690, and says that the scale was re-painted about 1870. Uffenbach saw it in 1709 (*Merkwürdige Reisen,* Vol. I, p. 38).

95 See for example Francesco Lana-Terzi, *Prodromo overo saggio di alcune inventioni nuove* [etc.] (Brescia, 1670).

96 Cf. my *The History of the Barometer,* pp. 88–92.

Fig. 3.3 Hooke's (or Huygens') two-liquid barometer. Hubin added the bulb shown by broken lines to convert it into a thermometer.

lines in Fig. 3.3.[97] This was really a very clever idea, especially to have come so soon after Huygens' invention was made known in Paris. Hubin admits that the hermetically-sealed bulb was "the only piece that [he had] added to M. Huygens' barometer."[98] But the liquid, instead of water, was *l'eau seconde,* an acid solution of copper nitrate produced in the refining of gold. Being green it would be easily visible.

Hubin kept the idea secret for a few weeks and then on January 21, 1673, showed the instrument to the Academy, who found it "much more sensitive than the other thermometers that have been used up to the present." Indeed it would be very sensitive; a rough calculation suggests that 1°C. might be about 15 mm. on the tube. Actually, such a thermometer would respond to the vapor-pressure of the *eau seconde* as well as the dilatation of the air in the bulb.

Apparently he had not kept his ideas secret enough, for he was beaten into print by the clockmaker Réné Grillet,[99] whom he accused of appropriating his thermometer.[100] Grillet, whose publication scarcely inspires confidence, showed a figure of two of the two-liquid barometers sharing a common vacuum chamber, one open and the other having a sealed bulb. This would show both pressure and temperature but would be hard to fill properly.

Hubin also described an interesting variation on this thermometer. One Toinard, "fils de M. le President d'Orleans," suggested that its sensitivity might be still further increased by inclining the tube containing the *eau seconde.* This is the principle of the diagonal barometer ascribed to Sir Samuel Morland, but not as yet assignable to any exact date.[101] Hubin's illustration shows the tube inclined to about 40° from the horizontal.

On February 3, 1685/6, Robert Hooke described to the Royal Society a three-liquid barometer, as shown in Fig. 3.4.[102] This has an extra open bulb at the top, and the right-hand tube contains two immiscible liquids, such as turpentine and alcohol. The reading is made at the interface *D* between these two liquids. In France this instrument was made into an air thermometer simply by closing the bulb *C.* This was done by Guillaume Amontons,[103]

[97] Hubin, *Machines nouvellement executées et en partie inventées par le sieur Hubin . . . 1re partie, où se trouvent une clepsydre, deux zigosimètres, un pèze-liqueur et un thermomètre* [etc.] (Pamphlet) (Paris, 1673).
[98] *Ibid.,* p. 10.
[99] *Curiositez mathematiques de l'invention de SrG.* [etc.] (Paris, 1673).
[100] Hubin, *Machines,* pp. 21–22.
[101] Middleton, *The History of the Barometer,* pp. 110–12.
[102] *Phil. Trans.,* Vol. 16 (1686), pp. 241–44.
[103] Amontons, *Remarques et expériences phisiques sur la construction d'une nouvelle clepsidre, sur les barometres, termometres, & higrometres* (Paris, 1695), pp. 146–57.

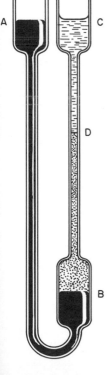

A
C
D
B

Fig. 3.4 *Hooke's three-liquid barometer. Amontons closed the bulb* C *to make an air thermometer.*

who said that he thought that he had himself invented the three-liquid barometer about 1685 until Hubin told him that it was Hooke's idea. The upper liquid in Amontons' thermometer was clear petroleum oil. But Amontons did much more than this in the study of the air thermometer, and we shall return to him in the next chapter.

IV

The Search for Rational Scales

1. Introduction. By the year 1700 it was just beginning to be realized that the value of meteorological observations would be vastly greater if the observations made in one place could be compared directly with those made in another. As far as the thermometer was concerned this could have been done in either of two ways. The first was that suggested, as we have seen, by Jurin: to have everyone use thermometers made by the same maker and adjusted in the same way. The second was to establish one or more scales that could be reproduced anywhere by using simple laboratory techniques; one scale, if possible, but if more than one, the readings would still be interconvertible.

Even if Hauksbee's thermometers had been as uniform as Jurin thought they were, the first scheme would have had no future, as Hooke had foreseen in 1664. The world was too large a place; too large even—up to now—for the adoption of any one thermometer scale in all countries and for all purposes. There were bound to be a large number, some better, some worse, and throughout the eighteenth century the history of the thermometer is largely that of the development of these competing scales. For all practical purposes, only three survived into the 19th century, characterized by intervals of 80°, 100°, and 180° between the freezing and the boiling points of water, and popularly associated with the names of Réaumur, Celsius,[1] and Fahrenheit.

There were also a large number of others, many used only by their makers, but several with a certain celebrity in restricted territories, or for one or two decades. By about the middle of the century it was not uncommon for thermometers to be made with more than a dozen scales on a wide board behind the tube. There is one with eighteen scales in the University Museum, Utrecht, dated 1754. None of the scales are centesimal. The man-

---

[1] Or with the term *centigrade.*

ufacture of such instruments went on for a long time, as witness one at the Museo Copernicano in Rome, dated 1841, and with the following eighteen scales, reading from left to right:

1. Old Florentine	7. Delisle	13. Amontons
2. New Florentine	8. Fahrenheit	14. Newton
3. Hales	9. Réaumur	15. Société Royale
4. Fowler	10. Bellani	16. De la Hire
5. Paris	11. Christin	17. Edinburg
6. H. M. Poleni	12. Michaelly	18. Cruquius.

The reader may expect to meet some, but not all, of these in this book. Some of them are of interest only to the small and gallant band of historical climatologists who will be very familiar with the excellent work by J. H. van Swinden to which I have already referred.[2] My main task in this chapter is to try to unravel the involved and indeed tangled history of the more important scales. I cannot hope to have gotten it completely right; but I think I shall be able to dispel the darkness in a few corners.

2. *Rømer and Fahrenheit.* The history of the scale known by the name of Fahrenheit has led to a very great deal of controversy, and in no other area of the subject are there so many quicksands. Nevertheless, twentieth-century research has at least disposed of some venerable misconceptions.

Daniel Gabriel Fahrenheit was born in 1686 at Danzig but lived for so much of his life in Holland that the Dutch often consider him as one of themselves.[3] Originally intending to go into business, he became a successful instrumentmaker, and it is undoubtedly because he was a tradesman rather than a "natural philosopher" that he published very little about his methods. Like a number of other eighteenth-century instrumentmakers he was brought into the orbit of the Royal Society, and in the year of his election, 1724, he sent his only papers to the *Philosophical Transactions*.

For the history of the thermometer it is very important that during the first decade of the eighteenth century Fahrenheit was

[2] *Dissertation sur la comparaison des thermomètres* (Amsterdam, 1778).

[3] For biographical details, see: A. Momber, *Schriften naturf. Gesellsch. Danzig*, n.F, Vol. 7, Teil 3 (1890), pp. 108–39; Ernst Cohen and W. A. T. Cohen-De Meester, *Kon. Akad. Wet., Verhand., Afd. Natuurkunde*, erste sectie, Vol. 16, no. 2 (1936), pp. 1–37.

in Denmark for some time,[4] and especially that he visited the famous Danish astronomer Ole Rømer, the discoverer of the finite speed of light.

Now Rømer kept a notebook in which he jotted down all sorts of experiments and calculations. After his death in 1710 this book remained with his widow, who gave it to the University Library in Copenhagen in 1739.[5] It is called simply *Adversaria,* which is Ciceronian Latin for "notebook." But it is not in the state it was in when Rømer died, for his successor, Peter Horrebow, added a large number of remarks in much blacker ink than Rømer had used. This piece of vandalism—as it would be termed nowadays—turns out to be of importance to the history of the thermometer.

The *Adversaria* was published only in 1910,[6] complete with Horrebow's annotations, but without editorial comment except for two pages of introduction. One of the editors, however, let the world know about Rømer's thermometry by way of a summary in *Nature* of part of a book she had written in Danish,[7] and also a fuller article in a German periodical.[8] It is illuminating to examine the *Adversaria* with these papers as a guide. Later Miss Meyer's book, in which she let her enthusiasm for Rømer have full play, appeared in German.[9]

The part of the *Adversaria* dealing with thermometers appears on pages 202 to 213 of the printed edition. It starts with several pages headed "De mensura tubulorum vitreorum pro thermometris" (On measuring glass tubes for thermometers) in which Rømer makes elaborate calculations to show how the degree of uniformity of such tubes may be investigated by measuring the length of a drop of mercury at various places. Finally, he gives instructions for the construction of a standard thermometer, as follows:

I. By means of a drop of mercury, find out whether the bore of the tube is regular, be it cylindrical or conical, before the bulb is blown. Discard those of irregular shape. Use the cylindrical ones without further examination. With the conical tubes we must proceed as follows:

II. From the middle of the tube towards the ends take the lengths of the drop of mercury.

[4] Cf. Kirstin Meyer, *Arch. Gesch. Naturw. Techn.,* Vol. 2 (1910), pp. 323–49.

[5] It is now in the Kongelige Bibliotek (Royal Library), ms. E don. var. 16.

[6] *Ole Rømers Adversaria . . . udgivne af det Kgl. Danske Videnskabernes Selskab, ved Thyra Eibe og Kirstine Meyer* (Copenhagen, 1910).

[7] Kirstin Meyer, *Nature,* Vol. 82 (1910), pp. 296–98.

[8] *Arch. Gesch. Naturw. Techn.,* Vol. 2 (1910), pp. 323–49.

[9] Meyer, *Die Entwicklung des Temperaturbegriffs im Laufe der Zeiten* (Brunswick, 1913). (No. 48 in the collection "Die Wissenschaft.")

III. When by this experiment the tube has been divided into two equal parts, these parts are again subdivided, according to their increase or decrease. The whole tube will thus be divided into four equal volumes.

IV. When the thermometer has been made, filled, and sealed, the point of division 7½ is fixed by means of snow or crushed ice, the point 60 by boiling.[10]

In his notes Horrebow dates these experiments of Rømer's. Five thermometers had survived and had been given to Horrebow in 1739. Although he records this gift as "5 vitra pro thermometris,"[11] in April, 1741, he states[12] that he took the thermometers off their bases and put them into snow and then into boiling water, finding after all these years, "precisely the same marks that Rømer himself had scratched on them."[13] He also compared them with a thermometer sent from France, made on Réaumur's principles by the Abbé Nollet.[14]

On April 10, 1741, he asked Rømer's widow when her late husband had made these five thermometers, and she said that it was at a time when Rømer had been confined to the house because of a broken leg. Horrebow at once deduced that it must have been before June, 1703, when he first went to work at Rømer's observatory. This was confirmed by some old servants, perhaps predictably; and on the 17th of April the widow came to see Horrebow and told him that she was now certain that the thermometers had been made in 1702.

It therefore appears that Rømer was the first to make reproducible thermometers using the melting point of ice and the boiling point of water as fixed points, and dividing the scale into equal increments of volume—precisely the method still used, at least in principle, for the construction of liquid-in-glass thermometers. Judging by Horrebow's recalibration after nearly four decades, he seems to have been very successful. But why did he choose such a number as 7½ for the freezing point? The answer that I find most reasonable is that he first chose 60—a number very familiar to an astronomer—for the boiling point and then numbered his scale in such a way that, as he thought, all meteorological temperatures would be represented by positive numbers.

[10] *Adversaria*, ed. cit., p. 210. In view of its importance I give the last sentence in the original Latin:

"IV. confecto impleto et sigillato thermometro per nivem vel glaciem contusam constituatur punctum divisionis 7½ per ebullitionem punctum 60."

[11] *Ibid.*, p. 210.

[12] *Ibid.*, p. 213.

[13] "Praecise eadem signa, quae ipse Roemerus per silicem fecerat."

[14] See below, p. 85.

So he put ⅞ of his entire scale above the freezing point, and ⅛ below "for greater degrees of cold," as Horrebow puts it.[15]

Horrebow asked Rømer's widow whether her husband had later made any changes in his thermometric scale. She did not know; but she gave Horrebow a *vade-mecum* of Rømer's, in which was found a loose leaf, "in which I see that Rømer fixed his point at 8 divisions by means of the snow, and so indeed, as far as we know, the spirit of wine never goes below zero at Copenhagen."[16]

This leaf, part of the front of which is reproduced in Fig. 4.1, contains a graph of daily temperatures from December 26, 1708, to April 6, 1709.[17] The winter of 1708–9 was one of the coldest ever recorded in Europe; but for us the interest in this document lies in the heading, which puts it beyond doubt that by this time Rømer had placed the freezing point at 8°. He had also thought of putting it at zero, as noted in the upper line of figures. Over this Horrebow has written, upside down, "muta-verat ergo Roemerus primum suum propositum."[18] We do not know what the boiling point would have been; logically it might have been 64° if the freezing point were at 8°, or 56°, if at 0°.

Rømer's thermometer would be of much less interest if a young instrumentmaker from Danzig had not visited him in 1708. The name of this young man was Daniel Gabriel Fahrenheit. Before we come to his visit to Rømer, it will be well to say something about his thermometric scale.

Nowadays it is defined rigorously by setting 32° at the temperature of melting ice, and 212° at the temperature of the steam over pure water boiling at normal atmospheric pressure, the intervals presumably being determined according to the volumetric expansion of mercury.[19] This scale closely resembles the last of the three scales used by Fahrenheit, but his scales were defined quite differently. In spite of the fact that in 1724 he gave a description[20] of his fixed points in the most famous of scientific journals, the literature abounds in extraordinary speculations about his scale. As late as 1827 P. N. C. Egen repeated an old story that it was defined by a freezing mixture (0°F.) and the

[15] *Adversaria*, ed. cit., p. 210 (Horrebow's note).

[16] *Ibid.*, p. 211.

[17] The original is preserved in the manuscript of the *Adversaria* at Copenhagen, and is reproduced in the 1910 edition, p. 214.

[18] "Therefore Rømer had changed his first intention." Horrebow has also marked some readings taken in 1740, another very severe winter.

[19] The international scientific community pays almost no attention to the Fahrenheit scale in its deliberations about the measurement and specification of temperature.

[20] Fahrenheit, *Phil. Trans.*, Vol. 33 (1724), pp. 78–84.

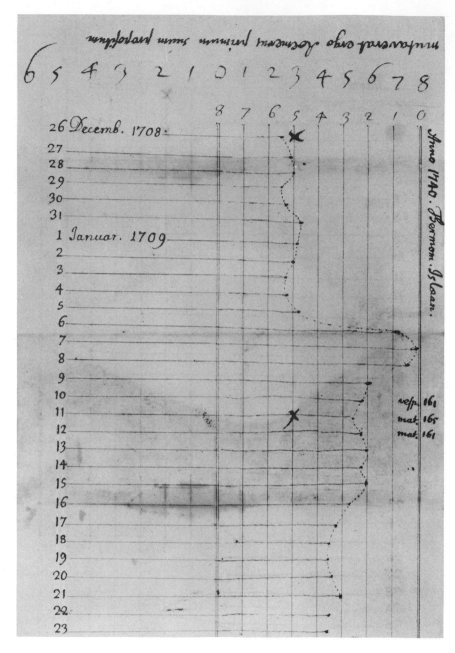

Fig. 4.1 Rømer's temperature curve, 1708–9.
(Courtesy of the Royal Library, Copenhagen.)

boiling point of mercury (600°F.)![21] I do not propose to go into detail about all these speculations, which would fill many pages.

Miss Meyer, finding evidence that Fahrenheit was in Denmark between 1702 and 1710,[22] strongly suspected that he may have learned from Rømer about thermometer-making. This could only be a speculation until Professor Ernst Cohen found among Herman Boerhaave's correspondence at Leningrad a letter from Fahrenheit to Boerhaave, dated April 17, 1729, apparently written in reply to a request for information, and stating clearly that Rømer had indeed given him his first ideas about it.[23] Professor Cohen writes with truth, "How much less printer's ink would have been used, if [this] letter had been known."[24] It is only fair to remark that a good deal has been used since; but first (using still more) I must record what Fahrenheit wrote.

Now concerning the way in which I came to begin improving thermometers,[25] I am glad to inform you that I obtained the first incitement to it in the year 1708 through conversation with the excellent Rømer in Copenhagen. For once, when I went to see him on a fine morning, I found that he had stood several thermometers in water and ice, and later he dipped these in warm water, which was at blood-heat (welches blutwarm war). And after he had marked these two limits on all the thermometers, half the distance found between them was added below the point in the vessel with ice, and the whole distance was divided into 22½ parts, beginning with 0 at the bottom, then 7½ for the point in the vessel with ice and 22½ degrees for that at blood-heat. I also used this graduation until the year 1717, but with the difference that I divided each degree into 4 smaller ones. And in this manner were also divided the two thermometers, about which Professor Wolf[26] wrote a report in the Acta Lipsiana for August 1714. As this graduation is inconvenient and awkward because of the fractions, I decided to alter the scale, and to use 96 instead of 22½ or 90; this I have always used since then. And I found, although this is only by chance, that it agrees approximately, though not exactly, with the graduation of the thermometer than hangs in the Paris Observatory. After I had thus laid the foundations for the improvement of thermometers at Mr. Rømer's, I began to read some books about barometers and thermometers, and as I heard that in the French Memoirs of the Académie des Sciences a great deal had

21 Egen, Ann. der Phys., Vol. 11 (1827), p. 293.

22 Meyer, Arch. Gesch. Naturw. Techn., Vol. 2 (1910), p. 344.

23 This was first published in its original Dutch in an article about Fahrenheit: Ernst Cohen and W. A. T. Cohen-De Meester, Chem. Weekblad, Vol. 33 (1936), pp. 374–93; and later in German in Verh. K. Akad. Wetensch, te Amsterdam, afd. Natuurkunde (1e sectie), Vol. 16, no. 2 (1936), pp. 1–37. I have used the German version, which is stated to be "möglichst wort-und stilgetreu" (ibid., p. 9, note).

24 Ibid., p. 9.

25 Note that he says "thermometers," not "my thermometers."

26 [Christian Wolff], Acta Eruditorum (1714), pp. 380–81. The article is not signed.

been reported about these things, I began, with a good grammar and a dictionary, to study the French language, of which in a short time, thanks to my Latin, I got so good a command, that I was able to read and translate the writings of the Society [the *Académie*]. In this way a great light dawned upon me, to which the papers of Maraldi, De la Hire, and Amontons contributed much, especially the last, because he has taken very great pains to give the thermometer a firm foundation. Of the Englishmen who have written about the thermometer I have read only Boyle's writings, as far as they are translated into Latin. Those of the [Royal] Society I never began to read before the year 1724, when I was elected a Fellow. Since then I have come so far with it that I can read their writings too, and understand most of them. These are, in brief, the means by which I was put in the way of these improvements, with which I hope, Sir, you will be satisfied. . . .[27]

The reader will have noticed a serious discrepancy between the process described in this letter and that given unequivocally by Rømer in the *Adversaria*. Nothing was said by Rømer about blood heat; his upper fixed point, numbered 60°, was the temperature of boiling water.[28] This discrepancy has supported some doubts about the extent to which Fahrenheit was indebted to Rømer.[29] It is certainly unlikely that Fahrenheit would have misremembered this important occasion to such an extent, even after twenty-one years, for he had been dealing with thermometers during the whole of the interval. I see no irrefragable solution to the problem unless further documents are discovered, but I shall set forth what I believe to be a reasonable guess at what had happened between 1702 and 1708.

In the first place, a thermometer graduated up to the boiling point of water is not a very handy instrument for meteorological use. Too much of the scale is superfluous. It may well be that Rømer had noticed that the temperature of the air never went above about 20° on his scale, and that he had calibrated some thermometers of shorter range by comparison with his earlier instruments, making the top of their scale 22½°, three-eighths of the way from his zero to his boiling point. Plainly, there was no means of holding a vessel of water at blood heat, or anything near it, without the aid of a thermometer; so one of the thermometers that Rømer "dipped" into the warmer of the two vessels must have been calibrated. Of course, if we assume the scale of the thermometer to be linear, this vessel was a long way from blood heat, as has been pointed out (e.g., by Dorsey); but

---

[27] E. Cohen *et al.*, *Verh. K. Akad. Wetensch.*, Vol. 16 (1936), pp. 9–10.
[28] One might quibble by suggesting that water is not mentioned.
[29] Cf. N. Ernest Dorsey, *J. Washington Acad. Sci.*, Vol. 36 (1946), pp. 361–72.

it must be remembered that Rømer's thermometers were spirit thermometers, of which the scale is far from linear, as Deluc found,[30] so that it might well have been fairly close to the temperature of the human body. It would be very natural for Rømer to refer to it as "blood-heat." I am aware that this is all very speculative, but at least there seems to be no escape from the conclusion that Rømer had a calibrated thermometer in the vessel, if Fahrenheit's account is correct.

Another point of interest is that at some time between Fahrenheit's visit and the end of the year, Rømer changed his scale so that the freezing point became 8 degrees instead of 7½. We may imagine that the younger man said something about the inconvenience of fractions; but Fahrenheit does not seem to have known that his mentor had made the change, and kept the less convenient scale for some time. Rømer died in September, 1710.

Even after the publication of the famous letter, Fahrenheit's dependence on Rømer was the subject of argument, I. Bernard Cohen taking the extreme view that the Fahrenheit thermometer "should, in all fairness, be called the Rømer thermometer,"[31] and N. Ernest Dorsey the opposite view that Fahrenheit learned almost nothing from Rømer.[32] I think that my readers will agree at this point that the latter view is too extreme, and in what follows it will also appear that what we now know as the Fahrenheit thermometer differs greatly from Rømer's. I am aware of the opinions expressed in 1937 by J. Newton Friend,[33] who could not believe that Rømer "could be so inartistic as to choose arbitrarily the curious figure of 7½ for his lower fundamental fixed point."[34] But we have seen[35] that this is just what he said he did, and I hope I have shown that this figure was not entirely arbitrary, being merely one-eighth of 60. Dr. Friend believes that Rømer based his scale on a freezing mixture, although he nowhere said so.[36]

We learn from a letter to Boerhaave dated March 3, 1729, that Fahrenheit was at Berlin in 1713, where he "investigated the exact dilatation of mercury in a thermometer made of Potsdam

30 See p. 124 below. With a linear scale, 22½° of Rømer's would correspond to about 28.3°C.; but this probably comes to about 33.5° on the basis of Deluc's corrections, and if Rømer's spirit of wine was rather dilute it might have been higher.

31 *Isis*, Vol. 31 (1940), p. 362.

32 *J. Washington Acad. Sci.*, Vol. 36 (1946), p. 370.

33 *Nature*, Vol. 139 (1937), pp. 395–98 and 586.

34 *Ibid.*, p. 586.

35 P. 68 above.

36 The notes by Horrebow that are discussed in another connection below (p. 94) seem to make Dr. Friend's position much less tenable.

glass, which almost agrees with one made of Bohemian glass."[37] At the beginning of 1617 he had settled in Amsterdam and had begun to make mercury thermometers.[38]

Meanwhile, he had received an enthusiastic advertisement from Christian Wolff of Halle in the article mentioned in his letter. But he had not remembered correctly, for it is clear from Wolff's detailed description of the thermometers that they had the 24-degree scale. They also had cylindrical bulbs, a shape that Fahrenheit early adopted as standard, and were filled with blue spirit. Although the bulbs were of slightly different sizes, the two thermometers shared the same scale, and Wolff notes that they read the same to within $\frac{1}{16}$ of a degree, which may surprise us as much as it surprised Wolff, who notes that Fahrenheit had his own reasons for concealing the means by which he made his instruments agree with one another.

Like the barometermakers of the time, the thermometermakers felt that words as well as figures were useful on their scales. Wolff's pair of thermometers had them, as follows:

0°–Frigus vehementissimus
4°–Frigus ingens
8°–Aer frigidus
12°–Temperatus
16°–Calidus
20°–Calor ingens
24°–Aestus intolerabilis

These may be compared with John Patrick's notations given on page 61 above. If the degrees are multiplied by four they will correspond fairly closely to the present Fahrenheit scale, and the descriptions then seem very appropriate, with some reservations about "calidus."

In 1724, the year of his election to the Royal Society, Fahrenheit contributed five papers in Latin to the *Philosophical Transactions*—his entire published work. One of these was about his hydrometer, another,[39] which interests us somewhat more, is on the boiling points of various liquids, in which he ascribes his use of mercury as a thermometric liquid to learning of Amontons' demonstration[40] that the readings of the mercury barometer should be corrected for its temperature. He gives the boiling point of water as 212° on his scale; but it is only in a later

[37] Quoted by Cohen *et al., Verh. K. Akad. Wetensch.,* Vol. 16 (1936), p. 10.
[38] *Ibid.,* p. 11.
[39] Fahrenheit, *Phil. Trans.,* Vol. 33 (1724), pp. 1–3.
[40] Amontons, *Mém. Acad. r. Sci. Paris* (1704), pp. 164–72.

paper,[41] in which he describes his accidental discovery of the supercooling of water—he slipped on the stairs while carrying a flask of supercooled water, and found that it suddenly became full of flakes of ice—that we get a description of his thermometers and the way they were calibrated. They were of two kinds, those filled with mercury and those filled with spirit of wine. They were of whatever length was suitable; he is careful to state that the length does not matter, because they are graduated between fixed points. Those intended only for meteorological observations were graduated from 0° to 96°. He tells us how the fixed points (*termini fixi*) are found:

> The division of their scales is based on three fixed points, which can be produced accurately as follows: The first is placed at the lowest part or beginning of the scale, and is attained with a mixture of ice, water, and sal-ammoniac or sea-salt; if the thermometer is placed in this mixture, its fluid descends to a point that is marked zero. This experiment succeeds better in winter than in summer. The second fixed point is obtained if water and ice are mixed together without the above-mentioned salts. If the thermometer is placed in this mixture its fluid takes up the thirty-second degree, which I call the point of the beginning of congelation, for in winter stagnant waters are already covered with a very thin layer of ice when the liquid in the thermometer reaches this degree. The third fixed point is found at the ninety-sixth degree; and the spirit[42] expands to this degree when the thermometer is held in the mouth, or under the armpit, of a living man in good health, for long enough to acquire perfectly the heat of the body. . . . The scale of thermometers for determining the heat of boiling liquids also begins at zero, and contains 600 degrees; for the mercury that fills the thermometer begins to boil at about that point.[43]

This passage contains the only authentic information about Fahrenheit's scale available for two centuries. I believe that much of the confusion has resulted from believing that he meant exactly what he said, and discounting the natural tendency of an instrumentmaker to wish to conceal his processes, or at least to obfuscate his readers. The mere fact that either of two salts was to be used in his freezing mixture, and the note that "the experiment succeeds better in winter than in summer," should have warned his readers that such a zero would not be even approximately a fixed point. Dr. N. H. de V. Heathcote has stated his belief that the temperature of melting ice and blood temperature were the real fixed points,[44] and I am sure that this is so. Yet as early as 1732 we find Pieter van Musschenbroek mentioning the

41 Fahrenheit, *Phil. Trans.*, Vol. 33 (1724), pp. 78–84.
42 *Spiritus*. For the moment he had forgotten about mercury.
43 *Phil. Trans.*, Vol. 33 (1724), pp. 78–79.
44 Heathcote, *Ambix*, Vol. 6 (1958), pp. 155–56.

two lower fixed points but saying nothing of the third, although he was using a thermometer made by Fahrenheit himself.[45] The authority of Musschenbroek was considerable and long-lasting, and we find his words almost repeated in an anonymous book on meteorological instruments ascribed to Michael Adelbulner, which went through three editions between 1768 and 1789.[46]

It is quite certain that Fahrenheit did not use the boiling point of water as a fixed point, and indeed he described[47] a "new barometer" based on his discovery[48] that the boiling point varies with the pressure. This instrument, the first hypsometric thermometer, is almost sufficiently described by reference to Fig. 4.2, in which it will be seen that he graduated the upper part *DE* of the scale directly in terms of barometer readings in inches of mercury, so that the atmospheric pressure could be determined merely by putting the instrument in boiling water.

It is, therefore, probable that his determination of the boiling point of water as 212° was made before he recognized its variability; at least it was reported a few months earlier. These figures of 212°, and boiling points of other liquids up to oil of vitriol at 545°, were certainly obtained with a thermometer having its scale extrapolated upward from 96°, a tricky business, depending critically on the uniformity of the tube at least, and of course begging all sorts of questions about the uniformity of the expansion of the thermometric liquid. Normal blood heat is 98.6° on the present-day Fahrenheit scale—instead of 96°—so that his 212° was probably fortuitous. Musschenbroek's instrument read 214° in boiling water. So did one used by Poleni,[49] though it is possible that he was merely copying Musschenbroek. But by about 1740 it seems to have become common practice to consider 212°F. both as the boiling point and as a fixed point, to the exclusion of blood heat.

The great chemist Herman Boerhaave was a faithful customer of Fahrenheit's and praised him highly. He once ordered two thermometers, one filled with mercury, the other with "the light-

[45] Musschenbroek, *Phil. Trans.*, Vol. 37 (1732), p. 358.

[46] *Kurze Beschreibung der Barometer und Thermometer, auch anderer zur Meteorologie gehöriger Instrumente* (Nuremberg, 1768; 2nd ed., Frankfurt and Leipzig, 1776; 3rd ed., revised by J. C. Heppe, Nuremberg, 1789). I have seen the 2nd edition; the passage is on p. 86.

[47] Fahrenheit, "Barometri novi descriptio," *Phil. Trans.*, Vol. 33 (1724), pp. 179–80.

[48] Johannis Poleni ("Dissertatio de barometris & thermometris" in *Miscellanea* [Venice, 1709], p. 13) says that Bernardus states that the temperature of boiling water depends on the pressure, but that he, Poleni, does not believe this. I have not traced the reference to Bernardus.

[49] J. Poleni, *Comm. Acad. Petrop.*, Vol. 8 (1736), p. 448.

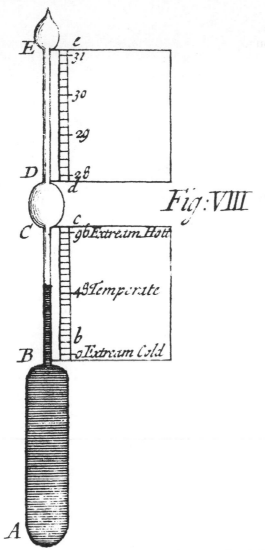

Fig. 4.2   Fahrenheit's "new barometer" or boiling-point thermometer.

est alcohol." Careful examination showed that they did not
quite agree in their readings. He told Fahrenheit, who acknowledged the defect but could not at first understand the reason.
After thinking about it, Fahrenheit suggested that it was because
they were made of glass from different places.[50] He missed the
explanation of the main part of the difference, which is that
alcohol and mercury do not expand proportionally.

Fahrenheit died in 1736, and the manufacture of his thermometers was continued by Hendrik Prins, as we are told in a

---

[50] Boerhaave, *Elementa chemiae* (Leiden, 1732), p. 141.

manuscript note, probably by Delisle.[51] And on July 12, 1743, Anders Celsius wrote from Uppsala to Antoine and Jean Grill of Amsterdam, acknowledging the receipt of a "Prince thermometer."[52] Prins and Fahrenheit seem to have been considered equally able by Pieter van Musschenbroek.[53]

Two thermometers signed by Fahrenheit survive in the Rijksmuseum voor de Geschiedenis der Natuurwissenschaften at Leiden.[54] One (inventory no. Th 1) is a mercury thermometer with a brass scale, signed on the back. It is graduated from 0° to 600°, and has a bulb about 15 mm. in diameter and 50 mm. long. The other (no. Th 1a) is signed "D. G. Fahrenheit 1727." Although it is graduated from −8° to +600° (marked in Dutch as being the boiling point of mercury), it is filled with a dark-colored liquid, but there is a strong probability that the glass parts of the instrument are not original.

There is also a spirit thermometer (inventory no. 477) at the University Museum, Utrecht, signed "D^L. G^L. Fahrenheit." This has scales from −104° to +400°F., and −61° to +170°R, which must mean that it is one of his later productions for details of Réaumur's experiments can scarcely have reached Amsterdam much before 1733. I think that its authenticity is somewhat doubtful.

Before leaving Fahrenheit and Rømer I had better give a brief summary of the tentative conclusions at which I have arrived:

1) By about 1702 Ole Rømer had settled on a thermometer scale having 60° at the boiling point of water and 7½° at the melting point of ice. He had a fairly well-developed method of investigating the bores of tubes, and had made several thermometers.

2) In 1708 Fahrenheit saw Rømer calibrating thermometers. By this time Rømer had realized the convenience of calibrating meteorological thermometers at a temperature of 22½° on his scale by comparison with one of his own thermometers in a vessel of warm water. Fahrenheit referred to this as blood heat.

3) Later in 1708 Rømer changed his scale so that the melting point of ice became 8° and made observations with such a thermometer during the cold winter of 1708–9.

[51] Observatoire de Paris, ms. A.7.4, item 28, fol. J. "Mr Prins fait et vend à Amsterdam des thermometres de mercure entierement conforme à la division de Mr Fahrenheit."

[52] Upsala, University Library, ms. A533, item 164. I have to thank Dr. G. H. Liljequist for translating this letter.

[53] Musschenbroek, *Beginselen der Natuurkunde* (Leiden, 1736), p. 599.

[54] See also C. A. Crommelin, *Descriptive Catalogue of the Physical Instruments of the 18th Century*, Rijksmuseum, Communication no. 81 (Leiden, 1951), p. 34.

4) The spirit thermometers that Fahrenheit made for Christian Wolff about 1714 were calibrated according to this scale.

5) In 1713 Fahrenheit began experimenting with mercury thermometers and in 1717 began to make them commercially. At about this time he divided his degrees into quarters.

6) Fahrenheit's final scale was really based on two "fixed" points: the melting point of ice (32°), and the heat of the healthy human body (96°). He did not use the boiling point of water as a fixed point, but stated it as 212°.

7) Soon after his death the boiling point replaced blood heat as the upper fixed point.

It would seem that the Fahrenheit scale quickly came into use in the Low Countries and in England. In France it remained unused and practically unknown even to the *savants,* and a French thermometer with a Fahrenheit scale is a rarity,[55] though toward the end of the eighteenth century a few were made with both Réaumur and Fahrenheit scales.[56]

3. *Réaumur and Delisle.* We now come to a pair of thermometric scales based, not on two fundamental points, but on one, together with numerical values of the dilatation or contraction of the working substance relative to its containing vessel. It has been argued that such scales are simpler, logically, than the other sort; but it cannot be maintained that they can be constructed as accurately in practice.

In contrast to the very meager documentation vouchsafed us by the instrumentmaker Fahrenheit, the well-born *savant* René-Antoine Ferchault de Réaumur has told us everything we could possibly wish to know about his thermometer scale in two memoirs of incredible verbosity.[57] Réaumur did a great deal of useful work in a number of subjects, notably in ferrous metallurgy, embryology, entomology, and botany.[58] I think it is fair to say that his work on thermometry was far below the standard of much of his other scientific work, and was far from being an

55 A barometer at Oxford (History of Science Museum, inv. no. 64–300) by Mazza, who lived "en Faubourg St. Antoine, rue St. Margueritte, à l'Enseigne des Baromètres," has a large thermometer with a Fahrenheit scale, or something like one. But the legend is in both French and Dutch, so that it was probably made for export.

56 Paris, Conservatoire National des Arts et Métiers (hereafter CNAM), inv. no. 1581 (but this was made in Amsterdam by Bianchy & Co.) and 8491 (by Cappy & Mossy in Paris).

57 Réaumur, *Mém. Acad. r. des Sci. Paris* (1730), pp. 452–507; *ibid.* (1731), pp. 250–96.

58 Cf. Centre International de Synthèse, *La vie et l'oeuvre de Réaumur (1683–1757)* (Paris, 1962).

improvement on existing techniques. As we shall see, his actual methods were very soon modified or neglected by those who claimed to be making "Réaumur thermometers," but nevertheless the scale that he devised, and its modifications, survived for well over a century in France and Central Europe. Its wide distribution was due initially to the prestige of the Académie royale des Sciences and the high reputation of its inventor, and later simply to habit[59] and academic conservatism. It was at least fortunate that by the end of the eighteenth century Réaumur's scale had been so modified as to make it possible to construct accurate and reproducible thermometers.

From the very title of Réaumur's first paper ("Regles pour construire des thermometres dont les degrés soient comparables, et qui donnent une idée d'un chaud ou d'un froid qui puissent être rapportés à des mesures connües") one suspects that he thought he was being entirely original. This is borne out in the fifty-six pages of the memoir. It is clear that he had never heard that Hooke had done almost the same thing nearly seventy years before; but few Frenchmen of the period were able, or bothered, to read English.

I shall try to summarize Réaumur's memoirs in a reasonable compass. He begins by complaining, entirely justly, of the chaotic state of thermometer-making in France at that period. Thermometers were usually fitted to a thin board covered with "a paper on which the degrees are printed. Papers similarly printed, or engraved, serve for different thermometers, as if the lengths of their degrees ought to be the same."[60]

Clearly, this was a senseless procedure. He then discusses the choice of liquids, fixing on spirit of wine because of its large dilatation, though he knows that the amount of the dilatation depends on the purity of the spirit. In the course of this discussion he criticizes Amontons' air thermometer, for he does not believe that air always has the same dilatability. It turns out that he has the presence of water vapor in mind. Indeed, the same conclusions had been reached by Philippe de la Hire in 1708.[61]

So he will start with spirit of wine of known properties. The principle of constructing a thermometer is that at the temperature of water beginning to freeze the instrument will contain some known volume of spirit. The tube will be divided into

---

[59] This was acknowledged in 1789 by Jean Gaussen, *Dissertation sur le thermomètre de Réaumur* (Beziers, 1789), p. 117.

[60] *Mém. Acad. r. des Sci. Paris* (1730), p. 454.

[61] *Ibid.* (1708), pp. 274–88.

degrees each containing a known fraction of this volume. In order that this can be done accurately, he proposes very large thermometers, and he suggests bulbs 4½ inches in diameter and tubes up to ¼ inch in bore, and several feet long. Why not? he asks.

He had made a series of small pipettes for calibrating the bulb and tube, and larger ones containing 25, 50, and 100 times as much as the smaller. The exact unit of measurement is arbitrary but it should occupy ⅙ to ⅓ of an inch of the tube.

After tying a fine thread around the tube at the place where he would like the freezing point to come, he puts in an integral number of hundreds of his unit measures. If this comes to an inconvenient place he corrects things by dropping some bits of gravel, or of glass, into the bulb, until the liquid rises to where he wants it. Water, not spirit, is used at this stage. He then attaches the tube to its wooden base covered with white paper and calibrates the scale by putting in single units of volume, not of water but of mercury, which runs into the bulb and displaces the water. Next he removes the glassware and draws the scale properly.

He then pours the water and mercury out, carefully preserving the grains of gravel, etc., and drying them, and also drying the tube and bulb as far as possible, although he says that this does not really matter. Next he pours in spirit of wine of the proper quality to a little above the thread that marks the zero. Presumably he has replaced the bits of gravel, though he does not say so. He puts the bulb into a cylindrical can, high enough to extend to the level of the zero mark, and freezes water in this by surrounding it with a freezing mixture in another vessel. Then

> As the water around the bulb becomes colder, the liquid descends in the tube. When the surface of the water has frozen, the liquid is very close to its lowest point. When it is judged to be about as low as it can go, and if it is below the point marked as the freezing-point, spirit of wine is put in little by little . . . until it rises to [the point marked by the thread]. Then we shall be careful to note whether the liquid keeps on descending. If it does, we add whatever is needed to bring it back to the marked point. When it remains steady there, the bulb may be taken out of the ice, but . . . it is better to let the ice melt, and wait until it lets the bulb come out freely.[62]

Réaumur then sealed the end of the tube, warming it "so that [the air] that remains above the liquid has neither the density nor the spring of ordinary air."[63] It is questionable, he believes, whether it is better to leave air in the tube, or to produce a near

[62] *Ibid.* (1730), p. 470.
[63] *Ibid.*, p. 471.

vacuum. Both, he thinks, have drawbacks, and he prefers to compromise.

The supposed effect of even moderate pressures in changing or preventing the dilatation of liquids was to hamper the progress of thermometry for the rest of the century at least. Another question that was wide open in 1730 was whether the freezing point and the boiling point of water were really constant, even apart from the effect of changing atmospheric pressure on the latter. There was a persistent tradition that the power of the air to freeze water was not solely determined by its temperature but was influenced by its content of "saline particles," which were thought necessary for the formation of ice. This tradition was evidently well known to Réaumur,[64] who says that he knows that water does not always freeze in nature when the air is at one particular temperature. On the other hand his artificial ice is not exposed to all these variations in the air.

> But what . . . seems to me to put the matter beyond contradiction is that I have made ice at different seasons of the year; I have made it on fine days and rainy days, during which different winds were blowing; and these specimens of ice have always made the thermometer go down to the point marked for artificial congelation.[65]

We may be surprised that he succeeded so well, but the enormous size of his thermometer bulb and his way of doing the experiment ensured that there was plenty of ice and water in thermal equilibrium by the time his great instrument had steadied down.

It was necessary to choose a standard dilution of spirit of wine, and Réaumur goes into an appallingly long-winded description of his way of doing this. In brief, he calibrates a narrow-necked flask (matras) and determines for various dilutions the dilatation between (1) the freezing point of water and (2) the point where the spirit itself just ceases to boil after it has come to the boil and cooled down below its boiling point several times, presumably so that any air it contains—and alas! some of the alcohol, too—will have been driven off. Then he summarizes this part of the paper in a sentence which proved highly unfortunate: "What I was trying to do was to find, in parts of this same volume [the volume at the freezing point], its difference from the volume of this same quantity of spirit of wine dilated by the heat of boiling water."[66] One can scarcely

[64] It had been aired by J. J. d'Ortous de Mairan in his *Dissertation sur la glace* (Bordeaux, 1716), pp. 29ff.

[65] *Mém. Acad. r. Sci. Paris* (1730), p. 477.

[66] *Ibid.*, pp. 482–83. "Ce que je cherchois étoit d'avoir en parties de ce même volume, sa différence avec le volume de la même quantité d'esprit de vin dilaté par la chaleur de l'eau bouillante."

blame people for forgetting what had transpired several pages earlier and thinking that the upper temperature in these experiments was the boiling point of water, though it was clearly the boiling point of whatever sample of diluted alcohol he was using at the time.

After five more pages we learn that he finally chose a dilution for which the expansion, measured in this way, was 80 parts in 1000, mainly because 80 is "a number convenient to divide into parts."[67] Then, in insisting that particulars of the spirit employed should be written on the scale of the thermometer, he makes confusion inevitable:

> We shall write, for example, at the top: *Spirit of wine, of which the volume is 1000 when condensed by the freezing of water, and 1080 when rarefied by boiling water.* In this case, if the thermometer goes high enough, the degree of dilatation marked 80 on one side[68] and 1080 on the other will be the boiling-water point (*le terme de l'eau bouillante*).[69]

I am inclined to doubt whether Réaumur was really clear in his own mind about what he was doing. In any event, the public came to believe that 80°R. is the boiling point of water.

There is a great deal more in that paper of 1730. For instance, he recognizes that his large thermometers are very sluggish and suggests that the remedy is to change the shape, rather than the volume, of the bulb. "Any shape is all right."[70] At any rate, if smaller thermometers are required—and of course they were— they can be graduated by comparison with the large ones.

He comes back to the supposed inconstancy of the fixed points. A few years earlier this had been urged by Carlo Taglini of Pisa in a curiously uneven dissertation[71] which ends in complete despair—his own word—of ever being able to construct an accurate thermometer because no fixed points can be obtained. On the way to this sad conclusion, Taglini did suggest that "Thermometers filled with the purest spirit of wine indicate the degrees of heat and cold more exactly, other things being equal,"[72] advice that Réaumur chose to ignore. Of course, Taglini was right about the boiling point, although he did not recognize that the difficulty lay in the variability of the atmospheric pressure. Réaumur did not make the boiling point one of his fixed points (though

[67] *Ibid.*, p. 489.

[68] Of the tube. He liked to mark his scales both from 0 to 80 and from 1000 to 1080.

[69] *Ibid.*, p. 489. The italics are after Réaumur.

[70] *Ibid.*, p. 498.

[71] Taglini, *De thermometro disputatio* [etc.] (Andreas Aloysius, *praeses*) (Pisa, 1725). There is a copy in the library of the *Muséum d'Histoire Naturelle* in Paris, DD 115D.

[72] *Ibid.*, p. 31.

he imagined that he was using it in choosing a suitable dilution of alcohol), but he was able to adduce his own experiments to refute Taglini's claim that the freezing point is variable. In any event, whatever other points may or may not be fixed, Paris physicists have one fixed point in the cellars of the Observatory. On his "1000°–1080°" thermometer, the temperature in these cellars is 1,010¼°. We shall hear more about this later.

Réaumur's paper of 1731,[73] almost equally verbose, is largely devoted to an investigation of the "air" that remains in the spirit of wine. His somewhat draconic method of getting rid of this must have got rid of a good deal of alcohol as well.

There is a fairly large unpublished memoir[74] in which Mairan, while praising Réaumur's new way[75] of making thermometers, also worries about the air left in the tube, thinking that it may dissolve in the spirit, or come out again, and suggesting that it would be better to leave the thermometer unsealed. But, of course, evaporation must be prevented, and he blows a small bulb near the top of the tube and adds petroleum oil so that it half fills this, the short length of tube remaining being open to the air. This construction has the advantage, Mairan adds, that it almost eliminates the change of hydrostatic pressure with change of temperature, and thus the elastic effects on the bulb.

As far as I am aware this idea was stillborn, but the manuscript contains evidence that the volatility of alcohol had been a difficulty for a long time. Mairan tells us that Hubin, who made thermometers for the Academy in the seventeenth century, used "la Simple Eau de vie" in order to reduce the formation of bubbles and "make good the lesser sensitivity of that liquid by making the tubes a little narrower in relation to the capacity of the bulbs.[76]

The subsequent fate of Réaumur's thermometric scale is interesting but rather complicated. In France, to which the Fahrenheit scale had not spread, it had no immediate competition, and Réaumur's great authority made any criticism of it almost lèse-majesté in academic circles. It is, therefore, rather surprising to find that it gradually suffered a change, until, by 1770 or thereabouts, what was referred to as Réaumur's scale differed both numerically and in principle from the version of 1730. I shall endeavor to explain how this came about.

[73] Réaumur, *Mém. Acad. r. des Sci. Paris* (1731), pp. 250–96.

[74] J. J. d'Ortous de Mairan, "Remarques sur la construction des thermomètres et des baromètres [etc.]" *Registres Acad. r. Sci. Paris,* February 10, 1731, fol. 15r–28v.

[75] The reading of Réaumur's first paper had been completed only a fortnight earlier, on January 27, 1731.

[76] Mairan, fol. 20v.

Réaumur himself soon came to realize that his methods, and especially his way of preparing a standard sample of alcohol, were no easy matter. His assistants, Henri Pitot (the inventor of the Pitot tube) and later the Abbé Jean Antoine Nollet, could follow them,[77] but probably not the average artisan.[78] By 1736, moreover, he seems to be losing sight of his own principles, so that he can write unselfconsciously about "the mercury of thermometers constructed on the same principles as those of spirit of wine,"[79] where the context makes it clear that it is his own spirit thermometers that he has in mind. In spite of the complete impossibility of applying *all* his principles to the construction of a mercury thermometer, such thermometers were made at about this time and taken on the famous expedition to Lapland (1736–37) which measured the length of a degree of the meridian near the arctic circle. On his return the leader of the expedition reported[80] that, "In January the cold was so great that our mercury thermometers *of Mr. de Réaumur's construction* . . . went down to 37 degrees [below zero]; those of spirit of wine froze."[81]

By the end of 1739 Réaumur began to be aware of other thermometers. In discussing some observations that Musschenbroek had sent him from Utrecht, he notes that they were made with a mercury thermometer by Fahrenheit, and makes the objection that the latter does not follow his volumetric method. "Whatever liquid one wishes to put into the thermometer . . . even mercury, the principles that I have established ought always to be followed."[82] But although mercury and spirit thermometers were made on these principles, they could not coincide everywhere on their scales, because the two liquids do not expand proportionately; and therefore

it follows that if we wish to have a mercury thermometer that expresses the degrees of cold and of heat by the same numbers as does the spirit-of-wine thermometer, we are obliged to graduate the former by means of the latter, as the Abbé Nollet has done, and continues to do with great care; and on the other hand we shall graduate a spirit thermometer by means of a mercury thermometer, if we want it to speak the language of the mercury thermometer.[83]

[77] Both these men became Academicians. I call them his assistants on the authority of Arthur Birembaut in *La vie et l'oeuvre de Réaumur*, ed. cit., p. 62.

[78] Cf. Réaumur, *Mém. Acad. r. Sci. Paris* (1734), p. 190.

[79] *Ibid.* (1736), pp. 489–90.

[80] P. L. Moreau de Maupertuis, *Mém. Acad. r. Sci. Paris* (1737), pp. 389–469.

[81] *Ibid.*, pp. 419–20. The italics are mine. The freezing of the spirit of wine suggests that it contained less than about 60 per cent of ethanol by weight. If the temperature had really been $-37°R$, on the principles that the scale was *supposed* to be based on, the mercury would also have frozen.

[82] Réaumur, *Mém. Acad. r. Sci. Paris* (1739), pp. 461–62.

[83] *Ibid.*, p. 462.

Réaumur deserves great credit for realizing this, but people soon began to want to make mercury thermometers, to correspond as closely as possible to his original scale, without going through the whole process. One of these was a doctor at Montpellier, François Boissier de Sauvages, who, in an appendix to a work on silkworms,[84] instructs his readers to calibrate a mercury thermometer in boiling water, and then in snow or crushed ice, and to divide the interval into 87 degrees.[85] This, he says, will agree with Réaumur's spirit thermometer.

But it was not long until it became general practice to define the "Réaumur" scale by the freezing point of water or the melting point of ice (0°) and the boiling point of water (80°), and to graduate mercury thermometers uniformly between these points. It turned out that for some purposes this was not much of a change. The celebrated Johann Heinrich Lambert pointed out much later that because of the nonlinear dilatation of spirit of wine, Réaumur's peculiar technique just happened to ensure that in the lower part of his scale—i.e., at ordinary meteorological temperatures—his spirit thermometer almost agrees with a mercury thermometer graduated between 0° and 80°.[86]

Some time in the 1730's even Réaumur, probably at the prompting of Nollet, realized that melting ice was a more convenient standard than freezing water.[87] Nollet made an excellent technical point: "If a vessel is specially made for holding the thermometers in the ice, it is well to have a tap, or something equivalent, near the bottom, in order to let the water out when it is seen to be getting too abundant."[88] It seems likely that Réaumur and Nollet made the change from freezing water to melting ice as early as 1732.[89]

It appears that one of Réaumur's large thermometers was preserved by the *Académie* until the revolution, for in the inventory made by J. A. C. Charles in 1793 we find the following entry: "Item 55. Large thermometer of Réaumur, preserved in a box. This thermometer may be precious, if it is a standard for the

[84] I have seen only an Italian version, "Modo di fare de' termometri d'argento vivo, e che si accordino con quelli del Sig. de Réaumur," in *Memorie sopra la fisica* [etc.], ed. O. A. Giuliani (4 vols.; Lucca, 1743–57), Vol. 1 (1743), pp. 243–45.

[85] All sorts of other figures, from 85 to 115, were suggested by various authors.

[86] Lambert, *Pyrometrie oder vom Maase des Feuers und der Wärme* (Berlin, 1779 [posthumous]), pp. 71–72.

[87] Cf. Nollet, *L'art d'expériences* [etc.] (3 vols.; Paris, 1770), Vol. 3, pp. 147–48.

[88] *Ibid.*, p. 148.

[89] Jean Gaussen, *Dissertation sur le thermomètre de Réaumur* (Béziers, 1789), pp. 70–82, argues plausibly for this.

thermometers of the true system of Réaumur, which is neither clear nor well known."[90] I do not know what has become of this instrument.

A thermometer scale analogous to that of Réaumur was invented in 1732 by Joseph Nicolas Delisle, a French astronomer who had been invited to St. Petersburg by Peter the Great and remained there from 1725 to 1747. In 1724 or earlier he and his brother had made some spirit thermometers that indicated 0° in boiling water and 100° in the Observatory cellars;[91] and being unable to take these thermometers to Russia, he determined to make some more. But at St. Petersburg there were no cellars of sufficient depth; and besides this, he found it difficult to adjust spirit thermometers in boiling water; so in 1732 he adopted mercury as a working liquid[92] and produced a scale with one fixed point—the temperature of boiling water—and characterized by the number of hundred-thousandths of its volume that the mercury contracted at lower temperatures. A description of this, which still exists in manuscript,[93] was sent to Paris and read to the Academy in February, 1734.[94] Nothing could testify more strongly to the Academy's commitment to Réaumur's thermometer than the fact that this paper, like Mairan's, was not published; unlike Mairan's, it was not even copied into the *Procès-verbaux*.[95]

I shall briefly indicate Delisle's method. A tube two or three feet long was attached to a cylindrical bulb after having been calibrated by means of a short thread of mercury. His bulbs

[90] *Inventaire des Instrumens de Physique Optique, Géométrie, Astronomie &c. Du Cabinet de la cy devt. Académie des Sciences de Paris.* Institut de France, ms. 1986, no. I.

[91] J. N. Delisle and L. Delisle de la Croyère, *Mém. Acad. r. Sci. Paris* (1724), pp. 316–19.

[92] J. N. Delisle, *Mém. Acad. r. Sci. Paris* (1749), p. 6.

[93] *Les thermometres de Mercure rendus Universels, en leur faisant en tout tems la quantité dont le volume du mercure est diminué, par la temperature presente de l'air, au dessous de l'etendue quil a dans l'eau bouillante.* Observatoire de Paris, ms. A.7.4, item 35. This bears a note in Delisle's hand stating that his memoir—presumably a copy—had been "given to Mr. [Daniel] Bernouilli on his departure from St. Petersburg in 173[3] to be taken to Paris and presented to the Academy, where it was read on the 10th and 13th of February, 1734, by Mr. Godin."

[94] According to the *Registres,* on the 3rd and 10th.

[95] It had been read to the St. Petersburg Academy in February, 1733, and was finally published in *Mémoires pour servir à l'histoire & aux progrès de l'astronomie & de la géographie physique* [etc.] (St. Petersburg, 1738), pp. 267–84. The Berlin Academy published, in Latin, excerpts from a letter of March 22, 1732, about it (*Misc. Berol.*, Vol. 4 (1734), pp. 343–49). Delisle also wrote in February, 1733, to the Secretary of the Royal Society, John Machin; this letter was published later in *Phil. Trans.*, Vol. 39 (1736), pp. 221–29. He was clearly out for publicity.

were about half an inch in diameter and 3 or 4 inches long. Then in cool weather the bulb and tube were weighed, filled completely with mercury, and weighed again, then immersed in boiling water. Some of the mercury came out. By weighing this and cooling the thermometer down again he was able to express lengths on the tube in terms of hundred-thousandths—later ten-thousandths—of the volume of the mercury at the boiling point of water. This was his scale, the thermometers usually being graduated down to 2,400 or 2,700 degrees, sufficient for the temperatures at St. Petersburg.

One rather interesting advantage claimed by Delisle for his scale was that it made it easy to correct the observed height of the barometer to what it would be at the boiling point of water! There exists a table for this correction with columns for barometer readings 26.00/0.50/30.00 inches and rows for temperatures 900/50/2,100° Delisle.[96]

In none of the sources mentioned so far is there anything about the freezing point of water. But in the winter of 1737–38, at Delisle's suggestion, Josias Weitbrecht made experiments on the freezing point of water from the river Neva and also measured the temperature of the water flowing under the ice on the river, finding it to remain quite constant at 149.5° Delisle all winter.[97] These observations, we may suppose, set Weitbrecht off on an excellent series of experiments of his own, in which, using techniques very like Delisle's, he determined that the contraction of the mercury between the boiling point and the freezing point of water was very close to 150/10000 of the volume at the boiling point. He therefore proposed to make thermometers by using the two fixed points, marking 0° at the boiling point, 150° at the freezing point, and extrapolating to 200° to take care of lower temperatures.[98] Weitbrecht was well aware that the expansion of mercury, obtained in this way, depends on the glass, "since the mercury is contained in an instrument of variable capacity."[99] He also knew that the thermometer should be pointed at the boiling point first, then at the freezing point, and that it should be sealed when at the boiling point so as to leave as little air in as possible. The boiling, he thought, should be done when the barometer is fairly high, so as to obtain as strong a heat as possible.

The Delisle scale, made in this way, remained in use for more

[96] Observatoire de Paris, ms. A.7.3, item 27.

[97] *Ibid.,* item 29. By this time the numbers had been divided by ten.

[98] J. Weitbrecht, *Comm. Acad. Petrop.,* Vol. 8 (1736), pp. 310–33. This was published in 1741.

[99] *Ibid.,* p. 332. The phrase is italicized in the Latin.

than half a century in Russia.[100] The scale had little to recommend it, but the thermometers were fairly well constructed, and, as we shall see later, one very important one survives.[101]

4. *The Centigrade Thermometers.* It is nothing more than a historical accident that our system of counting has a decimal base, so that the integral powers of ten are the "round" numbers. We are so used to this that we have come to think of it as if it were imposed on us by natural law; but, in fact, we could have chosen any number as a base, and there are others, notably the number 12, which might have been more convenient because of having more divisors. In our older systems of measuring length and mass, and in our division of time, can be found traces of a predilection for a duodecimal notation. If the digital computer had been invented long ago, we might all be counting in powers of 2! But however this may be, 100 is a round number for us today, and it was to be expected that sooner or later someone would propose a thermometer scale with 100 degrees between the fundamental points.

Nowadays this is taken to mean a scale with 100 degrees between the melting point of ice and the boiling point of water; but before discussing the invention of this "centigrade" thermometer, we must dispose of two earlier thermometers that had 100 degrees in their scales.

The first of these, and as far as I know the first thermometer of this kind, has already been mentioned. To measure air temperatures during the total solar eclipse of May 22, 1724, the Delisle brothers had made four spirit thermometers that indicated 0° in boiling water—we can suppose only that the compression of the contained air made this successful—and 100° in the Observatory cellars.[102] Nothing further seems to have been heard of this scale.

The second scale of this sort, about which we have a good deal more information, was invented by Jacques Barthélemi Micheli du Crest, a native of Geneva who ended his days as a political prisoner of the Canton of Berne. In 1741 he published an anonymous pamphlet at Paris, describing his "universal ther-

[100] Cf. Anon., *Acta Acad. Petrop.* (1782), *Hist.*, pp. 25–27 (published 1786).
[101] There is also an interesting thermometer with the Delisle scale in the Deutsches Museum at Munich (inv. no. 39079). This has the scale on a brass tube, and a cursor carrying a vernier, with a fine adjustment; it cannot be much earlier than 1800.
[102] J. N. Delisle and L. Delisle de la Croyère, *Mém. Acad. r. Sci. Paris* (1724), pp. 316–19.

mometer."[103] The term simply meant a thermometer that could be duplicated by anyone, and it will be remembered that Delisle had used the same designation. This was republished, with extensive additions, in 1757.[104] In the earlier work Micheli records almost at the outset his doubts about the constancy of the freezing point of water and the melting point of ice, and this for the usual reason: in colder countries ice may be "impregnated with a greater quantity of niter at its center, or with other kinds of salt differing from ours."[105] Because of this uncertainty, he takes the temperature of the cellar of the Observatory as his lower fixed point and marks it zero, and the boiling point of water under a pressure of 27¾ Paris inches of mercury as his upper one, marked 100°. He chooses spirit of wine as a thermometric fluid, having apparently made up his mind, without any evidence, that it dilates more regularly than mercury. He also takes it as axiomatic that the temperature in deep cellars and mines is everywhere the same.

It is not quite clear whether he obtained permission to calibrate his thermometers in the Observatory cellar, but it seems unlikely. In practice he

> founded the freezing-point of [his] thermometer on the degree of cold of ice in summer, crushed till it is just like snow, taken in quantity and pressed around all the liquid of the thermometer in a tarred bucket from which the water is drawn off.[106]

This point he took as −10.4° on his scale. As far as I can determine, this figure resulted from his comparisons with some of Réaumur's thermometers, but the matter is not at all clear. It is rather astonishing that he thought that the temperature in the crushed ice would always be the same, but we discover that he did not think of this as the melting point, but as the temperature "of water in ice."[107]

This scale, in principle exactly the inverse of that of the brothers Delisle, was centesimal in theory but not in practice. We must now consider the origins of the centigrade scale as we

[103] *Description d'un thermomètre universel* (Paris, 1741).

[104] Anon., "Recuil de diverses pièces sur les thermomètres et baromètres, par l'auteur de la methode d'un thermomètre universel," *Acta Helvetica*, Vol. 3 (1757), pp. 23–104. Also separately as a pamphlet (Basle, 1757), paged from page 1.

[105] Micheli, *Description* (1741), p. 3. But this passage is not in the 1757 paper.

[106] *Ibid.*, p. 12.

[107] *Ibid.* (1757), p. 43. In Teyler's Museum at Haarlem there is a thermometer (inv. no. 1131) with three scales, one apparently that of Micheli, the others Fahrenheit and Réaumur.

know it, with zero at the melting point of ice and 100° at the boiling point of water.

The name associated in the minds of most people with the centigrade scale of temperature is that of the Swedish astronomer Anders Celsius; so much so, indeed, that in 1948 the Ninth General Conference of Weights and Measures officially ruled that what had been called "degrees centigrade" should henceforth go by the name "degrees Celsius."[108] There is, as we shall see, some justification for this, but we must also examine the claims of the great botanist Linnaeus, the astronomer Märten Strömer, and Jean Pierre Christin of Lyon. The names of Horrebow and Réaumur, surprisingly, also come into the story, though not as contenders for the honor of the invention, and I had better get this episode out of the way first.

In the archives of the Académie des Sciences at Paris there is a large envelope of loose papers marked "Réaumur, thermomètre et baromètre." Among these papers are the two scraps reproduced as Fig. 4.3 (a) and (b), drawn and written on by Réaumur, whose handwriting is somewhat of a trial. At the top of the "thermometer" sketched in Fig. 4.3(a), he wrote "Römer. 1702. 0 eau bouillante"; at a point lower down, "100. congellation"; and at the left, "mon degre a [sc. à] celui de Roemer comme 4. a 5. 22." I have no idea what the "22" means, but the remainder is explained by the other piece of paper, fig. 4.3 (b), which reads as follows:

pour 1740 si j'ai la suite détaillée des observations de Mr. horrebou

Mr horrebou s'est trouve des thermometres dont la marche peut etre ramenée aux miens. si Mr Roemer n'a pas eu l'idée que chaque degre fut une portion connue d'un volume de liqueur pris dans l'etat de la congelation, il avoit pense a faire des thermometres dont les degres peuvent etre compares aux miens.

Rappeller l'histoire

La congelation est exprimee par 100, et l'eau bouillante par 0. audessous de la congelation les degres s'ajoutent a 100. en otant 100. les degres se comptent comme les miens, et au contraire au dessus de la congelation otant le nombre des degres marques de 100. ou prenant le complement de 100 on compte a ma maniere 80de de Mr Roemer en comptant a ma maniere seroient 20 degres. mais Mr horrebou a remarque que quatre de mes degres en valent 5 de Mr. Roemer, ainsi 20 degres de Mr. Roemer sont 16 des miens. &c.

This is almost a doodle—Réaumur thinking with his pen. If we may assume a little more punctuation, it might be rendered as follows:

[108] For more information see J. A. Hall and C. R. Barber, *British J. Appl. Phys.*, Vol. 1 (1950), pp. 82–86.

Fig. 4.3(a) A sketch by Réaumur. 4.3(b) a fragment in Réaumur's hand-writing. (Courtesy of the Académie des Sciences.)

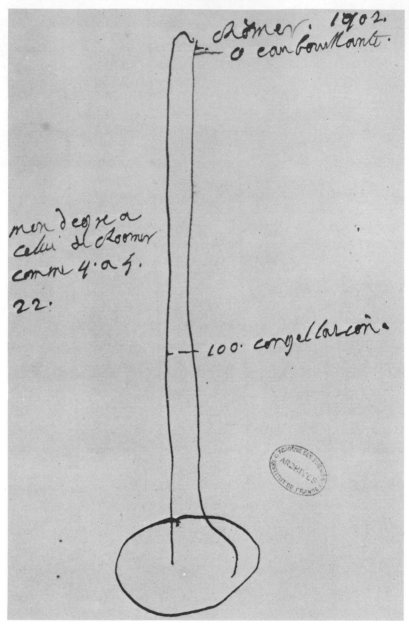

For 1740, if I have the detailed series of observations from Mr. Horrebow:

Mr. Horrebow found thermometers, the scale of which can be reduced to mine. [Even] if Mr. Rømer did not have the idea that each degree should be a known part of a volume of liquid taken when it is freezing, he had thought of making thermometers[109] of which the degrees can be compared with mine.

I have translated the last phrase word for word, and I submit it as an almost unexampled piece of egotism. Réaumur goes on:

Remember the story:

The freezing-point is expressed by 100, and boiling water by 0. Below freezing-point the degrees are added to 100; taking away 100 they are counted like mine; and above freezing, on the contrary, taking the number of indicated degrees from 100, or taking the complement to 100 we count in my way. 80 of Mr. Rømer's, counting in

109 Réaumur has crossed out "which can be reduced."

my way, would be 20 degrees. But Mr. Horrebow remarked that 4 of my degrees are equal to 5 of Mr. Rømer's, and so 20 degrees of his are 16 of mine, etc.[110]

I have been unable to find the letter that Horrebow must have written to Réaumur, probably in 1741, accompanying a copy of the meteorological observations for 1740, taken at Copenhagen.[111] He evidently told Réaumur about the five thermometers that had been given him by Rømer's widow.[112] What else he may have said may be guessed at from two separate notes in the manuscript of Rømer's *Adversaria*.[113] The first of these reads

> for 60 I take 100 and for 7½ I take 20, that is, ⅕ of the whole scale, in order to leave space for a greater cold than is observed in Denmark; this I do in Rømer's name, as he advised it.[114]

In the other note, after explaining that Rømer had divided his scale into seven parts between the freezing point and the boiling point and then added one part below freezing point "for greater degrees of cold," Horrebow continues:

> It seems to me more convenient as follows: between boiling-point and the snow four equal parts are taken, and one below; divide each of these five parts into 20, and you have 100 parts, a round number, below which the thermometer has never been observed to fall at Copenhagen. But nevertheless the invention is to be attributed to Rømer, for it is really his. P. Horrebow.[115]

These two notes, taken together with Réaumur's scribble, show us the origin of the latter but raise more than one problem. We should first remark that of Horrebow's two notes the first would have the boiling point at 100, which was simply substituted for

110 I must express my warmest thanks to Mme. Gauja, the Archivist of the Académie, for putting this bundle of papers on the table with the hope that "I might find something interesting in it."

111 No such observations appear in Réaumur's annual meteorological summary in *Mém. Acad. r. Sci. Paris* (1740), pp. 539–66.

112 See p. 68 above.

113 Copenhagen, Royal Library, ms. E. don. var. 16. Published as *Ole Rømers Adversaria . . . udgivne af det Kgl. Danske Videnskabernes Selskab, ved Thyra Eibe og Kirstine Meyer* (Copenhagen, 1910). See also p. 67 above.

114 *Adversaria,* fol. 115v (1910 ed.; p. 207). "Pro 60 sumo 100 & pro 7½ sumo 20, scilicet ⅕ totius graduationis, ut relinquatur spatium pro majori frigore quam in Dania observatur; quod monente Roemero facio nomine Roemeri." This must mean that Rømer believed in leaving space for the greatest cold.

115 *Ibid.,* fol. 117v (1910 ed.; p. 211). "Convenientius mihi sic videtur: Inter Ebullitionem & nivem sumantur quatuor partes aequales, quarum una sumatur deorsum; singulas has partes quintas divide in viginti, & habes partes 100, numerum rotundum, infra quas nunquam Hafniae observatum est thermometrum descendere. Sed inventio nihilominus tribuenda est Roemero, cujus revera est."

Rømer's 60,[116] while the second could be interpreted in the same way, or else with the boiling point at zero and 100 a low temperature below which the thermometer never sinks at Copenhagen.

More interesting still, neither of these alternatives corresponds to the scale sketched and described by Réaumur, in which the interval between freezing point and boiling point is 100 degrees. It is almost certain that Horrebow would write in Latin, so there could be no difficulty in communication. It is evident (1) that Horrebow told Réaumur about the scale, (2) that he ascribed it to Rømer, (3) that he "remarked" that four of Réaumur's degrees were equal to five of "Rømers." Except for this last remark we might suppose the Réaumur misinterpreted Horrebow's description of this scale. All that can be said, until Horrebow's letter is brought to light, is that *either* Horrebow or Réaumur devised a centigrade scale and then did nothing further about it.

This cannot be said of Anders Celsius, professor of astronomy at Uppsala from 1730 until his early death in 1744. The first indication that I have found of his interest in making thermometers dates from May 9, 1734, when one Giovanni Bianchi wrote from Rimini begging Celsius to "write . . . about that way of making a mercury thermometer, as you promised me when you were here,"[117] referring to a visit to Italy that Celsius had made the year before. What sort of a thermometer this was we do not know, but we are informed by his successor Märten Strömer that "the best and most accurate observations [had been] taken at Uppsala since 1726" with Hauksbee's thermometer.[118] This may disclose some degree of partiality, since Celsius had described his centigrade thermometer three years earlier in 1742, as we shall see. Meanwhile, we have confirmation from Celsius himself that he was using both a thermometer and a barometer made by Hauksbee for the official observations in 1731.[119] This instrumentmaker is so well known, he says, that description is superfluous.

But he had other thermometers, as we learn from a manuscript copy of observations, kept at Paris[120] in the file of loose papers

[116] See above, p. 68.

[117] Uppsala, University Library, ms. A533, item 19.

[118] *Kgl. Schwed. Acad. Wiss., Abh.*, Vol. 7 (1745), p. 168. (This is the German edition, tr. A. G. Kästner [Hamburg and Leipzig, 1752]. In the original *Handlingar* it appears on p. 166.)

[119] A. Celsius, *Misc. Berol.*, Vol. 5 (1737), p. 132.

[120] *Observationes Meteorologicae, habitae Upsaliae Anno 1740 ab And. Celsio* (Paris, Acad. Sci.), dossier "Réaumur, thermomètre et baromètre," (eight small leaves).

Fig. 4.4   A thermometer sent by Delisle to Celsius. (Courtesy of the Meteorological Institute, the Royal University, Uppsala.)

previously referred to. After giving his monthly maximum and minimum temperatures—1740 was a famous year for cold weather —he notes that "a thermometer constructed by the Abbé Nollet according to the principles of the illustrious Réaumur" went down on January 25 to −19°. At this time Hauksbee's thermometer had shown 126° and Delisle's 192°.[121]

We know where he got the Delisle thermometer for we have a letter in French from Delisle to Celsius dated from St. Petersburg, December 11, 1737, new style. Delisle is sending

> a small box in which are enclosed two mercury thermometers of my construction, that is to say adjusted in the way that I have thought the simplest and most exact for making universal thermometers. This method is described in the *Miscellanea Berolinensia* in one of my letters to Mr. Kirch.[122]

He is sending thermometers of this sort, calibrated at St. Petersburg, to all the places where meteorological observations have been made up to now [!], and "I have begged those to whom I have sent them to be kind enough to compare them with other thermometers, of whatever kind, that they have used in their meteorological observations."[123]

By the greatest good fortune, one of these two thermometers survives (Fig. 4.4), the treasured possession of the Meteorological Institute of Uppsala University.[124] The very slender tube, only about 2 mm. outside diameter, is tied over a paper scale to a wooden base. Delisle's scale runs from 0° at the top (*Chaleur d'eau bouillante*) past 150° (*Premiere Gelée*) to 205. On the right has been added part of Celsius' scale, defined by dots at 50° and then 70° onward. This scale is probably the result of a recalibration, for 100° Celsius corresponds not to 150° Delisle, as one might expect, but to 151.8°. I am almost sure[125] that the earlier scale and all the legends were put on by Delisle himself; but about the other I can come to no conclusion, though it is most unlikely that Celsius would delegate a job of this sort. On one edge of the thick wooden base someone has written, "Den första skalan af A. Celsius, inprickad på en gammal de L'Isle termometer."[126]

[121] *Ibid.*, fol. 2ʳ.

[122] This probably refers to *Misc. Berol.*, Vol. 4 (1734), pp. 343–49. Christfried Kirch was the astronomer of the Berlin Academy of Sciences.

[123] Uppsala, Univ. Lib., ms. A533, item 47 (one folded sheet).

[124] I am indebted to the Director, Dr. G. H. Liljequist, and to Dr. Birger Svensson, for this photograph and for much kindness.

[125] From a comparison with the handwriting in Obs. de Paris, ms. A.7.4, item 35.

[126] "The first scale of A. Celsius, drawn on an old Delisle thermometer."

Whenever it was that he marked his 100-degree scale on this thermometer, it was before 1742, when he wrote the paper[127] that shows how carefully he had been thinking about the problems of thermometry. He had also been reading the latest literature on the subject, namely, George Martine's "Essay on the construction and graduation of thermometers,"[128] to which I shall have occasion to refer in a later section.[129]

To begin with, Celsius does not like Réaumur's way of establishing his lower fixed point—we have seen that it probably had been abandoned even in France by this time—and prefers melting snow, quoting Newton as an authority for his preference.[130] Even when the snow is put in a kettle on the stove, Celsius has found, the thermometer does not rise as long as the snow remains tightly packed round the bulb. Regarding the boiling point, he finds that it depends to some extent on how violently the water is boiling. When the bubbles are large, and rise over the entire surface of the water, the thermometer takes up a steady temperature.

By careful experiments, he has confirmed Fahrenheit's conclusion that the boiling point varies with the height of the barometer and thinks that an accurate thermometer might be more easily transported than a barometer on voyages and in the mountains. He then describes his scale, the upper fixed point, marked 0°, being the temperature of boiling water when the barometer stands at 25¼ Swedish inches.[131] He gives a rule for marking the 0°-point if the water has to be boiled at other atmospheric pressures.

We know that Celsius had his new thermometer ready for use on December 25, 1741, for there exists a table of observations[132] in which a column headed "Cels. Th." is added to the observations of a Réaumur thermometer, beginning on that date, when we have −4.2 and 105.3. The next day we find −4.4 and 105.5. Regular observations of this thermometer or a similar one were begun by O. Hiorter at Uppsala Observatory on June 2, 1743,

---

127 A. Celsius, *Kongl. Svensk. Wet. Akad., Handlingar*, Vol. 3 (1742), pp. 171–80. It was translated into German as "Beobachtungen von zwei beständigen Punkten auf einem Thermometer" in *Abh. Schwed. Akad.* (trans. A. G. Kästner [Hamburg and Leipzig, 1750]), Vol. 4 (1742), pp. 197–205. References are to this version.

128 In *Essays Medical and Philosophical* (London, 1740), pp. 175–214.

129 Celsius refers to Martine's book on p. 198.

130 See p. 57 above.

131 This corresponds to 751.16 mm according to Hilding Köhler (*Uppsala, Kungl. Vetenskapssocietatens Årsbok*, 1944, p. 111), so that on the present-day definition Celsius' upper fixed point was at 99.67 °C.

132 Uppsala, Univ. Lib., ms. A530.

being added to observations of Hauksbee's, Delisle's, and two of "Prince's" [Prins's] thermometers.[133]

Celsius died in 1744. Some time later the Prins and Delisle thermometers ceased to be observed, but an instrument marked "Ekström" was added. This thermometer, which clearly had, or was intended to have, the freezing point at 0° and the boiling point at 100°, had been made by Daniel Ekström, a leading Stockholm instrumentmaker who had returned there in 1740 after studying his craft in England.[134] From September 1, 1747, another thermometer was added (Hauksbee's having been abandoned), and this bore the name of Celsius' successor Märten Strömer. Strömer's thermometer, which had the same scale as Ekström's, appears to have been developed in 1746.[135] This is interesting, because in the previous year Strömer wrote of "Hauksbee's thermometer, with which the best and most accurate observations have been taken at Uppsala since 1726."[136] As a matter of fact, this particular thermometer was about ten degrees off the supposed Hauksbee standard at the freezing point if the observations are to be believed.[137] However, it is important that by 1746 both Ekström and Strömer had made thermometers with the ice point at 0° and the boiling point at 100°. In the official observations Celsius' scale was replaced by Strömer's on April 13, 1750, and was no longer used.[138] This has given rise to the standard textbook statement that Strömer "inverted" his predecessor's scale in 1750. An examination of the note in the *Handlingar* makes the situation clear: "The thermometer of the late Professor Celsius has 0 at the boiling-point of water and 100 at the freezing-point; that of Professor Strömer, on the contrary, has 0 at the freezing-point and 100 at the boiling-point."[139]

Yet a very good case can be made for the assertion that the scale to which we are accustomed was suggested, not by Ekström or by Strömer, but by the celebrated botanist Carl von Linné (Linnaeus).[140] Indeed, Nordenmark has attempted to prove, not only that Linnaeus did this, but that he did it several years

[133] Uppsala, Univ. Lib., ms. A266c, quoted by N. V. E. Nordenmark in *Anders Celsius* (Stockholm, 1936), pp. 161–62.

[134] Nordenmark, *Svenska Linné-Sällskapets Årsskrift* (1935), p. 131. Ekström became a member of the Swedish Academy.

[135] Uppsala, Univ. Lib., ms. A313, quoted by Nordenmark, *Anders Celsius*, p. 162, note.

[136] Strömer, *Kongl. Svenska Wetenskaps Akad., Handlingar*, Vol. 7 (1745), p. 166.

[137] Cf. Nordenmark, *Anders Celsius*, p. 162.

[138] *Handlingar*, Vol. 14 (1753), pp. 254–55. The transition appears clearly in the published observations on p. 254.

[139] *Ibid.*, p. 253.

[140] Von Linné after he was ennobled in 1757.

Fig. 4.5   Part of the frontispiece of Hortus Cliffortianus, *1737.*

Fig. 4.5   Part of the frontispiece of Hortus Cliffortianus, *1737.*

before Celsius wrote the paper about his thermometer.[141, 142] This claim needs careful examination.

About 1735 Linnaeus was a guest of the wealthy banker G. Clifford, who had a magnificent garden at Hartecamp in the Netherlands, and in 1737 he published a sumptuous description of Clifford's garden and herbarium.[143] This has an elaborate engraved frontispiece with a typically eighteenth-century assortment of allegorical figures and *putti,* and in the lower right-hand corner (Fig. 4.5) one of these is holding a spade and another a thermometer nearly as big as himself, the scale of which is clearly visible, being marked 100 at the top, 90, 80, and so on down to 1 (not zero) in the middle, and then symmetrically every 10 down to 100 at the bottom.

---

141 N. V. E. Nordenmark, *Svenska Linné-Sällskapets Årsskrift* (1935), pp. 124–33 (A brief summary in English will be found on pp. 160–61).

142 Nordenmark, *Anders Celsius,* (*Lychnos-Bibliotek,* I). Celsius' thermometry is dealt with on pp. 155–67 (summary in French, pp. 263–66).

143 Linnaeus, *Hortus Cliffortianus* [etc.] (Amsterdam, 1737).

Nordenmark[144] jumped to the conclusion that this was a centigrade scale with 0° at the freezing point, and that "for the sake of symmetry" the artist had extended it downward to −100°. If Nordenmark had examined Linnaeus' preface he might have had doubts about this; for in writing of the temperatures required in greenhouses, Linnaeus refers to a very hot house (*calidissima hybernacula*) as being at 70°! Again, African succulents do not like a temperature of over 40° in winter, while American ones do not mind 70°.[145] Now whatever scale this is, it cannot be our centigrade scale. It is most probably a scale due to Fowler, which was designed specifically for horticulture and popular at the time.[146] It was graduated up and down from a zero at about 12°C., and 40° Fowler would be about 26°C., 70° about 37°C. Linnaeus had visited England in 1736 and would almost certainly have got to know Fowler's thermometer.

But, if it cannot be maintained that the centigrade scale dates back to 1737, it is clear that Linnaeus ordered from Ekström a centigrade thermometer with the zero at the ice point and showed it to the Senate of Uppsala University on December 2, 1745.[147] This thermometer was for the greenhouses in the botanical garden that Linnaeus had rehabilitated, as may be seen from a letter written, probably in October, 1745, to the secretary of the Academy of Sciences at Stockholm, Pierre Elfwius.[148] In the same year one of his students described the garden in a dissertation.[149] In his discussion of the *calidarium* or hothouse he states in a footnote that "our thermometer is 0 at the freezing-point and counts 100 to the degree of boiling water."[150]

In later life Linnaeus certainly believed himself to be the inventor of this scale. On October 30, 1758, he wrote in Latin to Boissier de la Croix de Sauvages, a botanist at Montpellier:

I was the first who decided to construct our thermometers in which the freezing-point is 0, and the heat of boiling water 100; and this for the greenhouses of our garden. I am sure that if you were accustomed to these, they would please you.[151]

[144] *Årsskrift* (1935), p. 130; *Anders Celsius*, p. 163.
[145] *Hortus Cliffortianus*, preface, sig.**, 4.
[146] Cf. Van Swinden, *Comparaison des thermomètres, ed. cit.*, p. 63.
[147] Nordenmark, *Anders Celsius*, p. 163.
[148] Th. M. Fries, ed., *Brief och skrifvelser af och till Carl von Linné*, Afd. I, Del. 2 (Stockholm, 1908), pp. 48–49.
[149] Samuel Naucler, *Hortus Upsaliensis* [etc.], Diss., Uppsala, Dec. 16, 1745.
[150] *Ibid.*, p. 23, note. "Thermometrum nostrum est 0 in puncto congelationis & numerat 100 ad gradus aquae coquentis."
[151] Louis Augustin d'Hombres-Firmas, ed., *Lettres inédites de Linné à Boissier de la Croix de Sauvages* [etc.] (Alais, 1860), p. 226. This letter had been found by one Requien, of Avignon, and communicated to François Arago, who read it to the Paris Academy in 1844. See *Compt. Rend.*, Vol. 18 (1844), p. 1063.

All this is very clear. But two things are not at all clear, and I can shed little light on them: Who had the idea of the centigrade thermometer with the freezing point at zero? And on what date? Earlier than December 2, 1745, certainly; but how much earlier? I do not know. I hope that some historian living in Uppsala or Stockholm may be persistent enough to find out.

Who thought of it, Linnaeus or Ekström? Probably Linnaeus, whose biographer assures us that after he moved to Uppsala in 1741—at the end of a particularly nasty display of University politics—Anders Celsius was one of his most intimate friends until Celsius' death in 1744.[152] Celsius had indeed been instrumental in defeating the determined opposition to Linnaeus' appointment. It is likely that the latter heard about the experiments with the thermometer.

Now we know that Celsius had been influenced by Delisle, and if the frontispiece of the *Hortus Cliffortianus* has any significance, Linnaeus had at least been accustomed to a thermometer scale in which greater heat is indicated by increasing numbers. We may surmise—and it is only a guess—that Linnaeus thought that the scale adopted by Celsius would be better upside down. It may be that he suppressed this idea until after the death of his benefactor.

While this was going on in Sweden, Jean Pierre Christin was thinking about thermometers at Lyon in France. Christin was one of the most active members, and for a time the secretary, of the Académie des Sciences, Belles-Lettres et Arts de Lyon, and the firsthand information about Christin's thermometers has to be sought in the excellently preserved manuscripts of the Academy.[153] These papers were studied more than a century ago by J. Fournet,[154] whose account is a valuable guide, even if rather overenthusiastic. A fair summary of Christin's conclusions was also published in 1743 by the President of the Academy, Borde.[155]

Christin seems to have become interested in thermometry in or shortly before 1740. In 1736, it appears, the Académie Royale des Sciences had sent to the Lyon Observatory, and also to several other parts of the kingdom, Réaumur thermometers that had been intercompared at the Royal Observatory of Paris.[156]

[152] T. M. Fries, *Linnaeus . . . the Story of His Life, Adapted from the Swedish . . . by Benjamin Daydon Jackson* (London, 1923), p. 298.

[153] I am greatly obliged to Mlle. P. Cotton, the City Librarian of Lyon, who put me in touch with the Secretary of the Academy, M. Marcel Chamaraud; and to M. Chamaraud, who graciously placed the relevant manuscripts at my disposal.

[154] Fournet, *Mém. Soc. Agric. Lyon* (1845), pp. 245–61.

[155] Borde, *Mém. de Trévoux* (July, 1743), pp. 2126–28.

[156] Christin, Lyon, Palais des Arts, ms. 199, fol. 123v.

On July 13 and September 14, 1740, Christin read two rather confused papers to the Lyon Academy which show him making up his mind that mercury is a better liquid than spirit of wine for thermometers.[157] At the end of the second paper he announced that he believed that he had "found a sure and easy method for making good thermometers," but would not publish it until he had finished his experiments.

This might lead one to suspect that the centigrade thermometer was invented in 1740, but there is clear evidence to the contrary in a letter of February 15, 1741 "to Mr. Joannon of Paris, to be read to Mr. de Réaumur," as we are told on the copy made and signed by Christin himself.[158] In this letter he asks his friend to try to get him a thermometer actually made by Réaumur, as he has found that some instruments sold as Réaumur thermometers disagree with the official one at the Observatory. It contains the following remarkable passage:

> Mr. de Réaumur used in the construction of his first [thermometers] a spirit of wine the dilatability of which was found to be 80 degrees from the freezing point to that of boiling water; I see that this is a division into a fixed number, which should no more be changed than that which has been fixed at 360 for the circle.[159]

The thing that strikes one in reading Christin's manuscripts is how the huge shadow of Réaumur hung over the subject of thermometry in France. Later on in the same letter, after some arguments in favor of mercury, he says that ". . . whatever liquids . . . thermometers are filled with, they must always be made on Mr. de Réaumur's principles to make them comparable."[160]

Réaumur did not send him a thermometer. Fournet says that this was a good thing, for otherwise Christin might have abandoned his experiments.

The next document of interest was read on August 22, 1742.[161] In this he makes a formal criticism of Micheli du Crest's thermometer scale as described in Micheli's memoir of 1741.[162] While defending the constancy of the ice point, and again emphasizing his belief in the superiority of mercury, Christin continues to

[157] His autograph drafts are in Lyon, Palais des Arts, ms. 199, fol. 125r–126r and 123r–124v respectively.
[158] *Ibid.*, fol. 127r–134r.
[159] *Ibid.*, fol. 131v. ". . . je vois que c'est une division en nombre fixe, et qui ne doit pas être plus changée que celle qu'on a fixé à 360 pour le cercle."
[160] *Ibid.*, fol. 133v.
[161] *Ibid.*, fol. 161r–170r. There is a rough draft on fol. 152r–160r, and a summary in the ms. *Journal des Conférences* of the Lyon Academy, under the date August 22, 1742.
[162] See p. 89 above.

praise Réaumur's principles. There is still no hint of a centigrade thermometer. Micheli replied to this criticism, which had been published in the *Mémoires de Trévoux* for February, 1743, at great length,[163] but his letter contains nothing on which we need dwell.

The centigrade thermometer did finally arrive on May 2, 1743, and when it did, it wore a curiously Réaumurian look. I shall translate part of the summary of Christin's paper in the *Journal des Conférences* for that date.[164]

> An experiment . . . had shown [Christin] that a quantity of mercury condensed by the cold of pounded ice, and then dilated by the heat of boiling water, formed, in these two states, volumes that were to each other as 66 to 67, and that a volume of 6600 parts, condensed, became one of 6700 parts by dilatation. The difference, 100 . . . is the number of degrees that he gives to the scale of a new mercury thermometer between these two points.

This seems a poor reason for the choice of a centigrade scale, but Borde goes on:

> This number is found to be advantageous for the precision of observations, and each degree represents one of 6600 condensed parts taken from zero, the freezing-point. . . . Mr. Christin has remarked that several advantages can be derived from this discovery; among others, that of being able to construct mercury thermometers by using boiling water, without the help of freezing, and conversely with ice, without the heat of boiling water.

The last sentence shows to what extent he was a disciple of Réaumur, and indeed there is further evidence that he thought he was simply doing what Réaumur would have done, had the great man used mercury instead of spirit of wine. It appears that on July 31, 1743, one De Moronval had written from Paris, plainly worried about the 100-degree scale. Christin wrote a twelve-page reply[165] and read it to the Lyon Academy on September 11, 1743, before sending it off. "If Mr. de Réaumur (he writes) had extended his researches to mercury thermometers, I am quite persuaded that he would have left us nothing to do."[166]

And yet, interestingly enough, this same document makes it clear that Christin, or perhaps the instrumentmaker Pierre

163 Lyons, Palais des Arts, ms. 199, fol. 71r–97r.

164 I have not found the actual paper. The summary, apparently made by Borde, was read, along with extracts from other papers, at a public meeting on 19 May 1743 and published in the *Mém. de Trévoux* (July, 1743), pp. 2126–28.

165 Lyon, Palais des Arts, ms. 199, fol. 171r–176v. A very careful search by M. Chamaraud, at my request, has failed to discover De Moronval's letter, which is a pity.

166 *Ibid.*, fol. 171v.

Casati[167] who may have helped him, was not really wedded to Réaumur's procedures. Apparently De Moronval had succeeded in making 100-degree thermometers, presumably after reading the latest number of the *Mémoires de Trévoux*. Christin writes:

> I find . . . that you have succeeded in using mercury in a thermometer that you have divided into 100 degrees between the two fixed points, . . . without determining the number of parts contained in the bulb. I confess to you that I have been fortunate enough, like yourself, to happen on all these things, which I had in view for a long time, with the exception of the division into 100 parts, which I thought of only after the experiments that the Sieur Casati spoke to you about.[168]

This sounds just a little disingenuous; but at least Christin made no protest at this flagrant departure from "the principles of Mr. de Réaumur." Yet on the next page he still protests that he has not feared

> to work at the perfection of the comparable thermometers invented by Mr. De Réaumur; and I have not desired any glory in this. My researches have never any other object than to find something useful, while working as an Academician.[169]

There was a good deal of discussion, much of it occasioned by the extraordinary respect for Réaumur to which I have referred. But on October 30, 1745, one Father Gregoire wrote very reasonably—though at unreasonable length—from Marseilles, objecting to the idea that mercury thermometers could be made with one fixed point, i.e., volumetrically, on Réaumur's principles.[170] He knew that this is "rigorously" possible, but the practical difficulties are too great.

Christin's thermometer soon became known as the *thermomètre de Lyon;* it was used fairly extensively at Lyon and in some places in the south of France for a time, but Réaumur's reputation was so overwhelming that the Réaumur thermometer, or what was fondly supposed to be the Réaumur thermometer,[171] became ubiquitous in France. Christin's thermometer scale was barely mentioned by Deluc and by Cotte but was recommended by Bossier in 1779.[172] Celsius does not seem to have been known

---

[167] Perhaps an ancestor of the Casati who made excellent thermometers at the end of the century. Cf. Daumas, *Les instruments scientifiques* (Paris, 1953), p. 382. Fournet, *Mém. Soc. Agric. Lyon* (1845), pp. 256–57, says that Casati made and sold nearly 700 of these "Lyon thermometers" in Paris.

[168] Lyon, Palais des Arts, ms. 199, fol. 171r–171v.

[169] *Ibid.,* fol. 172r.

[170] *Ibid.,* fol. 113r–116v.

[171] See p. 116 below.

[172] [L'Abbé Bossier], *Mémoires sur la réforme des thermomètres* (Tours, 1779), pp. 13 and 24.

to Bossier, nor is he mentioned, as far as I have been able to find, in Deluc's influential book.[173] Cotte[174] "does not know the construction" of the thermometer of Celsius, and in Hutton's *Mathematical and philosophical dictionary* the centigrade thermometer is referred only to Christin, and described as "a thermometer which has often been used in London, called the thermometer of Lyons, because Mr. Christin brought it there into use. . . ."[175]

There is one of these "Lyon thermometers" in the Science Museum, London, inventory no. 1951–581 (Fig. 4.6). The inscription is "Thermomètre de Lyon, Divisé Selon la Mesure de la Dilatation du Mercure, Trouvée en 1743. Par M. Christin de La Société Royale de Lyon. Fait par Pierre Casati."[176]

At this point the reader will be able to make up his mind about the "inventor" of the centigrade thermometer. As far as Sweden is concerned, there seems to be no good reason to doubt that Celsius, most probably basing his experiments upon Delisle's thermometers, produced his "inverted" scale on an actual instrument in December, 1741. Linnaeus certainly turned it "right way up," not later than 1745. In France, Christin had mercury thermometers in May, 1743; but his ideas at this time contained a good deal of Réaumur's technique. The name of the "inventor" will depend on the reader's definition of a centigrade thermometer.

5. *The Air Thermometer Again.* We must now return to the last years of the seventeenth century and to Guillaume Amontons, who was the first to make a serious study of the principles of the air thermometer. In 1699 Amontons wrote a paper, mainly about a hot-air engine of much ingenuity, which interests us because it begins with an experimental demonstration that different amounts of air have their "spring" increased equally by the same rise in temperature.[177] Between room temperature and that of boiling water this increase is about one third. He then deduces from Mariotte's (i.e., Boyle's) law that any volume of air

---

[173] J. A. Deluc, *Recherches sur les modifications de l'atmosphère* (Geneva, 1772).

[174] Louis Cotte, *Traité de Météorologie* (Paris, 1774), p. 136.

[175] Charles Hutton, *A Mathematical and Philosophical Dictionary* [etc.] (2 vols.; London, 1795–96), Vol. 2, pp. 589–90.

[176] It is fully described by J. A. Chaldecott in *Handbook of the Collection Illustrating Temperature Measurement and Control*, Part II (London, 1955), pp. 7–8.

[177] Amontons, *Mém. Acad. r. Sci. Paris* (1699), pp. 112–26.

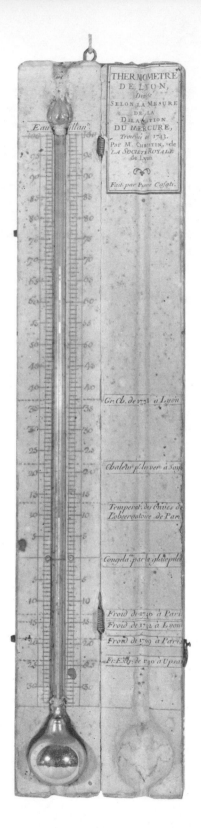

Fig. 4.6 A "thermomètre de Lyon."
(British Crown Copyright, Science Museum, London.)

Fig. 4.7 Amontons quantitative air thermometer, 1702.

will expand by the same fraction between room temperature and the boiling point if it is at liberty to expand without changing its "spring."

Having thus established the equivalence between the constant-pressure and constant-volume air thermometers (as we would say), Amontons goes on in a later paper[178] to show that, in our terms, the form of the relation between temperature and pressure is independent of the initial pressure. This being established, he made a very simple air thermometer out of a J-shaped tube with a bulb on the short end (Fig. 4.7). He described a means of introducing just enough air so that when the bulb was in boiling water, and the barometer at 28 inches, the level of the mercury in the tube was 45 inches above that in the bottom of the bulb, making the pressure of the air in the bulb 73 inches. In water with a good deal of ice in it, the mercury sank to a point 21 inches lower than in boiling water. Amontons realized that the volume of the air in the bulb changes a little as the mercury in the tube goes up and down, so that different thermometers of this sort will not in practice be strictly comparable. But the tube was narrow, so that the effect was not large. This thermometer had a great advantage over his earlier one[179] and that of Hubin, because the only liquid involved was mercury, which has a negligible vapor-pressure at ordinary temperatures. On the other hand it had the disadvantage that it had to be used in connection with a barometer. It is clear that his intention was to use it as a standard with which spirit thermometers could be compared.

Philippe de la Hire,[180] discussing some rather poorly controlled experiments by Lazare Nuguet,[181] drew attention to the necessity of having the air in the thermometer dry if reproducible results are to be obtained. In one of his own experiments he obtained an enormous thermal expansion of the air collected on a rainy day with a west wind.

It will be noted that Hubin's air thermometer was unaffected by changes in the barometric pressure. All that was necessary to make Amontons' instrument equally independent of them was to close the end of the long tube, filling the instrument like a siphon barometer before sealing the bulb with some air in it. The first to do this was probably Vittorio Francesco Stancari, a

[178] *Ibid.*, (1702), pp. 155–74.

[179] See p. 63 above.

[180] De la Hire, *Mém. Acad. r. Sci. Paris* (1708), pp. 274–88.

[181] Nuguet, *Nouvelle découverte d'un thermometre cherché depuis longtems* [etc.], pamphlet, 8 pp. + 1 pl. (Paris, 1706).

professor at Bologna; the year, about 1708.[182] A similar instrument was described in 1716 by Jacob Hermann of Basle,[183] but his idea was not to improve the air thermometer, as Hoppe stated,[184] but merely to demonstrate a theorem about heat. This, or a similar instrument, was known to Daniel Bernouilli, who suggested that by inclining it a constant-volume air thermometer could be obtained.[185] One was known to Theodore Balthasar in 1719;[186] and Balthasar's thermometer was praised by Mairan in the unpublished memoir already referred to.[187]

J. H. Lambert was a great believer in the air thermometer and made many experiments with it. He referred other thermometer scales to one of his own, directly arising from these experiments, in which the freezing point was 1,000° and the boiling point 1,370°, and indeed he assumed without question that "the air thermometer shows the actual degree of heat."[188] Comparing it with the spirit-of-wine thermometer, he naturally found the latter highly nonlinear.

Very careful experiments were made at the beginning of the new century by Louis Joseph Gay-Lussac, not only on air, but on several other gases. Within the accuracy of his measurements he found their expansion identical. In his report[189] he tells us that similar results had been obtained, but not published, by J. A. C. Charles several years before. On the strength of this handsome acknowledgment, the law of the linear expansion of gases with temperature is usually called Charles's law.

The accuracy of thermometry, and indeed of a good many physical measurements, was greatly improved by that superb experimenter Victor Regnault, whose results are largely assembled in a great memoir of 748 pages dealing with the physical quantities involved in the working of the steam engine.[190] From the standpoint of this chapter, the most interesting passage is his demonstration that the constant-pressure and constant-volume

[182] *Comment. Bonon.*, Vol. 1 (1731), pp. 209–10. Thermometers of this sort seem to have been known as "Stancari thermometers" at Bologna for many years; Cf. *Hist. Inst., Bologna, Coll. Académique, Partie étrangère*, Vol. 10 (1773), p. 587.

[183] Hermann, *Phoronomia sive de viribus et motibus corporum solidum et fluidorum libri duo* (Amsterdam, 1716), pp. 376–77. I have dealt with this passage in *British J. Hist. Science*, Vol. 2 (1965), pp. 247–50.

[184] Edmund Hoppe, *Geschichte der Physik* (Brunswick, 1926), p. 176.

[185] Bernouilli, *Hydrodynamica sive de viribus et motibus fluidorum commentarii* [etc.] (Strasbourg, 1738), pp. 205–6.

[186] Balthasar, *Acta Eruditorum* (1719), pp. 128–30.

[187] Mairan, *Acad. r. Sci. Paris, Registres*, February 10, 1731, fol. 27ᵛ–28ʳ.

[188] Lambert, *Pyrometrie oder vom Maase des Feuers und der Wärme* (Berlin, 1779), p. 78.

[189] Gay-Lussac, *Ann. de Chim.*, 1er ser., Vol. 43 (An 10[1802]), pp. 137–84.

[190] Regnault, *Mém. Acad. r. Sci. Paris*, Vol. 21 (1847), pp. 1–748.

air thermometers are very nearly equivalent. The constant-volume thermometer is to be preferred. Air, nitrogen, and hydrogen give almost the same results, but for each of them there is a slight dependence on the pressure (at the ice point) of the gas in the thermometer. Regnault's work has been extended, chiefly by the *Bureau International des Poids et Mesures,* in the succeeding century, with slight changes in the numbers that he found; but this is beyond the province of this book.

Since the time of Balthasar, air thermometers have been used hardly at all in meteorology, if we except one or two recording thermometers, which will be dealt with in Chapter 9.

6. *"Absolute" Temperatures.* I have dealt with the air thermometer at more length than might seem justified in a book such as this, mainly because the experiments with it were closely connected with the search for "absolute" temperatures and the specification of the absolute zero of heat. This is a matter that is likely to get us into all sorts of philosophical traps, as was brilliantly pointed out by Ernst Mach.[191] We have already seen some of these difficulties in Chapter 3, and I shall not insist on them further, except to point out that from the time of Amontons or even of Hooke there has been an assumption of a metaphysical sort, sometimes expressed but more often tacit, that there exists a "natural" or "true" scale of temperature. We have seen this as the mainspring of the experiments and arguments of Réaumur, Delisle, Micheli, and Christin. The preference for mercury as a thermometric liquid was largely due to the belief that its expansion was more "uniform" than that of others, such as spirit of wine.

The basis for such ideas seems to have been at first purely intuitive, but later they found strong support from experiments in mixing measured amounts of water at various temperatures. As early as 1723 Brooke Taylor, in a paper with a significant title,[192] made "a good linseed oil thermometer," and graduated it "with small divisions, not equal in length, but equal according to the capacity of the tube in the several parts of it, as all thermometers ought to be graduated." Then, by mixing measured amounts of cold and of boiling water, he found that the rise of

[191] Mach, *Die Principien der Wärmelehre historisch-kritisch entwickelt* (Leipzig, 1896), pp. 39–57 and *passim.*

[192] "An experiment made to ascertain the proportion of the liquor in the thermometer with regard to the degrees of heat," *Phil. Trans.,* Vol. 32 (1723), p. 291.

the thermometer was "accurately proportional to the quantity of hot water in the mixture, that is, to the degree of heat."

Here we have a rule for the construction of a thermometer scale implicitly stated. Taylor's success was certainly due to the imprecision of his experiments, for, as we shall see,[193] Deluc did not find such linearity for linseed oil. But Deluc expressed no doubts about the absolute validity of his own mixing experiments.

Amontons had stated his belief that the elasticity (pressure) of air is due entirely to the amount of heat in it. If there were no heat, then, there should be no elasticity. Therefore, if the elasticity is proportional to the amount of heat in the air, an extrapolation down to zero pressure should yield an absolute zero of heat, or as we should say, of temperature. This line of reasoning involves the entirely metaphysical assumption of a linear relationship between pressure and quantity of heat. It also contains an entirely arbitrary definition of a temperature scale. It seems to be merely a piece of good luck that Amontons' idea has turned out to be so fruitful.

Lambert, discussing the air thermometer, believed that "in absolute cold the air is packed so tightly together that its particles quite touch each other, or so that it becomes, as we might say, watertight."[194] He believed that the particles are so small in comparison with the space between them at ordinary temperatures that a linear extrapolation would be permissible. It must be noted that this is not a "kinetic theory" idea; the particles were kept apart not by their own motion but by the particles of "fire" stuffed between them.

If Amontons' and Lambert's principles are correct, then to find the absolute zero we have only to measure the volumes v_o and v_t (at constant pressure) of a sample of dry air, or alternatively the pressures p_o and p_t required to keep the volume constant, at two temperatures, say 0 and t degrees, on whatever scale is being used. Then the absolute zero on that scale will be at a temperature

$$t_o = -tv_o/(v_t - v_o) = -tp_o/(p_t - p_o).$$

The temperatures most generally used have been the freezing point and the boiling point, or more correctly the ice point and the steam point. Various experimenters throughout the eighteenth century determined the ratio of the volume (or the pressure) at these two points, but most of them did not take enough

[193] P. 124 below.
[194] Lambert, *Pyrometrie* (1779), p. 29.

trouble in drying their samples of air. It will give a more comprehensible picture if we think in terms of centigrade degrees. In these terms, it can be deduced from Amontons' figures that his value of p_{100}/p_o was 1.404, giving an absolute zero of $-248°C$. Lambert got 1.370 ($-270°C$.). Gay-Lussac's values for v_{100}/v_o are in the vicinity of 1.3750 for air, hydrogen, oxygen, and nitrogen;[195] but it was pointed out almost at once by L. W. Gilbert that he had not allowed for the expansion of a glass bulb, and if he had done so he would have obtained 1.380.[196] Strangely enough, Gay-Lussac's experiments on the production of cold by the expansion of gases led him to disbelieve in the existence of an absolute zero.[197]

Further experiments were made by Flaugergues,[198] Rudberg,[199] and others. In 1847 there appeared the great paper by Regnault to which I have already referred,[200] in which as an average of four methods he obtained $p_{100}/p_o = 1.3665$ for air, which would correspond to an absolute zero of $-272.75°C$. Regnault found that hydrogen is preferable to air in that the dependence of the dilatation on the initial pressure is less.

Meanwhile, there had been other ideas about how absolute zero should be determined. In his extreme old age J. J. d'Ortous de Mairan, relying on the unfortunate experiments of Braun on the freezing of mercury,[201] calculated[202] that absolute zero is $-1,000°R$. ($-1,250°C$.). The Irish chemist and physician Adair Crawford purported to show, from the heat produced by the combustion of hydrogen in oxygen, that the absolute zero is $-1,500°F$. ($-853°C$.).[203] John Dalton, who had made experiments on the dilatation of several gases—finding them all nearly alike in this respect—exercised his remarkable powers of speculation on the subject.[204] To explain how elastic fluids expand by heat, he made the hypothesis that "the repulsive force of each particle"—whatever that may mean—"is exactly proportional to

[195] Gay-Lussac, *Ann. de Chim.*, Vol. 43 (1802), p. 167.

[196] Gilbert, *Ann. der Phys.*, Vol. 12 (1802), pp. 396–98.

[197] Gay-Lussac, *Ann. de Chim.*, Vol. 9 (1818), pp. 305–10.

[198] Flaugergues, *J. de Phys.*, Vol. 77 (1813), pp. 273–92.

[199] F. Rudberg, *Ann. der Phys.*, Vol. 41 (1837), pp. 271–93; Vol. 44 (1838), pp. 119–23.

[200] Note 190, this chapter.

[201] These are discussed on p. 121 below.

[202] Mairan, *Mém. Acad. r. Sci. Paris* (1765), p. 209.

[203] Crawford, *Experiments and Observations on Animal Heat, and the Inflammation of Combustible Bodies* (2nd ed.; London, 1788), pp. 262 ff.

[204] Dalton, *Mem. Manchester Lit. & Phil. Soc.*, Vol. 5, part 2 (1802), pp. 595–602. I have dealt with his speculations on water vapor in my *A History of the Theories of Rain* [etc.] (London, 1965), Chap. 7.

the whole quantity of heat combined with it."[205] Then, since "the diameter of each particle's sphere of influence" is proportional to the cube root of the space it occupies, the absolute quantity of heat (i.e., the absolute temperature) will vary as the cube root of the volume at constant pressure. From this he got an absolute zero at −1,515°F. (−867°C.), and congratulated himself on the close agreement with Crawford's estimate. L. W. Gilbert, the editor of the *Annalen der Physik,* who had a very high opinion of Dalton, put Gay-Lussac's figures, corrected by Gilbert, into this, and got −1,566°F. (−888°C.).[206] Someone, more perspicacious than Gilbert, seems to have objected that calculations between different temperatures will produce widely different values for the absolute zero. Dalton, quite unperturbed, interpreted this as an indication that the mercury thermometer is not a true measure of heat, and should be graduated on the basis of his cube-root law![207]

There were more such speculations, but we have not space to deal with them. The reader may be referred to a paper by E. Gerland,[208] who gives a table of thirteen widely different estimates of the absolute zero made between 1702 and 1841.

In 1853 the famous engineer W. J. M. Rankine[209] took Regnault's values of the dilatation of air and of carbon dioxide at various initial pressures, and by extrapolating to zero pressure obtained −274.6°C. for the absolute zero of temperature. Gradual refinements in experimental techniques, resulting from the work of the great national and international standardizing laboratories, have led to the value now adopted— −273.15 ± 0.02°C.—and it will be hard to give it greater precision than this.

7. *The Thermodynamic Scale of Temperature.* In spite of the long search for a rational scale of temperature which I have endeavored to follow in this chapter, the subject was still in an unsatisfactory state in 1847. Regnault made the difficulty clear:

> Up to the present time we possess no direct way of measuring the quantities of heat that a body absorbs in given circumstances, and we recognize this absorption of heat only by the changes that occur in

[205] *Ibid.*, p. 601.
[206] Gilbert, *Ann. der Phys.*, Vol. 12 (1802), pp. 396–97.
[207] Dalton, *Nicholson's Journal*, Vol. 5 (1803), p. 35.
[208] Gerland, "Die Entdeckung der Gasgesetze und des absoluten Nullpunktes" [etc.], in P. Diergart, ed., *Beiträge aus der Geschichte der Chemie zum Gedächtnis von Georg W. A. Kahlbaum* (Leipzig and Vienna, 1909), pp. 350–60.
[209] Rankine, *Trans. Roy. Soc. Edinb.*, Vol. 20 (1853), pp. 561–63.

the state of the body, or by its dilatation. We give the name *ther-mometers* to instruments that are intended to determine the varia-tions of the quantity of heat contained in a medium. In general, these instruments are founded upon the expansion that bodies undergo through the action of heat, or on the changes of pressure (*force élastique*) that a given volume of gas experiences in the cir-cumstances to which the medium is submitted.

A perfect thermometer would be one of which the indications are always proportional to the quantities of heat that it has absorbed; or, in other words, one in which the addition of equal quantities of heat always produces equal expansions. For this condition to be fulfilled, either the specific heat of the thermometric substance must remain constant in the various phases of the experiment, or else these two elements [i.e., the specific heat and the expansion] must vary rigorously in an inverse ratio.[210]

He then points out that this is generally not so.

But a solution was at hand. In the following year William Thomson, later Lord Kelvin, repeated Regnault's warning,[211] adding that even the gas thermometer only gives us "an arbitrary series of numbered points of reference sufficiently close for the requirements of practical thermometry."[212] He then proposed a scale of temperature that would not depend on the properties of any actual substance.

Thomson's proposal depended on a theory of an ideal reversi-ble heat-engine, developed by the French engineer Sadi Carnot.[213] It would take us far outside the purpose of this book to go into details about this, which indeed would involve us in the difficult subject of thermodynamics.[214] In brief, then, Carnot had devel-oped an expression for the efficiency of an ideal heat-engine working between the temperature t and the temperature $t + dt$. This is called Carnot's function $F'(t)$. In the paper referred to above, Thomson suggested that the scale of temperature should be chosen so that $F'(t)$ is constant. In his own words:

> The characteristic property of the scale which I now propose is, that all degrees have the same value, that is, that a unit of heat descend-ing from a body A at the temperature $T°$ of this scale, to a body B at the temperature $(T - 1)°$, would give out the same mechanical effect, whatever be the number T. This may justly be termed an

210 Regnault, *Mém. Acad. r. Sci. Paris,* Vol. 21 (1847), p. 163.

211 Thomson, "On an absolute thermometric scale founded on Carnot's theory of the motive power of heat, and calculated from Regnault's observa-tions," *Phil. Mag.,* Vol. 33 (1848), pp. 313–17. Also in *Proc. Cambridge Phil. Soc.,* Vol. 1 (1848), pp. 66–71.

212 *Ibid.,* p. 314.

213 Carnot, *Réflexions sur la puissance motrice du feu* [etc.] (Paris, 1824).

214 The most readily understandable account for English-speaking readers is probably in H. L. Callendar's article "Heat" in the eleventh edition (1910) of the *Encyclopaedia Britannica.*

absolute scale, since its characteristic is quite independent of the physical properties of any specific substance.[215]

When the values of Carnot's function were calculated from Regnault's observations on steam, however, the new scale was found to be very different from that of the air thermometer, and some years later, in collaboration with Joule, Thomson proposed to define absolute temperature θ as proportional to the reciprocal of Carnot's function.[216] They had devised a very beautiful and delicate experiment, known as the "porous-plug experiment,"[217] which enabled them to calculate the extent to which the scale of the gas thermometer varies from the absolute temperature thus defined. Happily, the constant-volume hydrogen thermometer was found to agree almost exactly with the absolute thermodynamic scale at all ordinary temperatures, and it became the agreed practical realization of the absolute scale until it was superseded by the platinum resistance thermometer in the twentieth century (see Chapter 8).

As a tribute to William Thomson's inspired idea, the absolute thermodynamic scale is now referred to as the Kelvin scale, and temperatures measured on it are designated in degrees Kelvin ($^\circ$K.).

The search for a rational scale of temperature has finally met with success in a way that the early thermometermakers never dreamed of. In the next chapter, however, it will be necessary to start again in the eighteenth century and to discuss the practical difficulties of thermometry—especially in meteorology—and the efforts to solve them and to improve the instrument.

[215] Thomson, *Phil. Mag.*, Vol. 33 (1848), p. 316. If t is in degrees centigrade $T = t + 273$.
[216] J. P. Joule and W. Thomson, *Phil. Trans.*, Vol. 144 (1854), p. 351.
[217] *Phil. Trans.*, Vol. 143 (1853), pp. 357–65.

V

Difficulties and Refinements

1. The Reformers of Réaumur's Scale. Over most of Europe, except in Scandinavia and the British Isles, the 80° Réaumur thermometer quickly attained a commanding position, but nevertheless the more perceptive members of the scientific community, outside the Académie at Paris, soon came to recognize its serious defects. There is a touch of sadness in much of the criticism, a feeling that the thermometer must be an unfortunate lapse on the part of a man greatly esteemed. Indeed it was just that, but it was not a momentary aberration. It would appear that Réaumur had made up his mind in advance about how a thermometer should be constructed, and then proceeded to do it in this way without at any time re-examining his assumptions.

The defects were, so to speak, at both ends and in the middle. The methods of establishing the fixed points were soon criticized, and the principle of dividing the scale was attacked—most fundamentally in that it took no account of the differences in the expansion of various kinds of glass but also on technical grounds. We have already noted Josias Weitbrecht's understanding of the difficulty about the glass,[1] and in 1737 his colleague Georg Wolfgang Krafft suggested a way of estimating the expansion of this by noting the "jump" in the reading of the thermometer when the temperature of its environment is suddenly changed.[2] However, both Krafft and Weitbrecht were dealing with mercury thermometers, and it is fair to remark that in Réaumur's instruments this source of error would have been negligible in comparison with the others, which were certainly not.

The earliest serious critic of Réaumur's thermometer was the English physician George Martine, whose "Essay on the con-

[1] See p. 88 above.
[2] Krafft, *Comm. Petrop.*, Vol. 9 (1737), pp. 241–48 [published 1744].

struction and graduation of thermometers"[3] was in advance of its time. Martine came out strongly for the necessity of two fixed points, one being the boiling point of water—with due attention to the barometric pressure—the other the temperature of ice beginning to melt. He had no doubts about the constancy of this latter point, in spite of Taglini and Musschenbroek, for he had exchanged thermometers with various people over a range of nine degrees of latitude. He criticized Réaumur's methods of getting his freezing point because of his method of freezing, but also and mainly because of the very large bulbs of his thermometers. But Réaumur's "boiling-point," Martine said, is "still more vague and uncertain," because the spirit of wine cannot take the heat of boiling water. This brings him to a plea for the adoption of mercury as a thermometric fluid.

Soon most of the instrumentmakers, even on the Continent, turned to making mercury thermometers. In England they followed Fahrenheit, with the difference that they used the melting point of ice (32°F.) and the boiling point of water (212°F.) as fixed points.[4] Where the 80-degree scale of Réaumur was in vogue, the instrumentmakers made mercury thermometers in which the ice point was 0°R. and the boiling point 80°R., as for example, Jacob Bianchy of Vienna, who in 1762 cheerfully defines Réaumur's scale in this way,[5] with the recommendation that the boiling point be determined when the barometer stands at 28 [Paris?] inches. But since about 1740 it had been recognized that the dilatation of mercury and spirit were not proportional.[6] Micheli du Crest had in fact made comparisons, though assuming a priori that the expansion of spirit was linear.[7]

In the year of Bianchy's book a remarkable manuscript had been submitted for, and had received, the approval of the Académie des Sciences at Paris. This was the work of Jean André Deluc, a citizen of Geneva, who was such a perfectionist that even though the manuscript had been extravagantly complimented by the Académie in 1762,[8] he spent the next ten years

[3] In his *Essays Medical and Philosophical, a Collection of Six Essays* (London, 1740), pp. 175–214. Another of the essays was on the comparison of various thermometers (pp. 215–30). Editions of these two, with alterations by other hands, were published at Edinburgh in 1772 and 1792. Martine died in 1741.

[4] Cf. p. 76 above.

[5] Bianchy, *Das Merkwürdigste vom Barometre* [sic] *und Thermometre* [etc.] (Vienna, 1762), p. 71. There were also instrumentmakers named Bianchy (or Bianchi) in Paris (R. Bianchy) and in Amsterdam (Bianchi & Co.).

[6] Réaumur himself knew this. See p. 85 above.

[7] J. B. Micheli du Crest, *Description d'un thermomètre universel* (Paris, 1741), p. 9.

[8] De la Condamine and De la Lande had examined it, and on July 30 it was judged to be "one of the best with which physics has been enriched for a long time." It was certainly one of the most long-winded.

adding to it and polishing it. In 1772 it appeared in two quarto volumes of which the title summarizes the contents.[9] Perhaps this book had more influence than it deserved, but at least it drew attention to the necessity of reforming the thermometer, and especially the Réaumur thermometer. Deluc's experiments with the barometer are important,[10] and his meteorological ideas[11] spectacular, if also highly speculative. Unfortunately, the *Modifications* is incredibly discursive, causing the great Lambert to complain that four times as much might have been said in a work a quarter as long.[12] I have space only to mention Deluc's main contributions to the reform of the thermometer.

Starting with the lower fixed point, he was very severe on Réaumur's methods. In this he was flogging a dead horse, for by 1760 the use of the melting point of ice had become almost universal. Writing of the boiling point, he says that "The true principles [of Réaumur's thermometer] are almost entirely effaced. I have tried to discover them."[13] Obviously the 80° point on the new thermometers called "Réaumur" was not the same as on Réaumur's own thermometers. The relation between them was an important question which Deluc approached by stages. Believing firmly that mercury was superior to spirit as a thermometric fluid,[14] he made elaborate comparisons of their *marche*. Then he started from the well-established fact that Réaumur's original thermometer read 10¼° in the cellars of the Paris Observatory. He could not make experiments there himself, and asked Claude Varenne, a correspondent of the Academy, for help. Varenne brought Réaumur's nephew Mathurin Jacques Brisson into the affair. They made numerous experiments, with the result that the cellars are at a constant temperature of 9.6° on the 80° scale of the mercury thermometer established by Deluc, who, using his comparisons between mercury and spirit thermometers, calculated that Réaumur's 80° should correspond to only 59.3° on a *spirit* thermometer graduated on Deluc's princi-

[9] J. A. Deluc, *Recherches sur les modifications de l'atmosphère, contenant l'histoire critique du baromètre et du thermomètre, un traité sur la construction de ces instrumens, des expériences relatives à leurs usages, & principalement à la mesure des hauteurs & à la correction des réfractions moyennes* (2 vols.; 4°, Geneva, 1772). Reprinted in 4 vols. (8°, Paris, 1784). Since the paragraph (¶) numbers correspond in the two editions, references will be made to them and not to pages. The work will be referred to as *Modifications*.

[10] See my *The History of the Barometer* (Baltimore, 1964), pp. 135–39 and *passim*.

[11] I have dealt with these in *A History of the Theories of Rain* (London, 1965), pp. 115–31.

[12] J. H. Lambert, *Pyrometrie oder vom Maase des Feuers und der Wärme* (Berlin, 1779), p. 70. "Und so hätte Deluc in einem 4 mal kleinern Werke 4 mal mehr sagen als er wirklich gesagt hat."

[13] *Modifications*, ¶ 439.

[14] See below, p. 124.

Table 5.1. Deluc's Table Showing the Comparison of Three
Thermometers

Deluc's mercury thermometer	Thermometer of Réaumur's liquid on Deluc's scale	Réaumur's original thermometer	
80	80.0	100.4	Boiling point
75	73.9	92.8	
70	67.8	85.2	
66.6	63.7	80.0	Réaumur's upper point
65	61.8	77.8	
60	56.2	70.8	
55	50.5	63.7	
50	45.0	56.8	
45	39.8	50.4	
40	35.0	44.2	
35	30.1	38.3	
30	25.5	32.6	
25	20.8	26.7	
20	16.3	21.1	
15	11.9	15.6	
10	7.9	10.6	
9.6	7.6	10.25	Observatory cellars
5	3.9	5.7	
0	0.0	0.8	Melting ice
−0.8	−0.7	0.0	Réaumur's lower point
−5	−3.8	−3.9	
−10	−7.5	−8.5	
−15	−11.2	−13.1	

ples. This was unreasonable, and Deluc went on with his experiments, making a mixture of spirit and water as noted by Réaumur, and finding its boiling point to be 64.3°. This gave him two points, on the basis of which he deduced that Réaumur's zero was 0.90° lower than his. He prints a table (5.1)[15] in which historical climatologists may be surprised to note how close Réaumur's *original* scale is to the revised *mercury* one, at ordinary meteorological temperatures.

The Observatory cellars, incidentally, continued to fascinate

[15] *Ibid.,* ¶ 448b, abridged a little.

the Academicians right up to the Revolution. Jacques Dominic, the last of the four Cassinis to direct the Observatory, himself climbed the 210 steps almost every day for nearly two years in order to determine once and for all whether or not the temperature in the cellars is constant.[16] The thermometers that he used are of interest to us as showing that at that time much more attention was being paid to detail. They were made for Lavoisier[17] by Mossy and engine-divided by Richer. They were of mercury, one with a tube 20 inches long, carefully calibrated in ice and in boiling water. The other was a very special instrument with a bulb 2½ inches in diameter and a capillary tube 22 inches long. It was calibrated, by comparison with the other, with great care in a water bath, the process taking six weeks. This thermometer, on which 1°R., corresponded to about 4¼ inches, could easily be read to ½₀₀°R. It was set up in a large gallery in the cellars, with the bulb in a good-sized pot of fine sand, in order to nullify the effect of the visits by the observer.

During the twenty-three months August 5, 1783, to June 29, 1785, the extremes were 9.06° and 9.28°R. In the complete table it is hard to separate the change in zero of the thermometer from the annual variation, but it is quite clear that there would not be an annual range of temperature of more than 0.1°R.

There was so much discussion of the "Réaumur" scale between 1770 and 1790 that I shall have to be selective. After the severe winter of 1775–76 Lavoisier, whose interest in thermometry seems to have been boundless, collected no fewer than thirty-eight thermometers that had been observed in various places and compared them in the Observatory cellars, in melting ice, and in a freezing mixture. The most important of these instruments was one belonging to Brisson, which had been made by Réaumur in 1730 and observed during the cold winter of 1739–40. One of the results of the study, intended mainly to compare the two winters, was that "Réaumur" thermometers made since 1740 "had not conformed to his principles at all."[18] At various times Lavoisier ordered numerous thermometers from the best makers, such as Cappy, Mossy, and later Megnié, and

16 J. D. Cassini de Thury, *J. de Phys.*, Vol. 35 (1789), pp. 190–205.

17 Maurice Daumas (*Les instruments scientifiques aux XVIIe et XVIIIe siècles* [Paris, 1953], p. 281) believes that "the first thermometers of satisfactory precision seem, indeed, to have been those made by Mossy and by Fortin for Lavoisier." It is probable, nevertheless, that John Bird in London made Fahrenheit thermometers of comparable excellence a little earlier.

18 Lavoisier, "Observations sur le froid de l'année 1776," *Acad. r. des Sci., Paris, misc. papers*, session of April 17, 1776. This is not in Lavoisier's collected works.

Fortin;[19] and there is no doubt that his influence on French thermometermaking, and instrumentmaking in general, was tremendous.

A different approach to reforming the Réaumur thermometer was made by a priest of Tours named Joseph Louis Bossier, or Beaussier, who in 1775 submitted a paper on the subject to the Paris Academy, which was reported on by Leroy and Macquer on July 3, 1776.[20] They did not find anything new in it and Bossier was obliged to print it himself, with additions, three years later.[21] They also said that anyhow, spirit thermometers must be given up, as they do not give the same precision as those of mercury. Reading Bossier's extensive and fascinating footnotes with this statement in mind, it becomes clear that the Academy was still very solicitous for the reputation of the great Réaumur and felt that the safest course was to sweep the spirit thermometer under the rug.

For Bossier's suggestion was to rehabilitate the spirit thermometer by leaving air over the spirit column so that it could be calibrated in boiling water and in melting ice. He would then divide the interval into 100 equal parts. He wished to preserve Réaumur's principles while improving on his practice, and declared that comparable spirit-of-wine thermometers should be filled with spirit that dilates 100 parts in 1000, "a simple round number, convenient for the division of thermometers,"[22] between the melting point of ice and the boiling point of water. Another argument in favor of the 100° scale is that it agrees with Christin's division of the mercury thermometer, which he believes ought to be adopted. But his adherence to Réaumur's principles is shown by the fact that he is still impressed by Christin's estimate that 6,600 volumes of mercury at the ice point become 6,700 at the boiling point![23]

Ten years later Jean Gaussen of Montpellier,[24] after criticizing both Deluc and Beaussier [Bossier] for going on a wild goose

[19] See Maurice Daumas, *Lavoisier théoricien et experimentateur* (Paris, 1955), pp. 124–26. Many of these are in the Lavoisier collection at the CNAM.
[20] Acad. r. Sci., Paris, *Registres des procès-verbaux des seances*, tome 95, fol. 200v–202r. In this he is called Bossier; but Goubert, in *Recherches sur les différences qui existent entre les thermomètres* [etc.] (Paris, 1789), p. 9, note, is sure that it is Beaussier. The librarian of the Bibliothèque Municipale at Tours informs me that according to L. Clément de Ris, *La Typographie en Touraine* (Paris, 1878), the name is Baussier.
[21] L. A.[bbé] B.[ossier], *Mémoires sur la réforme des thermometres, avec des avis particuliers, & des notes justificatives, critiques & instructives* (Tours, 1779).
[22] *Ibid.,* p. 75.
[23] Cf. p. 103 above.
[24] Gaussen, *Dissertation sur le thermomètre de Réaumur* (Béziers, 1789), pp. 116 ff.

chase, says that the choice ought to lie between the thermometers of Deluc and of Christin. But in France they have been accustomed to the Réaumur thermometer for so long that it can scarcely be abandoned. So he proposes a scheme, starting from Deluc's thermometer, for producing a fair imitation of Réaumur's original scale.

Gaussen may have proposed, but the Revolution disposed. Arthur Birembaut[25] quotes a long passage by René Just Haüy, from pages 202–4 of *Instruction sur les mesures déduites de la grandeur de la terre, uniformes pour toute la Republique, et sur les calculs relatifs à leur division décimale; par la Commission temporaire des Poids et Mesures républicaines, en exécution des décrets de la Convention nationale.* The decision to adopt the centigrade scale was taken on 12 germinal an II (April 1, 1794), and gave it an official connection—though of course no logical one—with the metric system. But all change meets resistance, and in 1816 we find the wealthy amateur physicist Honoré Flaugergues writing: ". . . this division into 100 degrees presents absolutely no advantage, and it seems to me to be much more worth while to preserve the old division into 80 degrees, adopted by the very great majority."[26]

2. *The Freezing Point of Mercury.* I shall now digress briefly to deal with the question of the freezing point of mercury, a matter of much interest to physicists through most of the eighteenth century. It was at first almost universally believed that mercury would remain liquid at temperatures that would freeze spirit of wine; the observation by Maupertuis, already quoted,[27] is an example of an observation that seemed to prove it, though there can be no doubt that the spirit in his thermometer was diluted with water. It must be noted that the freezing mixtures used at the time, starting with snow or ice at its melting point, would not freeze mercury. If the snow were very cold, lower temperatures could be obtained. Joseph Adam Braun of the Academy at St. Petersburg knew this, and when on December 14, 1759, the temperature fell to 205° Delisle (= −36.6°C.), he thought he would try to find out what a freezing mixture would do.[28] He

25 In *La vie et l'oeuvre de Réaumur* (Paris, 1962), pp. 67–68, note.
26 Flaugergues, *J. de Phys.*, Vol. 82 (1816), p. 390.
27 See p. 85 above.
28 Braun, *Novi Comm. Petrop.*, Vol. 11 (1765), pp. 268–301. The paper was read to the Academy on Sept. 6, 1760, with a title that may be translated as "Dissertation on the wonderful artificial cold by which mercury or quicksilver is frozen."

mixed snow and nitric acid, and when he put the bulb of a mercury thermometer into this mixture the mercury went down to 260, 380, and finally 470° Delisle (= −220°C.!). Taken into a warm room the mercury, which had evidently frozen, rose again to agree with another thermometer that had not been in the mixture. On December 25 he froze the mercury in a thermometer and broke the bulb, becoming the first man to see mercury in the solid state. The column had descended to 530°D. (−253°C.). Later he got one to descend to 700°D. (−366°C.). What had happened, of course, was that the mercury in the bulb had contracted on freezing, and the mercury in the tube, still liquid, had gone down to fill the space that was left empty. It is curious that he did not suspect this, for he recounts how he took three thermometers made with the most highly rectified spirit of wine and put them in the freezing mixture with the mercury thermometer. Even though the mercury froze, they did not, but went down to 300°D. This is −100°C., but we need not be surprised, for such an extrapolation would be meaningless in the case of these spirit thermometers. He could not believe that the mercury thermometer could attain a much lower temperature than the spirit thermometers in the same freezing mixture. Here are his conclusions:

> It seems therefore, that the descent of the mercury, especially when it begins with a rush, no longer preserves any proportion in its contraction. From the observations it is at least certain that at the lowest degrees of cold, the harmony and concordance of mercury thermometers with those filled with spirit of wine entirely ceases. What is more, it can be seen from the observations reported here that the cold that is enough to freeze mercury does not always suffice to freeze the most highly rectified spirit of wine, even though of all fluids mercury may seem to need the greatest cold to congeal it. From this it may also be concluded that thermometers filled with very highly rectified spirit of wine may serve to indicate the various greater or lesser degrees of cold in a freezing-mixture, although they may not fix the measure of the cold. . . .[29]

In other words, although the spirit does not freeze, its indications are not to be trusted. Later in the paper, he suggests a freezing point of 650°D. (−333°C.) for mercury but admits that the decision is difficult.

The production of solid mercury created a small sensation in St. Petersburg. Braun found that it could be made whenever the natural cold was greater than 175°D. (−17°C.), and several Academicians repeated the experiment, among them F. U. T. Aepinus, M. W. Lomonosov, J. G. Model, and J. E. Zeiher.

Braun's conclusions were accepted by Jean André Deluc and

[29] *Ibid.*, p. 290.

publicized in his influential *Recherches sur les modifications de l'atmosphère*. Deluc believed that mercury would never freeze in any natural temperature and adduced this as one reason for preferring it as a thermometric liquid. He interpreted Braun's experiments as indicating a freezing point of about −261° on his own 80° scale,[30] or −326°C. On the other hand, Ernst August Strohmeyer of Hanover refused to accept Deluc's conclusions. On January 4, 1768, with an air temperature of −16°F., he put both mercury thermometers and spirit thermometers into a mixture of snow and saltpeter and froze the mercury but could not freeze the spirit, concluding that Deluc was quite wrong about the temperatures that mercury will withstand and that we must use spirit thermometers to measure very low temperatures.[31]

Clearly it was time for some well-designed experiments, and these were made at Fort Albany on Hudson's Bay in the winter of 1781–82 by Thomas Hutchins, at the suggestion of Henry Cavendish and Joseph Black.[32] The experiments were very extensive, made usually with freezing mixtures but sometimes with the natural cold of Fort Albany. Mercury was frozen in a small vessel around the thermometer bulb. In his discussion of the results, Cavendish points out that mercury, like other liquids, remains at a steady temperature while in the process of freezing. It also contracts when it freezes, and this was what Braun did not recognize.

Fortunately, it had been possible to recalibrate most of Hutchins' thermometers after they were returned to London. Examining all his experiments, made in various ways on both the freezing and melting of mercury, Cavendish derived a freezing point of −38⅔°F. (−39.3°C.), not far from the modern value (−38.87°C.), if we consider the difficulties under which the experiments must have been conducted.

In the same volume of the *Philosophical Transactions* Charles Blagden published a "History of the congelation of quicksilver,"[33] in which he pointed out how Braun's error had caused absurdly low temperatures to be reported at arctic stations. Deluc would have felt foolish, had he not been immune to such sentiments.

---

30 This is the scale now called by the name of Réaumur.

31 E. A. Strohmeyer, *Anleitung, übereinstimmende Thermometer zu verfertigen* [etc.] (Göttingen, 1775), pp. 11–12. There is a copy at Offenbach-am-Main. Strohmeyer is not in Poggendorf's *Biographisch-litterarisches Handwörterbuch,* but was known to J. H. Lambert.

32 Cavendish, *Phil. Trans.,* Vol. 73 (1783), pp. 303–28; Hutchins, *Phil. Trans.,* Vol. 73 (1783), pp. *303–70. (The paging is duplicated, and is so marked with asterisks.)

33 Blagden, *Phil. Trans.,* Vol. 73 (1783), pp. 329–97.

3. *Technical Matters.* While this diffuse but not entirely unprofitable argument had been going on, real advances had been made in the techniques of making and calibrating thermometers. Lavoisier's efforts in this direction seem to have been made by personal exhortation, and are largely unrecorded. The celebrated instrumentmaker John Bird, who worked in London for forty years after 1733, appears to have made excellent thermometers,[34] and according to Van Swinden he is supposed to have calibrated his tubes individually and divided his scales accordingly. But, again, written evidence is hard to come by.

There was a great deal of argument about the relative merits of mercury and of spirit of wine, beginning with Martine, who argued strongly for mercury.[35] As we have seen, Réaumur knew at least as early as this that the dilatation of alcohol with change of temperature followed a law different from that of mercury, but Deluc seems to have been the first to make careful quantitative experiments about this.

First of all, Deluc made excellent arrangements for comparing thermometers at various temperatures between the boiling point of water and a point 10° (on his 80-degree scale) below the ice point. He made thermometers of the same kind of glass, filled them with mercury, olive oil, oil of camomile, oil of thyme, rectified spirit of wine,[36] a saturated salt solution, and ordinary water respectively, and pointed them off at 80° and 0°. Then, taking his mercury thermometer as standard, he compared it with the others at each fifth degree on its scale. There is no need to reproduce his results here;[37] it is sufficient to note that, in comparison with the mercury thermometer, the expansion of the other liquids increased with increasing temperature. Similar comparisons between mercury and spirit of wine were published by Strohmeyer,[38] Lambert, [39] and Wildt.[40]

Realizing that such experiments have nothing absolute about them, Deluc then set out to discover whether the mercury thermometer really indicates the addition of equal amounts of heat for equal changes in the volume of the mercury. Acting on a

---

[34] Cf. Van Swinden, *Dissertation* (1792), pp. 117–18.

[35] Martine, *Essays* (1740), pp. 204–6.

[36] "Esprit-de-vin qui brule la poudre." The standard test for spirit was to put a few grains of gunpowder into a spoon, cover them with the spirit, and set it alight. If the powder finally burned, the spirit was judged to be free from water.

[37] See *Modifications,* ¶ 418m.

[38] Strohmeyer, *Anleitung.* His results will be found in Lambert's *Pyrometrie,* p. 68.

[39] *Ibid.*

[40] J. C. D. Wildt, *Archiv. für d. gesammte Naturlehre, Nürnberg,* Vol. 6 (1825), pp. 299–301.

TABLE 5.2. Deluc's Table of the Readings of the Mercury Thermometer, Divided into 80 Equal Parts between the Temperatures of Melting Ice and Boiling Water, that Correspond to the Division into 80 Equal Parts of the Excess of Heat of Boiling Water over That of Melting Ice

	Real amounts of heat	Corresponding readings of the mercury thermometer	Condensation of mercury by equal diminutions of heat
Boiling water	$z + 80$	80.0	
			5.3
	$z + 75$	74.7	
			5.3
	$z + 70$	69.4	
			5.2
	$z + 65$	64.2	
			5.2
	$z + 60$	59.0	
			5.2
	$z + 55$	53.8	
			5.1
	$z + 50$	48.7	
			5.1
	$z + 45$	43.6	
			5.0
	$z + 40$	38.6	
			5.0
	$z + 35$	33.6	
			4.9
	$z + 30$	28.7	
			4.9
	$z + 25$	23.8	
			4.9
	$z + 20$	18.9	
			4.8
	$z + 15$	14.1	
			4.8
	$z + 10$	9.3	
			4.7
	$z + 5$	4.6	
			4.6
Melting ice	z	0.0	
			80.0

suggestion by his mentor George Louis Le Sage the younger, he made a long series of experiments by mixing hot and cold water in various amounts, determined by weighing. These experiments were fairly well thought out, but probably not free from systematic error. It is interesting that he seemed to take the principle of these experiments—the laws of calorimetry—as axiomatic. His results are shown in Table 5.2, in which z is "the heat of melting ice."[41] We may note that the mercury thermometer differs from the thermodynamic scale of temperature[42] much less than Deluc found, and in the opposite direction.[43] The difference depends, of course, on what kind of glass is used for

[41] *Modifications,* ¶ 422rr.
[42] See p. 112 above.
[43] Cf. G. Ribaud, *Mesure des températures* (Paris, 1936), p. 48.

the thermometer. Nevertheless, if for no good reason, his results confirmed his conviction that mercury is the only good thermometric liquid.

Deluc's experiments were criticized on technical grounds by Flaugergues[44] and also, much more fully, by J. H. Lambert,[45] who based his thermometry on the air thermometer, an instrument that Deluc had given elaborate reasons for rejecting. There is no doubt whatever that Lambert's comparisons of thermometers with the air thermometer were much simpler and more exact than Deluc's mixing experiments, but his conclusion that "the air thermometer shows the actual degree of heat" was pure intuition, to be revealed as a very good approximation much later.

Although mercury was coming to be preferred as a thermometric liquid, spirit thermometers were still made in large numbers at the end of the eighteenth century. They might have been better than they were had it not been for an idea promulgated by Deluc, according to which the spirit had to be "purged of air," and if this was done, it would stand the heat of boiling water.[46] The process was to heat the thermometer after filling, until the spirit expanded to the top of the tube, then seal it. The "air" would come out as the spirit cooled, and after a period of hours or days, would accumulate at the end of the tube, which was then opened and the process repeated, until the liquid would stand the temperature of boiling water. If there was any more in this than self-deception, Deluc must have removed nearly all the alcohol by this process. Nevertheless, this idea gained currency on the authority of Deluc, and we find Louis Cotte[47] and even Angelo Bellani[48] taking it as gospel.

For meteorological purposes mercury and alcohol have held the field up to the present day, though the advantages of toluol at low temperatures down to $-70°$C. were emphasized in 1892 by Chappuis.[49] Wilhelm Donle[50] even suggested dilute sulphuric acid, the expansion of which is more linear, he said, than that of alcohol. A further advantage is that it does not distil into the end of the tube, the vapor pressure of any distillate being greater than that of the solution; but I am not aware that his suggestion has been adopted.

[44] Honoré Flaugergues, *J. de Phys.*, Vol. 77 (1813), p. 280.
[45] Lambert, *Pyrometrie, passim*.
[46] *Modifications*, ¶ 423.
[47] Cotte, *Obs. sur la Phys.*, Vol. 48 (An VII [1799]), pp. 285–86.
[48] Bellani, *Giornale di fisica*, Vol. 2 (1809), pp. 431–32.
[49] P. Chappuis, *Arch. Sci. phys. et nat., Genève*, Vol. 28 (1892), pp. 293–301.
[50] Donle, *Zeits. für Instrum.*, Vol. 13 (1893), pp. 238–42.

In the years following 1770 thermometers came to be calibrated with more and more accuracy. There is little doubt that Deluc's *Modifications* had given a strong push in this direction; yet the matter was clarified, in the main, by a number of Englishmen who probably thought it essential to let some light into that exasperating book, especially as most of them were interested in the elusive subject of barometric hypsometry.[51] Of these, Horsley introduced the excellent term "fundamental interval" for "the whole extent of the scale between melting ice and boiling water"[52] and recommended a standard barometric height of 30 English inches for the determination of the boiling point; it had always been done at this pressure by "that eminent mechanic, our countryman, Mr. John Bird."[53] So Horsley proposed to call a thermometer, thus constructed, "Bird's Fahrenheit," but there were no takers; the sporting English apparently felt that it was really Fahrenheit's bird.

In the same decade the Royal Society, prodded by the greatest of scientific *dillettanti,* Henry Cavendish, decided to have a good look at their meteorological instruments. In 1776 Cavendish published an extensive paper on these,[54] containing the suggestion that thermometers might well be adjusted in the steam from boiling water, if the conditions were carefully specified, instead of in the water itself. He wished that the Royal Society would recommend a standard method.

The Society immediately made him chairman of a committee *ad hoc,* with William Heberden, Alexander Aubert, Nevil Maskelyne, J. Planta, Horsley, and of course J. A. Deluc, who had come to England by this time and been given the position— apparently not a sinecure—of "reader" to Queen Charlotte. The terms of reference of the committee, and its assiduity, are indicated by the title and the length of its report.[55]

They found thermometry in a bad state; thermometers made by various makers were found to vary over a range of 3¼°F. in steam. So they made a great many experiments, and recommended a suitable vessel for determinations of the boiling point:

[51] Cf. Samuel Horsley, *Phil. Trans.,* Vol. 64 (1774), pp. 214–301; George Shuckburgh, *Phil. Trans.,* Vol. 67 (1777), pp. 513–97; William Roy, *Phil. Trans.,* Vol. 67 (1777), pp. 653–788. Note the enormous length of all three papers.

[52] Horsley, *Phil. Trans.,* Vol. 64 (1774), p. 221.

[53] *Ibid.,* p. 224. Although John Bird was one of the greatest of eighteenth-century instrumentmakers, I have not found any of his thermometers.

[54] Cavendish, *Phil. Trans.,* Vol. 66 (1776), pp. 375–401.

[55] "The Report of the Committee of the Royal Society to consider of the best method of adjusting the fixed points of thermometers; and of the precautions necessary to be used in making experiments with these instruments." *Phil. Trans.,* Vol. 67 (1777), pp. 816–57.

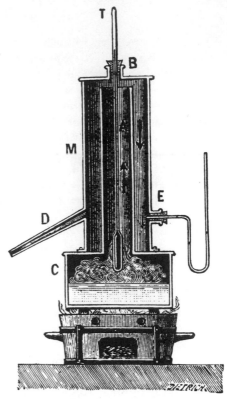

Fig. 5.1   Steam-point apparatus.

a cylindrical pot with a close-fitting cover and a "chimney" to carry off the steam. A small loose piece of tin-plate was placed on the top of the chimney to prevent the ingress of air without materially increasing the steam pressure. They picked 29.8 inches of mercury as a standard barometric pressure and provided a table of corrections for other pressures. The bulb of the thermometer should be in the steam, "at least one or two inches" above the boiling water, the vessel should be long enough to enable almost all the column of mercury to be in the steam, and the fire should be applied only to the bottom of the vessel.

The committee's general principles have been the basis of accurate determinations of the steam point ever since. The piece of tin-plate was eventually replaced by a U-tube manometer containing water, one end opening into the steam and the other into the atmosphere. A further improvement consisted in leading the steam down an annular space outside the upper parts of the boiling vessel, thus preventing the cooling of the thermometer by radiation. Both these improvements appear in the apparatus shown in **Fig. 5.1**.[56] A further refinement, quite superfluous for

[56] The importance of these features was emphasized by P. Tavernier, *Compt. Rend.*, Vol. 18 (1844), pp. 29–31.

any meteorological thermometry, was to provide a boiler and condenser separate from the calibration chamber.[57]

Small pieces of apparatus, now rather misleadingly called hypsometers,[58] were developed for mountain use, the first by Deluc[59]—though he put the bulb of the thermometer in the boiling water—later ones by Bellani,[60] Wollaston,[61] and many others. Wilhelm Gintl of Graz made one with the steam escaping down an annular space.[62] A particularly elegant one that folds into a length of only 15 cm. was described by Regnault,[63] and is shown in Fig. 5.2.

Regarding the ice point, the committee recommended that crushed ice should be piled nearly to the top of the mercury column. The additional desideratum that the melt-water should be allowed to run away was noted by Bossier at about the same time,[64] but, as we have seen,[65] Nollet had been aware of this in 1740.

By 1852 all these improvements in the adjusting of thermometers had been adopted as a routine at Kew Observatory,[66] though it is clear that the actual methods were those described by Regnault five years before. An important part of the process was the calibration of the tube before the construction of the thermometer. The first to do this was Ole Rømer, about 1702,[67] and his method, the measurement of a thread of mercury at different places in the tube, has always been adopted, with gradually increasing sophistication in dealing with the results. One of the earliest to give a formal theory was Ludwig Wentz,[68] but throughout the eighteenth century the better makers undoubtedly used rough-and-ready methods of their own. The astronomer F. W. Bessel developed an elaborate procedure that was the basis of many modifications.[69] Here I have space only to refer to two

[57] Such an apparatus, due to P. Chappuis, is described in the *Traité pratique de la thermométrie de précision* of Charles Edouard Guillaume (Paris, 1889), pp. 112–15.

[58] *hypsos,* height; *metron,* a measure.

[59] Deluc, *Modifications,* ¶¶ 867–79.

[60] Angelo Bellani, *Giornale di fisica, Pavia,* Vol. 2 (1809), pp. 413–41. He found that the temperature of the boiling water depends to some extent on the material of the vessel. But that of the steam does not (F. Rudberg, *Ann. der Phys.,* Vol. 40 (1837), pp. 54–55.

[61] Francis Hyde Wollaston, *Phil. Trans.,* [Vol. 107] (1817), pp. 183–96.

[62] Gintl, *Zeits. f. Phys. u. verwandte Wiss., Wien,* Vol. 6 (1840), pp. 91–100.

[63] Victor Regnault, *Ann. Chim. et Phys.,* Vol. 14 (1845), pp. 196–206.

[64] Bossier, *Réforme des thermometres,* pp. 16–17, note.

[65] Page 86 above.

[66] John Welsh, *Proc. Roy. Soc.,* Vol. 6 (1852), pp. 178–83.

[67] See page 67.

[68] Wentz, *Acta Helvetica,* Vol. 3 (1757), pp. 105–8.

[69] Bessel, *Ann. der Phys.,* Vol. 6 (1826), pp. 287–308.

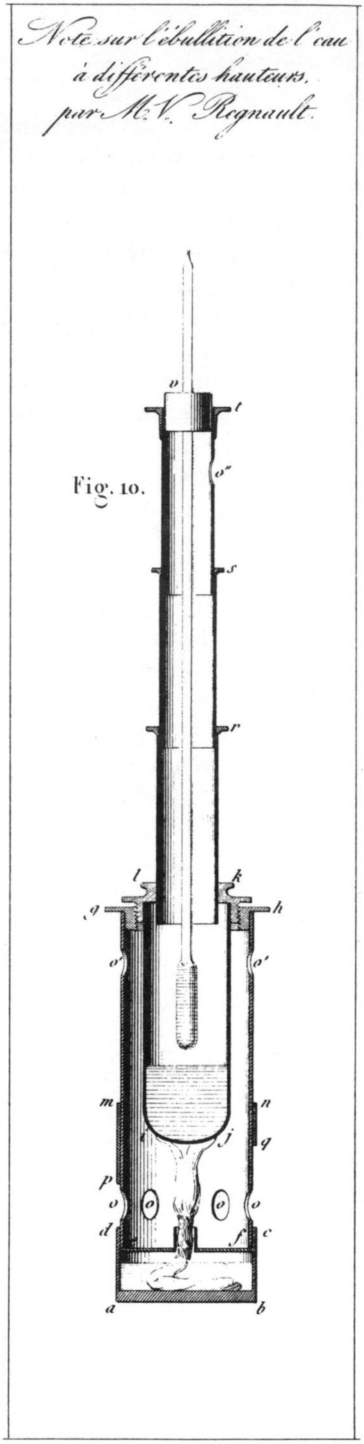
Note sur l'ébullition de l'eau
à différentes hauteurs,
par M. V. Regnault.
Fig. 10.
v
t
o''
s
r
l
k
g
h
o'
o'
m
n
j
q
p
o
o
o
o
d
c
f
a
b

Fig. 5.2 Regnault's pocket hypsometer.

critical summaries of the methods of calibrating such tubes.[70, 71]
A further problem arose in the calibration of alcohol thermometers for meteorological use, although C. S. M. Pouillet had found as early as 1837 that the alcohol thermometer practically agreed with the air thermometer when pointed off in melting ice and in a mixture of solid carbon dioxide and sulphuric ether.[72]
He found the temperature of this mixture to be $-78.8°C$. Perhaps only the Canadians and the Russians could see any need for such a technique. In 1891 Alfred Angot of the Office National Météorologique, after careful comparisons of mercury and spirit thermometers in a thermostat between $+34.7$ and $-23.7°C$., deduced a power series which he felt to be adequate down to about $-40°C$. even if only two calibration points, at $0°$ and about $+30°C$., had been used.[73] If more calibration points can be employed, there remains the purely technical problem of engraving a nonuniform scale, and in 1867 William Ackland of London, described as an employee of the opticians Horne and Thornthwaite, Newgate Street, had invented an "interpolating dividing engine" for this purpose.[74]

When a thermometer has its bulb at one temperature and its stem at another, a correction is needed, as was known to Henry Cavendish, who calculated a table for the mercury thermometer, pointing out that for a spirit thermometer the correction will be much greater.[75] While of much interest to chemists, the stem correction is not very important in ordinary meteorological observations, though Leyst has shown that it should be applied to wet-bulb thermometers in very hot, dry regions.[76]

Toward the end of the nineteenth century tremendous efforts were made in national and international standardizing laboratories to push the mercury thermometer to the limits of its possible accuracy. A consideration of these researches is beyond the scope of this book, but some readers may find interest in the long article with which the Physikalische Reichsanstalt at Berlin inaugurated their impressive series of *Abhandlungen*.[77] This sort

[70] J. Pernet, *Zeits. österr. Ges. Meteorol.*, Vol. 14, (1879), pp. 130–37.

[71] British Association, "Report of the Committee on the Methods Employed in the Calibration of Mercurial Thermometers," *B.A.A.S. Report, Southampton (1882)*, pp. 145–204.

[72] Pouillet, *Compt. Rend.*, Vol. 4 (1837), pp. 513–19.

[73] Angot, *Annuaire Soc. meteorol. de France*, Vol. 39 (1891), pp. 85–88.

[74] Ackland, *Proc. meteorol. Soc.*, Vol. 4 (1867), pp. 23–27.

[75] Cavendish, *Phil. Trans.*, Vol. 66 (1776), p. 377.

[76] Ernst Leyst, *Zeits. für Instrum.*, Vol. 14 (1894), pp. 143–44.

[77] J. Pernet, W. Jaeger, and E. Gumlich, *Berlin, Phys. Reichsanst., Abh.*, Vol. 1 (1894), pp. 1–102. The publications of the Bureau International des Poids et Mesures, Sèvres, may also be consulted.

of activity has been rendered much less useful by the development of electrical resistance thermometry.

4. The Shape of the Instrument. We have discussed bulbs and tubes and liquids and scales, but up to this point very little has been said about how these elements were put together; in other words, what liquid-in-glass thermometers actually looked like, at least after about 1665. As we have seen, the Florentine thermometers were entirely of glass; things of beauty, beyond the capability of the ordinary artisan, but fragile, and scarcely suited to everyday use. If it had not been for the happy accident that a large number of them were carefully packed away, to be discovered in an age when they would be valued for their historical importance,[78] it is doubtful whether any would have survived.

Workmen to the north of the Alps found it difficult enough at first to make a plain bulb and tube and fill it with spirit of wine. In the seventeenth century the glass parts were usually mounted on a wooden board that had been covered with paper. On this the scale was drawn, very often with calligraphic decorations, sometimes over a colored drawing. The new interest of the upper classes in science resulted in much very elaborate carving and gilding according to the prevailing fashion. There is a typical instrument, its bulb unfortunately broken, in the possession of the Académie des Sciences at Paris. An inscription on the front shows that it was made by "Prieur à l'image St. Geneviève à Paris," and one on the back states that a new tube was fitted on November 7, 1789, by the celebrated Mossy. It probably dates from the beginning of the eighteenth century; the scale has 100 divisions, but is not identifiable.[79] At this period the bulb of the thermometer usually lay snugly in a suitable depression carved in the wood—a position that must have added to the sluggishness of the instrument. Sometimes it was in a hole bored right through the plank.

Fahrenheit, as far as I know, was the first to make the thermometer look like a scientific instrument in our sense. The two original Fahrenheit thermometers at Leiden[80] are mounted on

[78] See page 34 above.

[79] Prieur is not mentioned by Daumas (*Les instruments scientifiques aux XVIIe et XVIIIe siècles* [Paris, 1953]). This thermometer is probably no. 528 of the inventory of the instruments of the *Académie royale des Sciences* made in 1793 by J. A. C. Charles (Institut de France, ms. 1986, no. 1).

[80] Rijksmuseum voor de Geschiedenis der Natuurwetenschappen, Inventory nos. Th 1 and Th 1a.

neat strips of sheet brass on which the scales are engraved. This tradition was continued by Hendrik Prins;[81] but in France, wooden bases and paper scales continued to be used until the time of Lavoisier. When it was suggested to Réaumur that thermometer scales should be on metal or glass, he wrote that this was pushing precision to a ridiculous length.[82] Even the thermometers sent to many parts of the world by the Meteorological Society of Mannheim were mounted on walnut bases,[83] and it is interesting that one of the reasons for making the bulb cylindrical, rather than spherical, was that "in forming the hole or depression in which it will lie, the board need not be as deeply cut."[84] Deluc, noting the possibility of parallax, advised letting the tube into a groove so that the plane of the scale coincides with the diametral plane of the tube.[85] But toward the end of the eighteenth century, metal and glass scales were used by the best makers, as can be seen particularly well in the collection of the Conservatoire National des Arts et Métiers at Paris.

The English makers often used ivory for the scales of their smaller thermometers. At Utrecht there is a particularly interesting one signed "J. Newman Lisle Street London," which puts its date between 1817 and about 1825.[86] In this the scale is hinged a short distance below the freezing point, so that it can be folded up out of the way when the temperature of a liquid is to be measured.

A way of protecting the scale from the weather was devised by Angelo Bellani about 1810. This was to draw the scale on paper, which was then rolled into a cylinder and enclosed in a glass tube. Sometimes this was a separate tube about one centimeter in diameter, fastened to the thermometer tube;[87] in other instruments the entire thermometer, and the scale, were enclosed, which must have made the thermometer very sluggish. Both types are represented in a group of instruments by Bellani in the Museo Copernicano at Rome.

These are rather clumsy attempts to do what was done by the *Einschlussthermometer*, which has been almost universally used

81 E.g., Leiden, Inv. no. Th 6a.

82 Réaumur, *Mém. Acad. r. Sci. Paris* (1731), pp. 295–96.

83 J. Hemmer, *Ephemerides Societatis Meteorologicae Palatinae. Historia et observationes anni 1781* [etc.] (Mannheim, 1783), p. 69.

84 *Ibid.*, p. 64, note. A thermometer at the Deutsches Museum, Munich, inv. no. 2761, is almost certainly one of these instruments, though it is stated to have been repaired at Regensburg in 1833.

85 Deluc, *Modifications,* ¶ 458c.

86 This is illustrated in *De Natuur*, Vol. 50 (1930), p. 28, by P. H. van Cittert. It is in the University Museum at Utrecht, inv. no. W.16.

87 This construction was later re-invented by John Ronketti of London (British Patent 756 of 1862, Mar. 18).

Fig. 5.3 Einschlussthermometer, *a group, 1890.*

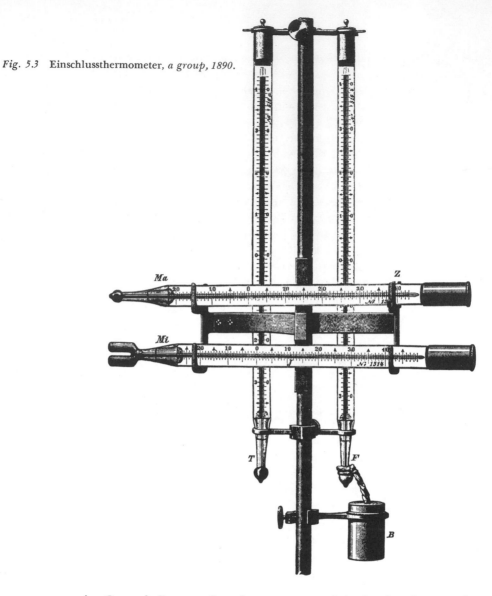

in Central Europe for the purposes of both chemistry and meteorology. In this type of thermometer the scale, usually etched on a thin flat piece of opal glass, is attached to the narrow thermometer tube and the whole enclosed in an outer tube of clear glass which is reduced in diameter and joined to the top of the bulb. Fig. 5.3 shows a group of these thermometers as mounted for the Prussian service. The idea seems to have occurred to the instrumentmaker Goubert, who worked in the rue Dauphine, Paris. On December 10, 1776, he presented a thermometer to the Société royale de Médicine in which the tube and the paper scale were enclosed and sealed in a glass tube, but the

134

bulb was left quite free.[88] It was intended for baths, but Cotte, who made a favorable report, said that it was excellent for meteorological observations because it measured the temperature of the air, "and not merely [that] of the board which serves it as a support, or of the wall against which it rests."[89]

The *Einschlussthermometer* was made into a most elegant instrument by the German makers, but the problem of maintaining the scale immovable in relation to the tube was not easily solved,[90] finally yielding to the ingenuity of R. Fuess of Berlin.[91]

I have not been able to find out who first etched the scale on the tube itself. It was probably done before 1800, for at the CNAM in Paris there are four thermometers in a case,[92] signed "Crichton fecit," whose thick glass tubes each have a plane face cut in them to take the graduations. Crichton flourished about 1780, according to Daumas.[93] Outside of Central Europe such thermometers, but without the flat face, have long been universally used in laboratories; but they were not so popular in meteorology, probably because the black, that was put in the graduations to make them more visible, gradually disappeared under exposure to the weather. A compromise was reached about 1850, in which the stem was graduated, but the numbers and the main divisions were carried on the support, typically of porcelain[94] as in Fig. 5.4. The firm of Casella started supplying such thermometers to the Board of Trade in 1854, according to records at the Meteorological Office, Bracknell, which has the first one, marked "B.T.1," in its collection.[95]

For naval use, brass frames were naturally preferred, and 'a standard model was designed at Kew in the same year.[96] It is interesting that a thousand of these thermometers were immedi-

[88] Goubert, *Description et usage des barometres, thermometres et autre instrumens météorologiques* (Paris, 1781), pp. 28–30.

[89] *Ibid.*, p. 29.

[90] J. Pernet, *Zeits. österr. Ges. Meteorol.*, Vol. 14 (1879), p. 135.

[91] D. R. P. 389, August 2, 1877.

[92] Inv. no. 19,912.

[93] *Les instruments scientifiques*, p. 396. Crichton was still active in 1803, when he had a paper in the *Philosophical Magazine*, Vol. 15 (1803), pp. 147–48. There is a passage in H. B. de Saussure's *Voyages dans les Alpes* [etc.] (4 vols., 4°; also 8 vols., 8°, Neuchâtel, 1779–96), ¶ 2053, which might be interpreted to indicate that Ramsden had made such thermometers. See also p. 171 below.

[94] Negretti & Zambra (*A Treatise on Meteorological Instruments* [etc.] [London, 1864], p. 65), claim to have been the first to use this. The graduations and figures were etched in with hydrofluoric acid.

[95] Inventory no. 3117B.

[96] Kew Committee (J. P. Gassiot, Chairman), *B.A.A.S., Liverpool, 1854, Report of Council*, p. xxvii.

Fig. 5.4   Thermometer with porcelain base.
(Courtesy of C. F. Casella & Co., Ltd.)

Fig. 5.5 *Sheathed thermometer.* (Courtesy of C. F. Casella & Co., Ltd.)

ately ordered by the Smithsonian Institution in Washington, half from Casella & Co. and half from Negretti & Zambra.[97]

In the United States, metal—in later times, stainless steel—became standard; the forming of the groove for the tube in a strip of sheet metal resulting in a very light and at the same time inflexible base. These constructions have the great advantage that a small motion of the tube in relation to the base causes no error, but on the other hand the graduations on the tube are exposed to the weather.

The remedy, used widely in the British Commonwealth, is to seal the thermometer tube proper in an outer glass tube which does not, however, cover the bulb. This construction seems to have been first applied to the so-called grass minimum thermometer.[98] I have not been able to trace the early history of this form of protection in detail, but according to an article in the *Meteorological Magazine*[99] one G. Leach, about 1845, surrounded the stems of his thermometers with a glass tube sealed with cork, and "thirty years later" G. Symons suggested the use of a glass sheath fused to the stem near the bulb. Symons may have suggested it, but in 1877 Negretti & Zambra patented it.[100] At the instigation of E. Gold, thermometers of this sort (Fig. 5.5) were made official in the United Kingdom in 1931, after extensive tests. They have proved very strong and durable.

The legibility of a thermometer graduated on the stem, particularly a mercury thermometer, is improved by a light-colored background. A particularly happy way of providing this is to produce a glass tube with a ribbon of white enamel at the back. This seems to have been effected in 1844 by Bodeur,[101] who noted that the enamel must not be on the outside, but must be protected by clear glass. The invention was made all over again by Negretti & Zambra of London, who were congratulated by a Jury of the International Exhibition of 1862 for not patenting it. All makers, the Jury said, had availed themselves of this.[102]

The vernier, employed on many instruments, has found little application to the thermometer. A few examples can be found in museums;[103] but the idea was not really very useful, a possible

[97] *Ibid.*

[98] See p. 162 below.

[99] Anon., *Met. Mag.*, Vol. 69 (1934), pp. 68–69.

[100] British Provisional Patent 718 of 1877, Feb. 21.

[101] Bodeur, *Compt. Rend.*, Vol. 18 (1844), p. 1132.

[102] London, International Exhibition of 1862. *Reports by the Juries* [etc.] (London, 1863), (paged in classes), p. xiii–34.

[103] E.g., Florence, Museo di Storia della Scienza, no. 525; Munich, Deutsches Museum, no. 39079. Both of these have the Delisle scale. Paris, CNAM, four thermometers under no. 19909.

88.
SCALE ABOUT 1-3RD.

Fig. 5.6   Thermometer with hollow, cylindrical bulb.

exception being for the thermometer of a "hypsometer," or
boiling-point apparatus.[104]

The easiest sort of bulb to blow is a spherical one. As we have
seen, other shapes having a higher ratio of surface to volume
had been suggested, notably the cylinder by Fahrenheit, but also
lens-shaped bulbs, spiral tubes, and so forth.[105] Delisle, it will
be remembered, liked pear-shaped bulbs (Fig. 4.4). Determined
efforts were made to reduce the sluggishness of spirit thermometers by means of complicated bulbs in the form of a two-pronged
fork, or a loop, or even a hollow cylinder, as in the thermometer
devised by the instrumentmaker James Hicks and described in
1873 (Fig. 5.6).[106] His competitor Francis Pastorelli objected that
changes in atmospheric pressure would alter its readings, but
Hicks replied that he had exposed it to a pressure of 50 lb./in.^{2},
and "the effect was very trifling."

People like to have instruments indicate on dials; indeed the
popularity of Hooke's wheel barometer[107] is evidence of this, if
any were needed. The mechanism of the wheel barometer is
exactly duplicated in the instrument devised by Ferdinand
Berthoud (Fig. 5.7), he says in 1756, and described in 1763.[108]
The figure is description enough, if we mention that the liquid is
spirit of wine in the parts *acd*, mercury in the central tube *ab*.

104 As in the one described by Wollaston, *Phil. Trans.*, Vol. 107 (1817), pp.
183–96.
105 See, for example, *Traittez des baromètres, thermomètres, et notiomètres,
ou hygromètres. Par Mr. D**** [Joachim Dalencé] (Amsterdam, 1688).
106 J. J. Hicks, *Quart. J. Meteorol. Soc.*, Vol. 2 (1873), pp. 96–99.
107 Cf. Middleton, *The History of the Barometer*, pp. 94–99.
108 Berthoud, *Essay sur l'horlogerie* [etc.] (2 vols.; Paris, 1763), Vol. 1, pp.
215–16.

Fig. 5.7   Berthoud's dial thermometer, 1763.

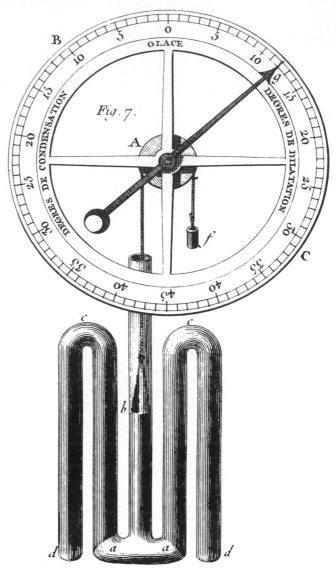

The mercury would probably have to go a little way up the
tubes *ac* for stability.

   This instrument antedates by more than two decades the
better-known one of Henry Cavendish, made in 1779, in which
the large cylindrical bulb full of spirit of wine is connected to a
U-tube containing mercury.[109] The mechanism is otherwise the
same, with the addition of two light pointers for indicating the
maximum and minimum temperatures, which are pushed by the

---

[109] *Scientific Papers of the Honourable Henry Cavendish, F.R.S.* [etc.] (2
vols., Cambridge, 1921), Vol. II, pp. 395–97.

138

main index. This instrument, which is now at the Royal Institution, London, was calibrated at Chatsworth on June 12, 1779, and used for meteorological observations. Such a use would not have suited the instrument in a painted and gilt Rococo case in the Deutsches Museum,[110] which was obviously intended to measure the temperature of the state apartments. It has a similar mechanism except that the bulb is a spiral with an outer diameter of 13 cm., of four turns of approximately 5 mm. tubing; and there is an inner and an outer scale and two pointers, with an elaborate and well-made gear train that causes the inner pointer to make several revolutions for one turn of the outer one. It is signed "Thermometre selon Réaumur invente et fait par Bianchy Vienne 1767." There is another rather similar one at Paris,[111] but with only one pointer. The dial of this is inscribed "Thermometre sur Echele de Fahrenheit et de Réaumur échelé le baromètre sur la hauteur de 29–8/12 Pouces d'Angleterre par Bianchy et Comp. à Amsterdam," which sounds appropriately scientific. There is no mention of thermometers of this kind in the book published in 1762 by the Vienna Bianchy,[112] which makes it likely that he designed his instrument soon afterward.

Spiral bulbs were used a good deal in more conventional thermometers, and examples will be found in the larger museums. It is probable that such instruments suffered severely from the slow changes in the volume of the bulb that will be discussed in the last section of this chapter.

5. *Earth Thermometers*. Rather special thermometers have been made from time to time for the purpose of measuring the temperature of the soil at various depths. Lambert in his *Pyrometrie* refers to measurements made at his suggestion at Zurich, from 1762 to 1767, by a well-to-do amateur whose name was Ott.[113] Spirit thermometers with tubes of appropriate length had been used, graduated on Micheli du Crest's scale[114]—which apparently was used to some extent in Switzerland even later than this.

Another formal study was made by Robert Ferguson of Raith in Scotland, who used four large mercury thermometers with very long stems of narrow bore, and thick bulbs. These were

[110] Inventory no. 63196.
[111] CNAM, Inv. no. 1581.
[112] Jacob Bianchy, *Das Merkwürdigste vom Barometre und Thermometre* [etc.] (Vienna, 1762).
[113] J. H. Lambert, *Pyrometrie*, pp. 356–57.
[114] See above, p. 89.

139

enclosed in wooden cases, and sunk side by side to depths of one, two, four, and eight feet respectively.[115]

One of the difficulties of this sort of thermometry is the possibility of large corrections because of the gradient of temperature in the long stems. The Belgian astronomer L. A. J. Quetelet, who made similar investigations at Brussels,[116] reports that Arago had attempted to estimate the stem correction by putting beside each thermometer another tube, similar in all respects, but without a bulb. Quetelet preferred to reduce the readings of the lower thermometers by using the readings of the upper ones and gave a theory of this procedure.

A similar technique was employed at Edinburgh by James D. Forbes.[117] Forbes had the instrumentmaker Alexander Adie make three sets of alcohol thermometers in lengths of 3, 6, 12, and 24 feet. These were French feet, presumably to facilitate comparison with the experiments on the Continent.[118] The bulbs of the thermometers were cylindrical, 6 to 8 inches long and 1½ to 2 inches in diameter. Observations were made at three sites from February, 1837, to May, 1842. A hole was bored in the soil and the thermometers inserted in three wooden boxes, the two shortest in one box. At one of the sites they were sunk in solid sandstone, and in this case the hole was 6 or 7 inches in diameter at the bottom and three inches at the top. Forbes managed to get the thermometers in without any sheathing, filling the hole with fine sand. This was rather a *tour de force*.

It also underlined Forbes's awareness that a sheath for the thermometer, or even the disturbance of the ground, might make the readings of the thermometers unrepresentative of conditions in the undisturbed soil. Long before, in 1785, this must have been in the mind of that excellent experimenter Horace Benedict de Saussure, who took a wooden staff 1¼ inches in diameter, and a little over 6 feet long, and

> had two thermometers placed in the interior of the staff, one at its end, the other two feet higher. Opposite the scale of each of these thermometers I have had a door made, which I can open to read the thermometer without exposing the bulb. The bulb is buried in the wood, and also surrounded with wax or cotton, which makes it difficult for the air to affect it.[119]

[115] Described by Sir John Leslie in *Supplement to the 4th, 5th, and 6th Editions of the Encyclopaedia Britannica* (Edinburgh, 1824), s,v, "Climate," Vol. 3, p. 179.

[116] Quetelet, *Nouv. Mém. Acad. r. Sci. et Belles-Lettres de Bruxelles*, Vol. 10 (1837), 80 pp. (paged separately).

[117] Forbes, *Trans. Roy. Soc. Edinb.*, Vol. 16 (1849), pp. 189–236.

[118] I owe this suggestion to Mr. Robert W. Plenderleith of the Royal Scottish Museum.

[119] De Saussure, *Voyages dans les Alpes*, ¶ 1419. (There is a quarto ed. in 4 vols., and an 8vo ed. in 8 vols., each numbered in paragraphs throughout.)

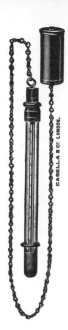

Fig. 5.8   *Earth thermometer for moderate depths.*
(Courtesy of C. F. Casella & Co., Ltd.)

He had an iron auger 7 feet long, just a little bigger than the wooden staff. A hole was bored in the earth, and the thermometers put in for at least an hour—three or four hours the first time, because the process of boring the hole produces heat.

The wooden stick was used ninety years later by Ewald Wollny, a professor of agriculture at Munich, for depths of 30 to 180 cm.[120] But Wollny lined the hole with a strong glass tube, closed at the bottom. The convection of air was prevented by a ring of greased cotton thread surrounding the shaft just above the thermometer, and water was kept out of the glass tube by a double cap.

At about the same time G. J. Symons must have decided that conduction down the sheath was less damaging than digging a hole in the ground; for he provided an iron tube with a steel point, which could be driven in.[121] His thermometers were also at the end of wooden rods; but at some later period they were hung on chains, and enclosed in strong glass tubes, with the bulb in a mass of paraffin wax, as shown in Fig. 5.8, to prevent the temperature changing while it is being read.

This obviously will not do near the surface, and for such observations a thermometer is bent at right angles, with the vertical leg as long as the desired depth, the horizontal part carrying the graduations and lying on the surface of the ground. I have not been able to trace the origin of this form; Filippo Eredia[122] ascribes it to the brothers Alvergniat, who flourished in Paris in the middle of the nineteenth century. It is not mentioned in the *Treatise on Meteorological Instruments* published in 1864 by Negretti & Zambra.

This simple solution to the problem did not find favor in Central Europe, conditioned to the *Einschlussthermometer,* and the firm of Fuess provided an instrument such as that shown in Fig. 5.9, elegant but rather fragile.

It must be recorded that many local and national variations on these themes have been composed.

[120] Wollny, *Zeits. österr. Ges. Meteorol.,* Vol. 10 (1875), pp. 149–51.
[121] Symons, *Quart. J. Meteorol. Soc.,* Vol. 3 (1877), pp. 420–26.
[122] Eredia, *Gli strumenti di meteorologia ed aerologia* (Rome, 1936), p. 113.

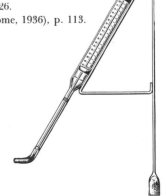

Fig. 5.9   *Earth thermometer, German pattern.*

6. The Changes in the Zero. It was natural to assume that after a liquid had been sealed into an enclosure made of a material such as glass a fairly permanent instrument would result. There had, it is true, been doubts about the permanence of the properties of spirit of wine, but by the middle of the eighteenth century these had largely vanished; and when mercury became the favorite fluid, things seemed even more secure. Deluc, indeed, emphasized the difficulty of getting all the air out of thermometric liquids and believed that any such air, at first hidden in an extremely fine state of division in the "pores" of the liquid—and so taking up no additional space—would collect into bubbles, larger though still minute, and increase the apparent volume of the liquid in the thermometer.[123] But even Deluc did not fear such a process if mercury were used.

As far as I am aware, the first to express doubts about the stability of a mercury thermometer was Jacques Dominic Cassini de Thury in his discussion of his rather heroic observations in the cellars of the Paris Observatory,[124] to which I have already referred.[125] There seemed to be signs of a very slow rise mingled with the very small annual variation of temperature, and Cassini suspected something:

> I shall not try to explain the details of the variations, but I think I am entitled to suspect that some peculiar cause, independent of the state of the external atmosphere, is acting, and participates in the variations of the subterranean thermometer.[126]

He did not pursue the matter. Thermometry was not his subject, and at any rate the Revolution soon left him with no time for such matters.

The subsequent history of this question is very complicated and full of apparent contradictions, and at this point it will be well to note that there are three different effects to be explained:

1) The temporary depression of the zero of a thermometer just after it has been taken to a high temperature, as for instance in a determination of the steam point,

2) the slow rise of the zero of a thermometer with time, often going on for several years, and particularly noticeable in some mercury thermometers, and

3) a gradual fall in the zero of some spirit thermometers.

Of these the first was recognized in the eighteenth century, for in 1775 we find Ernst August Strohmeyer of Hanover insisting

[123] Deluc, *Modifications,* ¶ 413b. He refers this hypothesis to Nollet.
[124] Cassini, *J. de Phys.,* Vol. 35 (1789), pp. 190–205.
[125] Page 119 above.
[126] *J. de Phys.,* Vol. 35 (1789), pp. 198–99.

that, "the boiling-point . . . must be determined first, because the freezing-point can become incorrect again if it is the first to be marked."[127] The phenomenon, for which Strohmeyer suggested no cause, is due to thermal hysteresis in the glass of the bulb and tube, which do not immediately regain their former dimensions. It seems to have remained unknown to many instrumentmakers even a century later, to judge by an editorial comment in a paper by one Zink.[128]

The slow rise in the zero of mercury thermometers was first described clearly by a Canon of Milan, Angelo Bellani, whose acute sensitivity in matters of priority was given full scope by his habit of publishing his discoveries in Italian journals of relatively small circulation. In 1808 he announced the phenomenon in question,[129] noting with some relish that neither Deluc nor the Royal Society's *ad hoc* Committee[130] had discovered it. Bellani quotes Nicholas Casbois[131] as stating that a thermometer, the ice point of which was determined in winter, will not go down as far if it is put in ice during the summer, and draws the conclusion that Casbois missed. He suggests that newly made thermometers should be kept for a year before calibration.

The fall in the zero of spirit thermometers formed the subject of a paper by Honoré Flaugergues in the same year.[132] He had a thermometer that had been made in 1734 by Nollet "on Réaumur's principles and under his supervision." On March 7, 1807 its ice point, measured in melting ice with the water removed, was $-1\frac{1}{4}°R$. Another, made by Romieu of Montpellier in 1758, had its zero at $-2\frac{1}{4}°R$. in 1807. In an additional note,[133] Flaugergues remembers that the Nollet thermometer had probably been calibrated in freezing water rather than in melting ice, which would make its original zero about 0.8° too low,[134] so that the zeros of both instruments had probably fallen by about 2°R. It had been possible to establish that neither scale had shifted relatively to the tube. Surprisingly, Flaugergues ascribed this result to a lessening of the *dilatability* of the spirit, and this caused Bellani to write that if spirit thermometers do suffer a secular fall in their zeros—which he doubted—it is not due to a

[127] Strohmeyer, *Anleitung,* p. 25.

[128] Zink, *Württemburg. Jahreshefte,* Vol. 28 (1872), pp. 124–25. The editor Zech says that the freezing point should be determined first.

[129] Bellani, *Giornale di Fisica* (Pavia), Vol. 1 (1808), pp. 429–39.

[130] See p. 127 above.

[131] Casbois had been a Benedictine prior at Metz, and had disappeared during the Revolution.

[132] Flaugergues, *J. de Phys.,* Vol. 66 (1808), pp. 295–96.

[133] *J. de Phys.,* Vol. 67 (1808), pp. 123–24.

[134] From Deluc, *Modifications,* ¶ 448b.

decrease in the dilatability of the spirit, but to a decrease in its *volume*.[135] Bellani was quite right.

The matter seems to have received no further attention until 1822, when the slow rise in the zero of the mercury thermometer was rediscovered by L. Gourdon,[136] and announced in a letter to Pictet, the editor of the *Bibliothèque Universelle,* a Geneva publication that tried to keep abreast of scientific developments everywhere. Gourdon did something else. He opened the end of the tube of a mercury thermometer, and saw a sudden fall, about equal to the amount that the zero had seemed to rise. He did this with several thermometers and speculated that a small quantity of air contained in the mercury might have collected into a small bubble, to raise the zero—the old idea of Nollet and Deluc. Why the sudden imposition of the atmospheric pressure should have released this bubble, which must surely have been somewhere in the bulb, is not clear.

Flaugergues repeated Gourdon's experiment and went further,[137] deducing that the rise in the zero is the effect of atmospheric pressure in compressing the bulb. Two thermometers, not sealed, that he had had for several years, came back exactly to zero when he placed them in melting ice, and this led him to propose that mercury thermometers should be left unsealed. Spirit thermometers—which presumably have air in them—do not show the effect: "a spirit thermometer, constructed by the Abbé Nollet in 1734, comes back in melting ice exactly to the thread fixed round the tube to mark the zero."[138]

If we compare this with what he had written in 1808 we may suspect him of insincerity or of a very poor memory, for it is almost incredible that he should have possessed at different times, two thermometers made by Nollet in 1734.

In an editorial footnote Pictet objected that the pressure of the atmosphere ought not to displace the zero, because calibration is done after thermometers are sealed.

When Bellani saw this paper he wrote to Pictet, referring to his 1808 article and claiming that he had since proved that the rise is due not to the mercury but to the gradual contraction of the glass.[139] Again he was right. As to the objection that spirit thermometers do not suffer this change, he asserts that they really do, but because of the greater thermal expansion of spirit, the effect is relatively less important. If he had believed in the secular

[135] Bellani, *Giornale di Fisica,* Vol. 1 (1808), p. 438.
[136] Gourdon, *Bibl. Univ.* (Geneva), Vol. 19 (1822), pp. 154–56.
[137] Flaugergues, *Bibl. Univ.,* Vol. 20 (1822), pp. 117–22.
[138] *Ibid.,* p. 118.
[139] Bellani, *Bibl. Univ.,* Vol. 21 (1822), pp. 252–55.

fall in the zeros of spirit thermometers discovered in 1808 by Flaugergues, he might have had an even stronger argument.

In spite of the unanswerable argument in Pictet's footnote, this second paper of Flaugergues set a good many people to breaking the ends off thermometers, often under conditions not very well controlled. Thermometers were also put under vacuum pumps, as by Delarive and Marcet[140] of Geneva, who gave the useful warning that, while there is no doubt that an external pressure or vacuum causes a change in the indications of a thermometer by changing the size of the bulb, it is necessary to avoid confusing this effect with the change in the temperature of gases when they are rarefied or compressed. They also recognized Pictet's argument and concluded that the *elasticity* of the glass diminishes with time. Four years later Egen, reviewing the evidence, realized that the *volume* of the glass must change,[141] but still believed that the change is caused by the pressure of the air, supporting this conclusion by the observation that the zero of a thermometer with a cylindrical bulb rose four times as much as one with a spherical bulb.[142] If such a ratio did occur, we would now suspect that it was due to the difference in the working of the glass, if not to different sorts of glass.

Nevertheless, the full explanation was getting nearer, though it was not helped by the great Arago,[143] who in the year of Egen's paper accepted without question the old hypothesis of Nollet and Deluc about tiny bubbles in the mercury,[144] demonstrating perhaps that not even an Arago can be omniscient, no matter how hard he tries.

A good deal of experiment was done in the next decade, and the year 1837 saw several papers of some importance.[145, 146, 147] It would take too much space to deal with these in detail, but there seems to have been a general recognition that thermometers should be made and sealed several months before they are calibrated. Legrand in particular had emancipated himself from a belief in the importance of atmospheric pressure in the process, referring it to changes in the glass, which, he thought, are complete in about four months. For some kinds of glass, at least, this was a wild underestimate, for that most careful experimenter

[140] Auguste Delarive and François Marcet, *Bibl. Univ.*, Vol. 22 (1823), pp. 265–90.

[141] P. N. C. Egen, *Ann. der Phys.*, Vol. 11 (1827), pp. 282–83.

[142] *Ibid.*, pp. 348 ff.

[143] D. F. J. Arago, *Ann. de Chim.*, Vol. 33 (1827), pp. 422–25.

[144] See p. 142 above.

[145] W. Gintl, *Zeits. für Phys. u. Math.*, Vol. 5 (1837), pp. 8–29.

[146] J. N. Legrand, *Compt. Rend.*, Vol. 4 (1837), pp. 173–76.

[147] F. Rudberg, *Ann. der Phys.*, Vol 40 (1837), pp. 39–62, 562–82.

James Prescott Joule reported how he had observed the ice po┄
of two thermometers for twenty-three[148] and finall╲
nine years.[149] They had risen gradually and wi
speed for the whole period.

By the middle of the century at least some of the instrumentmakers were aware of the seriousness of the matter and anxious
to do something about it, as can be gathered from a paper by
John Adie.[150] Careful scientists now took the precaution of
checking the zeros of their thermometers before and after important experiments.

It had also come to be generally recognized that while the
readings of a thermometer could be affected by external pressure
on the bulb, the pressure of the atmosphere on the evacuated
thermometer was not the main cause of the secular rise in its
zero, as had too hastily been concluded from early experiments
in opening old thermometers. Thirty years later there was a
controversy between J. M. Crafts[151] and J. Pernet,[152] both experts
in the field, as to whether the pressure had any effect at all.
Crafts, with the support of experiments, maintained that the
entire phenomenon is a result of the slow rearrangement of the
molecules in the glass.

Why, then, not complete the process as far as possible before
the thermometer is calibrated? In 1885, G. M. Whipple reported
to the British Association that at Kew Observatory it had "for
many years" been the practice to anneal mercury thermometers
in order to prevent the change of zero. "Mr. Hicks, of Hatton
Garden, has erected special apparatus for the purpose, and [his
thermometers] apparently show that the desired result has been
attained."[153] Hicks patented the process, which consisted in providing the thermometers with a large chamber at the top in
order to give the mercury plenty of room. After being filled and
sealed they were "annealed" for two or three weeks before calibration; this was done in an oil bath at a temperature higher
than any to which they would afterward be exposed.[154]

Meanwhile, it had been suspected that the composition of the
glass might be important, and in 1880 Crafts had shown that
glasses containing lead oxide should be avoided.[155] The so-called

[148] Joule, *Mem. Manchester Lit. and Phil. Soc.*, 3rd ser., Vol. 3 (1868), pp. 292–93.

[149] Joule, *Proc. Manchester Lit. and Phil. Soc.*, Vol. 12 (1873), p. 73.

[150] Adie, *Edinburgh Phil. J.*, Vol. 49 (1850), pp. 122–26.

[151] Crafts, *Compt. Rend.*, Vol. 91 (1880), pp. 370–72, 574–76.

[152] Pernet, *ibid.*, pp. 471–73.

[153] Whipple, *B.A.A.S. Report, Aberdeen, 1885*, p. 938 (abstract only).

[154] J. Hicks, British Patent 2027 of 1885, Feb. 13.

[155] J. M. Crafts, *Compt. Rend.*, Vol. 91 (1880), pp. 291–93.

"hard glasses" were to be preferred, as was clearly demonstrated ___ __e Bureau International des Poids et Mesures by Charles ___ __rd Guillaume, the greatest authority on mercury ther- ___meters.[156] The rise in zero when such glasses are used is less than a tenth of that experienced with the lead "crystal" glasses. But even better materials were on the way. At his famous Jena glassworks, Friedrich Otto Schott was working on the problem, and in 1891 was able to announce a glass for thermometers that was markedly more stable,[157] and with this glass F. Allihn[158] found a shift in zero of only 0.03°C. in three years. With such glasses the temporary lowering of the zero after being exposed to high temperatures is also much less.[159] These improvements rendered superfluous an expedient such as that of L. Marchis,[160] who built and tested two thermometers with bulbs made of single pieces of sheet platinum, without welding. Taken through many cycles of temperature, they kept a very nearly constant zero.

We must now recall that in alcohol thermometers the zero often falls with time. The spirit thermometer received much less attention from the physicists, but it finally emerged that the decrease in the volume of the spirit is due to polymerization, the aggregation of the molecules, under the influence of light. This is especially prominent if there is a trace of acetone in the alcohol.[161]

[156] Guillaume, *Arch. Sci. phys. et nat.*, Vol. 16 (1886), p. 524. His *Traité pratique de la thermométrie de precision* (Paris, 1889), should be consulted for an account of the ultimate refinements of such thermometry, which are outside my present purpose.

[157] Schott, *Zeits. f. Instrum.*, Vol. 11 (1891), pp. 330–37.

[158] See *Zeits. f. Instrum.*, Vol. 12 (1892), pp. 27–28.

[159] See for example A. Bartoli, *Rendiconti Ist. Lomb.*, Vol. 29 (1896), pp. 247–54.

[160] Marchis, *J. de Phys.*, Vol. 4 (1895), pp. 217–19.

[161] See W. F. Higgins and E. G. Bilham, *Great Britain, M.O., Professional Notes*, no. 51 (1929).

VI

Maximum and Minimum Thermometers

1. Introduction. The first idea for thermometers to indicate the highest or the lowest temperature, or both, since the last visit by the observer, seems to have occurred to the great mathematician Jean[1] Bernouilli, who communicated it to G. W. Leibnitz in a letter dated July 5, 1698.[2] These were air thermometers with many appendices (*varices, seu tumores*) as shown in Fig. 6.1. The third form, he says, he thought of while he was writing the letter. This was probably only an example of the sort of intellectual exercise that the two great men liked to indulge in by correspondence,[3] and needs no further discussion, except to note that in 1743 G. W. Krafft[4] made a maximum thermometer of this sort, but hermetically sealed, like Stancari's thermometer.

The other maximum and minimum thermometers that we have to discuss in this chapter are liquid-in-glass thermometers. There are dozens of them, some quite impracticable, some re-inventions, some not durable, some almost impossible to carry about. Only three or four are still in general use. It will be helpful to suggest a classification, and then, disregarding those ideas that were entirely without issue, deal with each of the main types in more-or-less chronological order. Here, then, is an attempt at classification:

a) Instruments depending on overflow.

b) Spirit minimum thermometers with indices.

c) Mercury maximum thermometers with indices.

[1] Or John or Johann; the first of three of that name in that extraordinary family.

[2] This is in *Virorum celeberr. Got. Gul. Leibnitii et Johann Bernouillii commercium philosophicum et mathematicum* (2 vols.; Geneva, 1745), Vol. 1, pp. 371–78.

[3] In 1698 Leibnitz suggested the aneroid barometer. See my *The History of the Barometer* (Baltimore, 1964), pp. 398–99.

[4] Krafft, *Comm. Petrop.*, Vol. 13 (1741–43), pp. 346–47.

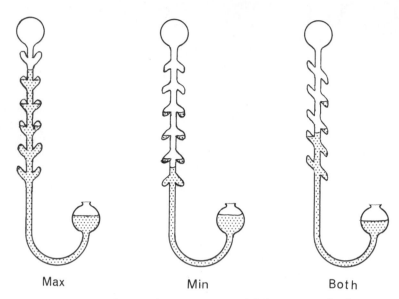

Max   Min   Both

d) Mercury maximum thermometers with interrupted columns.

e) Mercury maximum thermometers with side tubes.

f) Mercury minimum thermometers.

g) Combined maximum and minimum thermometers.

There are thermometers that do not belong clearly to any of these classes, but I think none of importance.

2. Instruments Depending on Overflow. The first maximum and minimum thermometers depending on the expansion of liquids seem to have been invented by Lord Charles Cavendish, the father of the famous chemist, and described in 1757.[5] As will be seen from Fig. 6.2, the art of working glass for scientific purposes must have been fairly well-advanced in England at that time.

The two on the left are maximum thermometers, differing in that the first depends on the expansion of mercury, the second on that of spirit. The former is like an ordinary thermometer with a large bulb, the end of the tube being drawn out fine and surrounded by a bulb C. There is spirit over the mercury in the tube, and the bulb C also contains some mercury and some alcohol; the space remaining contains only the vapor of alcohol. The instrument was "set" by inclining it until the end of the tube was submerged and warming the bulb until the spirit in

[5] Cavendish, *Phil. Trans.*, Vol. 50 (1757), pp. 300–10.

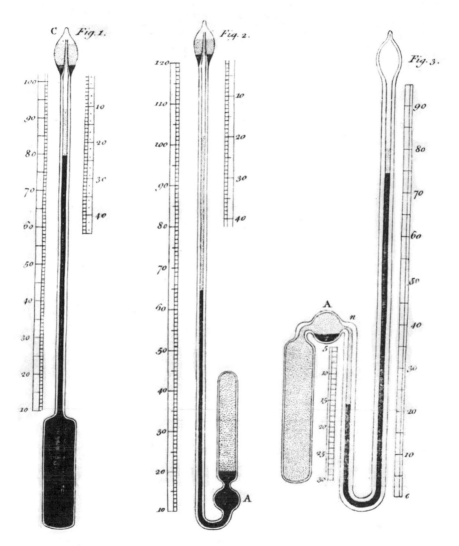

Fig. 6.2 *The thermometers of Lord Charles Cavendish.*

the tube joined up with that in *C*. The bulb was then allowed
to cool to the ambient temperature while in this position, so
that spirit was sucked in, filling the whole tube. The instrument
was then put upright and left. If the temperature rose, some
spirit would overflow into *C*; when it fell again, a space would
be left at the top of the tube. The maximum temperature was
obtained by adding the length of this space, measured on the
right-hand scale, to the current temperature at the time of the
observation, read on the left-hand scale at the top of the mer-

cury column. The drawing gives the impression that the volume of the reduced part of the tube has been allowed for.

The minimum thermometer on the right is constructed on the same general principles. It should be noted that a fine thread of glass goes from A through the slight constriction n as far as the bottom of the instrument, which is set by tilting it until n is covered by the mercury in A, and then warming the bulb so that— we are told—the mercury is forced past n in drops until the shorter arm of the siphon is full of it. The minimum temperature before the next observation is found by subtracting the reading of the top of the mercury on the right-hand scale from the current temperature given by the left-hand scale.

Other such thermometers depending on overflow were devised,[6, 7, 8] but they were hard to set and to transport, and found few admirers.

3. Maximum and Minimum Thermometers with Indices.

Before the end of the eighteenth century a pair of thermometers (Fig. 6.3) were invented, of which the minimum is in its essentials the one used almost universally by meteorological services at the present day. On April 5, 1790, Daniel Rutherford described these to the Royal Society of Edinburgh,[9] making it clear that they were the invention of a namesake, John Rutherford, a country doctor. The maximum thermometer was simply a mercury thermometer with a conical index of ivory. The minimum was a spirit thermometer with a glass index, conical in shape, its point toward the bulb, and immersed in the spirit. The two instruments were placed horizontally on the same frame, one above the other, the bulb of the minimum and the tip of the maximum toward the right. Inclining the frame to the left was all that was needed to set both instruments.

The Rutherford maximum thermometer was finally found to be unsatisfactory, the mercury tending to get past the index. The minimum, its index of blue glass now in the shape of a dumbbell, is ubiquitous. This change in the form of the index had taken place by 1826, and the index of the maximum thermometer was also a little dumbbell, of blued steel.[10] Also by this time, for some unaccountable reason, the assemblage of maximum and

6 James King, *Edinb. J. Sci.*, Vol. 9 (1828), pp. 113–16.
7 "Delta," *ibid.*, Vol. 10 (1829), pp. 159–63.
8 F. H. Walferdin, *Bull. Soc. géol. France*, Vol. 7 (1835–36), pp. 354–60.
9 D. Rutherford, *Trans. Roy. Soc. Edinb.*, Vol. 3 (1794), pp. 247–49.
10 K. L. G. Winckler, *Ann. der Phys.*, Vol. 6 (1826), pp. 127–32.

Fig. 6.3 *Rutherford's thermometers.*

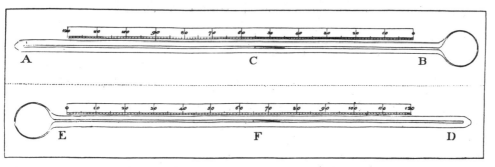

minimum thermometers had become known over much of the Continent of Europe as a "thermometrograph"—which should, one would think, denote a recording instrument—and the appellation stuck for many decades.

Attempts were made to improve the Rutherford maximum thermometer by putting a lighter liquid above the mercury, apparently with some success. We are told in 1859 by John G. Macvicar[11] that

> between twenty and thirty years ago, Mr. Adie,[12] the optician in Edinburgh, merely to prevent oxidation in the tubes of Rutherford's maximum thermometer, introduced above the mercury, naptha; and I saw the other day one of these thermometers, which, during that long interval had preserved the mercurial column unbroken, and the steel index pure and all right.[13]

Even the great Arago had a try, putting between the mercury and the index "a little glass *D*" with a concave surface to receive the convex extremity of the column of mercury.[14] The last attempt of which I am aware was in 1881, when Carl Greiner & Co. of Munich patented[15] the iron index enclosed in a nail-shaped glass envelope with a springy "tail" which, as we shall see, had been devised by James Six in the eighteenth century. But by 1881 other forms of maximum thermometers, and one in particular, had gained favor.

Another sort of index that appealed to several inventors was a short column of mercury in a column of spirit. Count Marsiglio Landriani invented both minimum and maximum thermometers

[11] Macvicar, *Chem. Soc. J.,* Vol. 11 (1859), pp. 106–7.

[12] Alexander Adie was a famous Edinburgh instrumentmaker at that time, being succeeded in 1857 by his son John. I am indebted to Mr. Robert W. Plenderleith for this information.

[13] *Ibid.,* p. 107.

[14] Arago, *Compt. Rend.,* Vol. 13 (1841), p. 967.

[15] D.R.P. 17122 (1881).

153

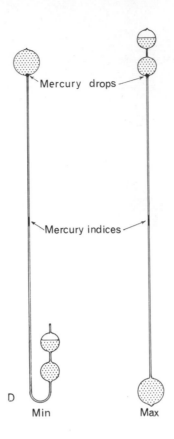

Mercury drops

Mercury indices

D

Min   Max

Fig. 6.4   Landriani's thermometers.

with indices of this sort,[16] as shown diagrammatically in Fig. 6.4. They were to be installed in a vertical position, as shown. A small drop of mercury in the neck of the upper bulb was supposed to permit the spirit to pass it in an upward direction, but if the spirit tended to move downward, it would force the drop of mercury into the tube, which had to be very narrow. The maximum thermometer, for example, would be "set" by warming its main bulb until the drop of mercury reached the first upper bulb, inclining it to get the drop out of the way and cooling the thermometer to air temperature in an inclined position. It was then set upright, when the drop of mercury would again act as a valve. At the next observation the ambient temperature would be read from the lower mercury index and the maximum found by adding the number of degrees that the upper one had descended from the top of the tube. The reader may be allowed to deduce the *modus operandi* of the minimum thermometer.

The mere fact that it takes so long to describe the operation of

16 Landriani, *Giornale di fisica, Decade* II, Vol. 1 (1818), pp. 413–20.

such instruments underlines their inadequacy. They had a more fundamental defect: the alcohol wets the glass, and eventually some will be transferred past the column of mercury, rendering all the readings inaccurate.

4. Mercury Maximum Thermometers with Interrupted Columns. An extremely simple sort of maximum thermometer was devised in 1832 by John Phillips, a geologist.[17] This was nothing more than an ordinary mercury thermometer in which about a centimeter of the column is separated from the remainder by a small bubble— a "speck"—of air. The thermometer being installed horizontally, the short column acts as an index. This thermometer had a fairly long history. In 1856 Phillips reported again to the British Association,[18] stating that a number had been constructed and were still serviceable. John Welsh at Kew Observatory had made even better ones,[19] and Louis Casella had become interested. If the detached column is of the correct small length, the thermometer can be used in any position. In a discussion *ad hoc* held at the Meteorological Society (London) in 1872,[20] Phillips' maximum thermometer was preferred for use at sea, that of Negretti & Zambra for land stations. The firm of Pastorelli & Co. had standardized on Phillips' maximum.[21]

It was reinvented in 1855 by François Hippolyte Walferdin; a senior civil servant in Paris who amused himself with problems in thermometry.[22] He could scarcely have been expected to have seen the report of the meeting of the British Association in 1832, but the same excuse cannot serve Émilien Renou, who, in a long historical article published in 1876,[23] ascribed the invention to Walferdin with no reference to Phillips.

[17] Phillips, *B.A.A.S. Report, Oxford, 1832*, Sections, pp. 580–81.

[18] *B.A.A.S. Report, Cheltenham, 1856*, Sections, p. 41.

[19] They were first used at Kew in 1851, according to Louis Casella. See *An Illustrated and Descriptive Catalogue of Surveying, Philosophical, Mathematical, Optical, Photographic, and Standard Meteorological Instruments, Manufactured by L. Casella . . . 147, Holborn Bars, London, E.C.* (London, 1871), pp. 10–11.

[20] *Quart. J. Meteorol. Soc.*, Vol. 1 (1872), pp. 224–26.

[21] F[rancis] Pastorelli & Co., *Standard Meteorological Instruments, Barometers and Thermometers of Every Description . . . Manufactured and Sold by F. Pastorelli & Co., Scientific Instrument Makers, 2–8, Piccadilly, London* [etc.] (London, 1874).

[22] Walferdin, *Compt. Rend.*, Vol. 40 (1855), pp. 951–54.

[23] Renou, "Histoire du thermomètre," *Ann. Soc. météorol. France*, Vol. 24 (1876), pp. 19–72. This paper must be used with caution.

Fig. 6.5   The constriction of Geissler's maximum thermometer.

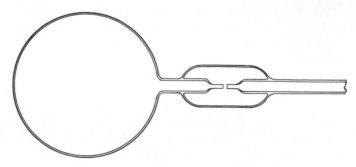

I mentioned Negretti & Zambra's maximum thermometer. This is the well-known instrument with the constriction in the tube near the bulb, now almost universally used at meteorological stations, and of course as a clinical thermometer. It was patented on March 8, 1852,[24] and it is interesting to note that, as an alternative to the constriction, the patent claimed the use of a piece of wood [!], glass, or wire inserted into the tube, the tube then being bent at a sharp angle.

The thermometer with the constriction was an immediate success, though it had to be well made. The well-known Berlin instrumentmaker Chr. Geissler made what he thought was an improvement, using the arrangement shown in Fig. 6.5; but the famous meteorologist Heinrich Wilhelm Dove reported on this unfavorably.[25] Outside of England there seems to have been a resistance to the thermometer with the constriction, and we have A. Lallemand writing that a good one can be made only by chance.[26] The same for the one with the air bubble. Indeed, a meteorological congress held at Leipzig in August, 1872, put it on record that while the Rutherford minimum thermometer was satisfactory, there was no maximum that could be generally recommended; a statement of which the Meteorological Society in London recorded its strong disapproval,[27] as well it might. This may account for the observation of a later President of the Society, Robert H. Scott, that in 1873 he had "found that many foreign stations did not possess" maximum and minimum thermometers.[28]

There is one other maximum thermometer, which is *sui generis* but may perhaps be mentioned here. It was patented by James

[24] British patent 14,002 of 1852.
[25] Dove, *Ann. der Phys.,* Vol. 123 (1864), pp. 657–58.
[26] Lallemand, *Compt. Rend.,* Vol. 66 (1868), pp. 812–13.
[27] *Quart. J. Meteorol. Soc.,* Vol. 1 (1872), pp. 224–26.
[28] Scott, *Quart. J. Roy. Meteorol. Soc.,* Vol. 10 (1884), p. 171.

Fig. 6.6 Hicks's mercury maximum thermometer, 1864.

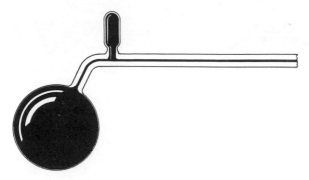

Fig. 6.6 Hicks's mercury maximum thermometer, 1864.

Hicks[29] and is shown in Fig. 6.6. The appendix on the side of the tube is of much larger bore than the capillary tube. After the appendix has been filled by lowering the bulb end of the thermometer, it will register the ambient temperature as long as this is rising; but when the temperature falls mercury will come from the appendix, leaving it undisturbed in the tube. This was the theory, but the instrument does not seem to have been a success.

5. *Mercury Minimum Thermometers*. In spite of the undoubted usefulness of Rutherford's spirit minimum thermometer, there was a strong demand for one using mercury as the thermometric liquid. This was because of a certain lack of confidence in the alcohol thermometer, dating from the days of Deluc. London instrument-makers tried very hard to meet this demand; indeed the Jury of the 1862 exhibition noted that since the Great Exhibition of 1851 no less than five mercury minimum thermometers had been invented.[30] It is a pity that none proved successful, though James Hicks was given a medal for his.[31]

The earliest of these was patented in 1855 by Negretti & Zambra[32] and publicly described in the following year.[33] In it there is a steel "needle" in the form of a double cone, the end nearer the bulb being blunter. It is stated that when the temperature falls the needle rides down on the surface of the mercury; when it rises again the mercury flows up past the needle

[29] British Patent 809 of 1864, April 1. See also *Proc. British Meteorol. Soc.*, Vol. 2 (1864), p. 208.

[30] London, International Exhibition of 1862, *Reports by the Juries* [etc.] (London, 1863) (paged in sections), pp. xiii–34.

[31] *Ibid.*, pp. xiii–38.

[32] British Patent 2306 of 1855, October 15.

[33] British Meteorol. Soc., *Report of the Council at the 6th Annual General Meeting, May 27, 1856*, pp. 11–14.

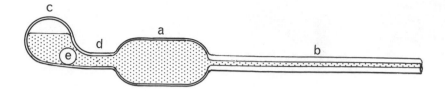

Fig. 6.7 *Negretti & Zambra's second mercury minimum thermometer, 1862.*

and leaves it at the minimum reading. It is reset with a magnet. This instrument cannot have been very successful, but Negretti & Zambra seem to have valued it highly.[34] Nevertheless, they patented another type a few years later,[35] the principle of which is shown in Fig. 6.7. In this diagram *a* is the main bulb, *c* an extra one joined to it by a tube *d*—somewhat wider than the thermometer tube *b*. *e* is a plug of platinum amalgamated by immersing it in boiling mercury. This plug may be fixed or loose, as long as it is too large to get into *a*. The thermometer tube being horizontal, the "adhesion" of the mercury to the platinum is supposed to cause the mercury to retreat in the main tube when the temperature falls; but when it rises again, it is easier for the mercury to flow through *d* than along *b*. Both of Negretti & Zambra's mercury minimum thermometers were tricky applications of the phenomena of surface tension.

So was the thermometer invented by James Hicks,[36] shown diagrammatically in Fig. 6.8, which made use of a platinum wire *p*, fixed to the tube and extending on each side of a constriction. There is a speck of air *s* in the tube, and this is supposed to be kept out of the bulb by the constriction; but the platinum wire is supposed to lead the mercury into the bulb past the air-speck. To set the thermometer, the air-speck is brought up to the constriction, and the distance in degrees to the end of the mercury column is read. After the desired period, the length of the col-

[34] See their *Treatise on Meteorological Instruments* [etc.] (London, 1864), pp. 78–80.

[35] *Ibid.*, pp. 80–81. See also British Patent 1223 of 1862, April 25.

[36] British Patent 1244 of 1861, May 15.

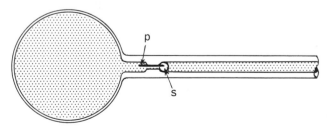

Fig. 6.8 *Hicks's mercury minimum thermometer, 1861.*

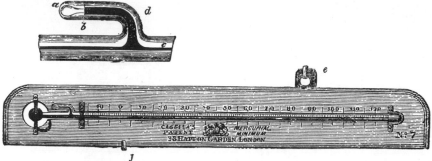

Fig. 6.9 Casella's mercury minimum thermometer, 1861.

umn above the air-speck—a sliding scale is provided—gives the minimum temperature.

In the same year a mercury minimum thermometer was patented by the younger Casella,[37] and described to the British Association by the Director of Kew Observatory, Balfour Stewart.[38] Figure 6.9 shows the illustration of it from Casella's 1871 Catalogue. I quote Balfour Stewart's explanation:

> To set this instrument, incline it slightly until the mercury in the side chamber comes to the abrupt termination between the two chambers. The mercury in the capillary tube will then denote the true temperature. Let this be 60°. If the temperature rise above 60°, the rise will take place in the side tube, and if it then begin to fall, the fall will also take place in the side tube until it reaches 60°; but below this the fall will take place in the capillary tube, as there is a disinclination of the mercury to recede from the abrupt termination between the two chambers towards the capillary tube. The instrument thus acts as a minimum thermometer.

The hopes for this construction, as for all the other mercury minimum thermometers, were disappointed. In 1872 it is recorded in the report of a discussion at the Meteorological Society that "Mr [Louis] Casella himself does not recommend the general use of the mercurial minimum invented by his son,"[39] so that there was no choice but the spirit minimum thermometer of Rutherford. Greater confidence in the spirit thermometer, and better methods for its calibration, ended the search for a substitute.

6. *Combined Maximum and Minimum Thermometers.* Even before Rutherford, an instrument that combined the functions of maximum and minimum thermometers was invented by James Six of Can-

[37] British Patent 2100 of 1861, Aug. 22, to Louis Marino Casella.
[38] Stewart, *B.A.A.S. Report, Manchester, 1861*, Sections, p. 74.
[39] *Quart. J. Meteorol. Soc.*, Vol. 1 (1872), p. 225.

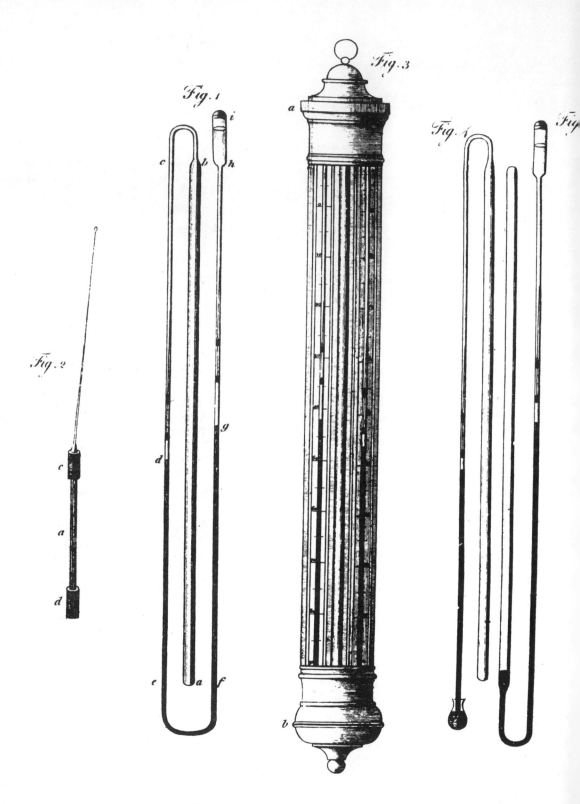

Fig. 6.10   Six's thermometer, 1782.

terbury.[40] Six's thermometer in its modern "household" form is probably the most familiar meteorological instrument ever invented, with the possible exceptions of the aneroid barometer and the wind-vane, and an extended description seems unnecessary; but it must be emphasized that the thermometric fluid is alcohol, contained in the long cylindrical bulb *ab* of Six's Fig. 1 (our Fig. 6.10), the mercury *defg* being only a means of indication, and confined between two volumes of alcohol, of which the second is given a little room to move in the bulb *hi*. Six's Fig. 2 shows on a much larger scale one of the little indices, made of steel wire and covered with glass, that were pushed up by the mercury. These had long glass "tails" to act as springs.

There is a Six's thermometer in the Museum of the History of Science at Oxford which, in its mahogany frame, looks almost exactly like the figure in his paper. It may well be the original, especially as R. J. Gunther records that this was in Oxford in 1923.[41]

The difficulty with Six's thermometer, and indeed with all thermometers containing both spirit and mercury, is that the spirit wets the glass, and can at length pass between the glass and the mercury. This was clearly recognized by the middle of the nineteenth century,[42] and led to the abandonment of such thermometers as serious meteorological instruments. We need not record all the modifications and "improvements" that were suggested.[43] In a special category, perhaps, were those using mercury for the thermometric liquid, that is to say with a spirit column between two mercury columns. One of these, albeit with a "dense transparent fluid" instead of spirit, was described in 1874 by S. C. Denton.[44] In discussing this design J. W. Zambra said he had already made "Six's thermometers" with mercury as the thermometric liquid. A similar thermometer was described in Germany in 1882[45] and is shown in Fig. 6.11. The bulb at the top is partly filled with air, the pressure of which keeps the columns of liquid united.

[40] Six, *Phil. Trans.*, Vol. 72 (1782), pp. 72–81.
[41] Gunther, *Early Science in Oxford* (14 vols.; Oxford, 1923–45), Vol. 1, p. 264.
[42] Cf. Richard Adie, *Edinb. New Philos. J.*, Vol. 54 (1853), pp. 84–86.
[43] See, for example: T. S. Traill, in: Society for the Diffusion of Useful Knowledge, *Library of Useful Knowledge, Natural Philosophy*, II (London, 1828), part 2, p. 39; Aimé, *Ann. de Chim. et Phys.*, Vol. 15 (1845), p. 6; R. H. C. Wilson, British Patent 2203 of 1860, Sept. 12; Casella, *An Illustrated and Descriptive Catalogue* [etc.] (London, 1871), p. 49; J. W. Zambra, *Quart. J. Roy. Meteorol. Soc.*, Vol. 6 (1880), pp. 159–61; H. J. Kappeller, D.R.P. 21082, Apr. 22, 1882.
[44] Denton, *Quart. J. Meteorol. Soc.*, Vol. 2 (1874), pp. 193–95.
[45] [Spitta], *Zeits. für Instrum.*, Vol. 2 (1882), pp. 28–29.

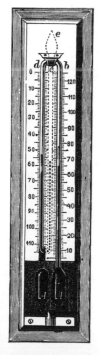

Fig. 6.11 Spitta's thermometer, 1882.

Glass index

Min. scale

Max. scale

Iron index

Fig. 6.12   Hicks's thermometer.

There were many other combined maximum and minimum thermometers, of which there is a distinct class having mercury as the thermometric liquid, with a column of a lighter liquid above the mercury. The lighter liquid contained two indices, one pushed up by the mercury to show the maximum temperature, the other drawn back by the spirit to show the minimum. They were of various shapes, straight,[46] rectangular,[47] V-shaped,[48] U-shaped;[49] I shall illustrate the rectangular one of James Hicks (Fig. 6.12), who was then "the intelligent foreman of Mr. L. P. Casella, Optician." I do not think it needs further explanation, except to note that the iron index had a hair tied round it to prevent it slipping. On balance, one would think that these instruments might work at least as well as Six's thermometer; but there would be the problem that occurred with Rutherford's maximum thermometer, of keeping the lower index out of the mercury—perhaps the second liquid, carefully chosen, might help.

7. *Radiation Thermometers.* There is a natural interest in "how hot it is in the sun," and in how cold it gets "in the open" at night, particularly in the incidence of ground frost. It has therefore been the practice to expose maximum and minimum thermometers specially for these purposes.

As far as the "grass minimum" thermometer is concerned, nothing need be said about the instrument itself, for it is merely a minimum thermometer exposed horizontally just above short grass. As both the glass bulb of the thermometer and the green leaves are fairly good radiators in the infra-red, the temperature indicated by such a thermometer is a good approximation to that of the grass. The "solar maximum" thermometer is a much less satisfactory instrument, for various reasons.

In 1773 Richard Watson, Regius Professor of Divinity at Cambridge, found that a thermometer painted black and exposed to the sun indicates a much higher temperature than does one left

[46] John G. Macvicar, *Chem. Soc. J.,* Vol. 11 (1859), pp. 106–7. He used "naphtha."

[47] By James Hicks. Described by Balfour Stewart in *Proc. Roy. Soc.,* Vol. 10 (1859–60), pp. 312–15. He used alcohol.

[48] W. Symons, British provisional patent 479 of 1860, Feb. 22. He used dilute sulphuric acid.

[49] Ulisse Marchi, *Descrizione di un nuovo termometrografo a massima e minima* (Florence, 1868), pamphlet. He used "a transparent liquid, much less volatile than alcohol." There is one of his thermometers at the Museo Copernicano, Rome (no. 3030).

Fig. 6.13   Negretti & Zambra's vacuum-jacketed thermometer.

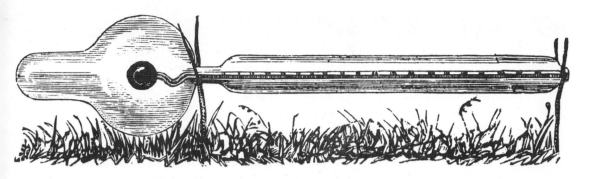

unpainted.[50] After the nearly simultaneous and entirely independent discoveries of Leslie[51] and of Rumford,[52] it came to be recognized that the temperature of a black object in the sun had some relation to the strength of the incident solar radiation. Unfortunately, the temperature of a blackened thermometer is also strongly affected by the movement of air past it, and although such instruments were still being sold in the 1860's,[53] their readings had absolutely no scientific value.

It was to be expected, therefore, that an attempt would be made to protect the blackened bulb from the wind, and this was done by enclosing it in an evacuated jacket. The earliest reference to such an instrument that I have been able to find is dated 1864, when Negretti & Zambra categorically claimed to have invented it,[54] giving an illustration (Fig. 6.13). The expression of their hopes for the instrument—"Important results are anticipated from this arrangement"—suggest that it was very new at the time. The important results, alas! did not materialize, partly because of the unsatisfactory state of vacuum technique at the time. To try to overcome this trouble, Negretti & Zambra built a miniature U-tube vacuum gauge into the jacket, which would show up a serious leak.[55] At about the same time James Hicks employed a more sensitive indicator of the state of the vacuum,[56] inserting two platinum electrodes (Fig. 6.14) so that the phenomena of the electrical discharge through gases might be examined. It is unlikely that the vacuum was really good enough

[50] Watson, *Phil. Trans.*, Vol. 63 (1773), pp. 40–41.

[51] John Leslie, *Experimental Inquiry into the Nature and Propagation of Heat* (London, 1804).

[52] Benjamin Thompson, Count of Rumford, *Phil. Trans.*, Vol. 94 (1804), pp. 77–182.

[53] Negretti and Zambra, *A Treatise on Meteorological Instruments* [etc.] (London, 1864), p. 86.

[54] *Ibid.*, pp. 86–87.

[55] G. J. Symons, *B.A.A.S. Report, Bradford, 1873*, Sections, pp. 47–48.

[56] Hicks, *Quart. J. Meteorol. Soc.*, Vol. 2 (1874), pp. 99–102.

for the purpose, for though the barometric vacuum pump had been invented in 1828, and the excellent design due to Sprengel was described in 1865,[57] it was not widely used. However, even if the vacua had been excellent, it would not have been enough for the standardizing of the instrument. It was shown by Herbert McLeod in 1889[58] that the indications of the black-bulb thermometer also depend on the thickness of the glass envelope and on the size of the bulb. He did not say so, but they must also depend on the way the bulb is blackened. Some people seem to have used black glass for the bulb, and the serious objections to this had been pointed out forcibly by John Tyndall as early as 1872.[59] Francis Nunes found that apparently similar instruments made by different firms differed more than instruments made by the same firm, *ad hoc,* with and without a vacuum.[60]

These many difficulties led to the gradual abandonment of the black-bulb as a serious instrument for measuring radiation, in favor of much more complex apparatus which is outside the province of this book.

[57] Hermann Sprengel, *Chem. Soc. J.,* Vol. 3 (1865), pp. 9–21.
[58] McLeod, *B.A.A.S. Report, Newcastle, 1889,* pp. 505–6.
[59] Tyndall, *Contributions to Molecular Physics in the Domain of Radiant Heat* [etc.] (London, 1872), p. 306.
[60] Nunes, *Meteorol. Mag.,* Vol. 5 (1870), pp. 169–72.

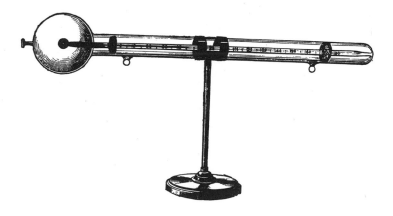

Fig. 6.14   Hicks's improved black-bulb thermometer, 1874.

VII

Deformation Thermometers

1. Introduction. I shall use the term "deformation thermometer" to refer to any thermometer which indicates a change of temperature by a change in the shape or configuration of some system of solid bodies. Such thermometers fall naturally into two main classes: (1) those in which the entire thermometer consists of solid substances, usually, but not always, metals; (2) those in which the deformation of a solid is produced by the expansion and contraction of a liquid. Each of these main groups can be subdivided.

The differential expansion of solids was known and used before it was applied to thermometry, notably by John Harrison, who invented the "gridiron pendulum" of brass and steel in 1725.[1] Apart from clocks, the first instrumental use of it was made by Pieter van Musschenbroek, who described a very well designed "pyrometron" for making numerical comparisons of the dilatation of various metals.[2] It used bars only about 15 cm. long, the motion of the free end of the bar being communicated to a pointer by a rack, a pinion, a spur gear, and a second pinion. It was not, however, intended as a thermometer.

I shall deal with the deformation thermometers in their various classes in the remaining sections of this chapter, apart from recording instruments, which are treated in Chapter 9.

2. Thermometers Using Straight Bars or Tubes. The first deformation thermometer was probably made about 1735 by Cromwell Mortimer, a physician who was secretary to the Royal Society, and who

---

[1] James Short, *Phil. Trans.,* Vol. 47 (1752), p. 518. George Graham (*Phil. Trans.,* Vol. 34 [1726], p. 40) had measured the dilatation of several metals in 1715, but thought the effect too small to use for this purpose.

[2] Musschenbroek, *Tentamina experimentorum naturalium captorum in Academia del Cimento* [etc.] (Leiden, 1731), Part 2, pp. 12–16. This was the first Latin translation of the *Saggi;* part 2 contains additions by Musschenbroek himself.

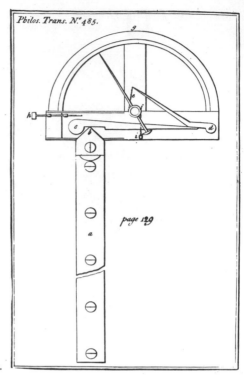

Philos. Trans. N.° 485.

page 129

Fig. 7.1   *Frotheringham's metallic thermometer.*

read a paper about thermometers on May 8, 1735, which was
printed only in 1747.[3] His was a large instrument intended for
measuring high temperatures, up to 900°F., in fact. It made use
of the differential expansion of a brass rod, thirty-seven inches
long, and its iron frame. A magnifying lever, cord, pulley, and
pointer indicated on a dial the relative motion of the brass rod.

It is impossible to decide who made the first such thermometer
to measure ordinary meteorological temperatures. The first to
be described was made by John Ingram of Spalding, Lincoln-
shire, at the suggestion of Samuel Frotheringham, and purchased
by the Gentlemen's Society of Spalding for their museum.[4] It is
shown in Fig. 7.1. A rectangular brass bar four feet long was
screwed to an iron bar at the lower end, and held to it at intervals by screws working in slots. At the top of the brass bar was a
steel chisel-edge which communicated the relative motion of the
top of the bar to the first of two magnifying levers and a chain

[3] Mortimer, *Phil. Trans.,* Vol. 44 (1747), pp. 672–95.
[4] Maurice Johnson, *Phil. Trans.,* Vol. 45 (1748), pp. 128–30.

and pulley. A pointer was fastened to the pulley, and its extremity must have had a magnification of about 500. This design is good in one respect which we may assume that the maker never thought of, namely, in that the thermal lag of the two elements is about the same.

At about this time, or a little earlier, Count Hans von Löser invented several metallic thermometers, which were made by J. G. Zimmer in the Count's workshops at Reinhartz, near Wittenburg,[5] where many notable astronomical instruments were constructed.[6] The thermometers were not described until 1764, a year after the death of the Count. They each embodied a brass or steel frame and several lead bars, the latter arranged so that their relative motions were added by levers at their ends. The motion of the final free end was magnified by a sector and a train of gears, and there was an adjustment for the magnification. I shall illustrate only the earliest (Fig. 7.2), made in 1746 according to Titius, which had four lead bars about nine inches long. It is plain that these instruments were not intended for use out of doors.

On similar principles, but less decorative, was a thermometer described in 1760 by Keane Fitzgerald.[7] In 1761[8] he presented an improved instrument with the addition of two pointers that could be pushed by the main pointer to indicate the maximum and minimum temperatures. All these pointers were on "friction wheels," i.e., antifriction rollers, and the work was done by Vuillamy, the Queen's watchmaker.

A somewhat more rugged instrument was developed at about the same time by Johann Ernst Zeiher, then at St. Petersburg.[9] This thermometer had silver bars and an iron frame, the long pointer indicating on a brass scale. Zeiher suggested that there might be a pencil underneath the pointer to mark a segment on paper, so that the maximum and minimum temperatures might be indicated.

Although there is no full description of it, Deluc may have made a thermometer of lead bars in a wooden frame about 1750. At any rate, in an essay on pyrometry published in 1778, he

[5] Johann Daniel Titius, *Descriptio thermometri metallici ab inventione Comitis ab Loeser* (Leipzig, 1764). This seems to be rare; I have found a copy at Offenbach-am-Main. Poggendorf cites only an edition at Wittenburg in 1765.

[6] Ernst Zinner, *Deutsche und niederländische astronomische Instrumente des 11.–18. Jahrhunderts* (Munich, 1956), p. 429.

[7] Fitzgerald, *Phil. Trans.*, Vol. 51 (1760), pp. 823–33.

[8] *Phil. Trans.*, Vol. 52 (1761), pp. 146–54.

[9] Zeiher, *Novi Comm. Petrop.*, Vol. 9 (1762–63), pp. 305–13.

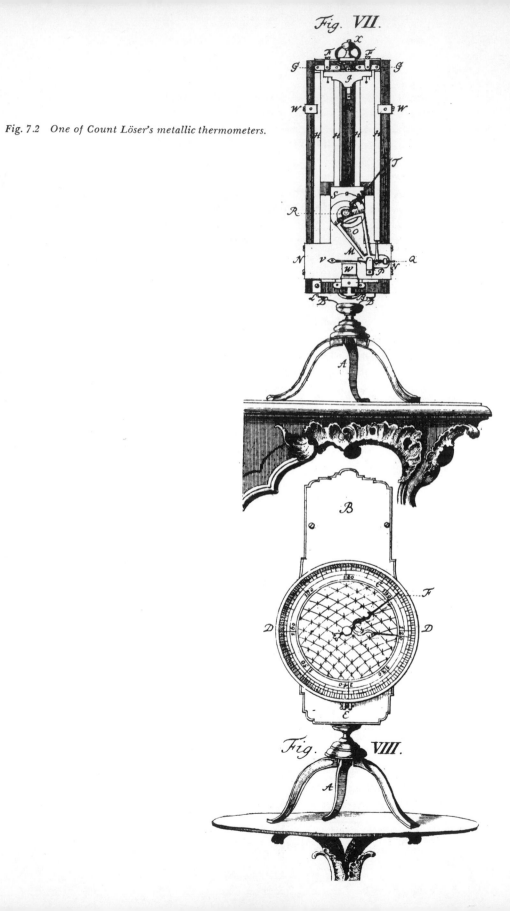

Fig. 7.2 One of Count Löser's metallic thermometers.

claims to have made one "27 or 28 years ago."[10] This is an incident in an argument to show that the expansion of metals is "irregular." One may suspect the action of varying humidity on the wooden frame, though Deluc discounts this possibility.

It was not easy to be original in the design of thermometers of this sort, but J. H. W. Felter, an instrumentmaker of Brunswick, at least deserves credit for thinking about problems of exposure.[11] An iron rod and a brass one, each four feet long, were fastened firmly together at the top and supported there; at the bottom a horizontal pointer three feet long was fastened [hinged?] to the brass rod and rested in a slot in the iron one. The instrument was graduated empirically in Fahrenheit degrees, and it was suggested that the rods be installed out of doors, the pointer coming through a slot in the wall. A patent was taken out on this general sort of thermometer as late as 1856.[12]

Finally, there is the simplest of all metallic thermometers, envisaged by Mathurin Jacques Brisson:

> I would like a thermometer made with a gold, platinum, or silver wire, or even a brass one, stretched along a wall. One extremity would be attached to a fixed point, and the other would end at a pulley, furnished with a weight and a pointer.[13]

Brisson's consistent use of the conditional tense would lead us to believe that it was just an idea; but it would work pretty well, with the reservation that the wall would also expand. In fact, a thermometer of exactly this kind was installed in the Loggia dei Lanzi at Florence in 1860 by Filipo Cecchi, as a companion to an elaborate barometer for public use.[14] The marble dial of this instrument, removed in the 1930's, is now in the Museo di Storia della Scienza.

3. Thermometers Using Compound Strips

The invention of a way of uniting two or more metals into a compound strip, which changes its curvature as the temperature changes, greatly simplified the design of metallic thermometers, making them at once more compact and more sensitive. Such strips are generally composed of

[10] Deluc, *Phil. Trans.*, Vol. 68 (1778), p. 440.

[11] Felter, *Mag. für Neueste im Phys.*, Vol. 4, pt. 3 (1786), pp. 89–90.

[12] Gauntlett, British Patent 846 of 1856, April 7.

[13] Brisson, *Dictionnaire raisonné de physique. Seconde edition, revue, corrigée, et augmentée par l'auteur* (7 vols.; Paris, an VIII [1800]), Vol. 6, p. 192.

[14] Maria Luisa Bonelli, *Florence*, Vol. 13 (1962), no. 3, pp. 30–31. The barometer is fully described in my *History of the Barometer*, pp. 104–7.

two metals of differing coefficients of expansion and are called bimetals, but one celebrated thermometer had a strip composed of three different metals, to reduce the stresses at the surfaces of junction.

The earliest reference to a bimetallic strip that I have been able to find is by Lambert and dates from 1779,[15] but must have been written before his death in 1777. He has been told, he says, that someone in England has had the idea of making bimetallic strips of copper and iron, and—which may surprise us—that this can be done by rolling, without soldering. "But such thermometers do not seem to be much in use."

This is confirmed a few years later by Jean Hyacinthe de Magellan, or Magalhaens, a Portuguese who settled in England and became greatly interested in the instruments of physics and meteorology. In 1782 we find him writing of the "metallic thermometer" as if it were well known. And what is it? It is a bimetallic thermometer.

> To construct it, a strip of steel and one of brass are solidly riveted or even soldered[16] together; for heat and cold make this double strip curve more or less, according to the reading of the thermometer. It is better to give this double strip a spiral form, so as to have it long enough to enlarge the movement. . . . This strip, being fastened at one end, moves the pencil that is attached to the other end (or to a rod fastened to this) according to the different temperatures of the atmosphere.[17]

But a metallic thermometer, which surely must have been bimetallic because it was a pocket instrument, had been constructed in 1767 by that very talented American David Rittenhouse at Norriton in Pennsylvania.[18] We are told that it was

> an ingeniously contrived thermometer, constructed on the principle of the expansion and contraction of metals, by heat and cold, respectively. This instrument had, under glass, a face upon which was a graduated semi-circle: the degrees of heat and cold corresponded with those of Fahrenheit's thermometer. . . . Its square (or rather parallelogramical) form, its flatness and thinness, and its small size—together with its not being liable to the least sensible injury or irregularity, from any position in which it might be placed,—rendered it safely portable; insomuch, that it could be conveniently carried in the pocket.[19]

[15] J. H. Lambert, *Pyrometrie oder vom Maase des Feuers und der Wärme* (Berlin, 1779), p. 124.

[16] "Ou même on [les] soude ensemble." The verb *souder* can mean to solder, to braze, or to weld.

[17] Magellan, *Obs. sur la Phys.*, Vol. 19 (1782), p. 353.

[18] Brooke Hindle, *David Rittenhouse* (Princeton, 1964), p. 25. I am indebted to F. R. Maddison for this reference.

[19] William Barton, *Memoirs of the Life of David Rittenhouse* (Philadelphia, 1813), p. 155, note.

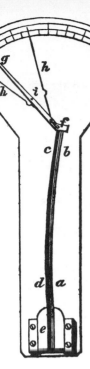

Fig. 7.3   *Crichton's metallic thermometer.*

It ought to be added that Barton had actually seen this thermometer.[20]

The invention of the bimetallic thermometer has been attributed to the physicist J. A. C. Charles,[21] but this can scarcely be correct. In France the instrument is often ascribed to Abraham Louis Breguet, the founder of the famous firm of clock- and instrumentmakers, who indeed built very sensitive and delicate thermometers with helical *trimetallic* strips—made of platinum, silver, and gold (the silver inside). The exact date of this instrument is hard to establish but is probably in or just before 1817, when Thaddaeus Siber was greatly impressed by the extremely rapid response of this "new metallic thermometer."[22] G. de Prony[23] wrote an instruction book about it, explaining that three metals were used instead of two for fear that if only two were used the *soudure* would loosen—a disaster by no means rare, at least in the nineteenth century. The total thickness of the trimetal was only 0.04 mm., and the thermometer is more a scientific curiosity than a meteorological instrument; as Prony admits, it cannot be used in the slightest breeze. A. L. Breguet was thinking about the dilatation of metals years before he made this thermometer. Through the kindness of M. François J. Breguet I was permitted to examine the notebooks of his distinguished ancestor, and in one of these, dated Fructidor An X (August–September, 1802), there are accounts of experiments on dilatation, and a vague sketch that suggests a bimetallic helix.

In 1803 J. Crichton of Glasgow described a very simple thermometer with a bimetal of iron and zinc (Fig. 7.3).[24] In this, *f* is a pin working in a slot in the short end of the pointer *g*. The stud *i* moves the auxiliary pointers *hh* to indicate the maximum and minimum temperatures. An instrument of this sort would have the advantage of large operating forces, as long as no attempt was made to have its thermal lag very small. There is a

[20] Letter from Professor Hindle to J. A. Chaldecott, Sept. 23, 1961. I have to thank Mr. Chaldecott for a copy.

[21] Maurice Daumas, *Les instruments scientifiques aux XVIIe et XVIIIe siècles* (Paris, 1953), p. 281. M. Daumas may have been led to this conclusion by the existence of a metallic thermometer by Breguet labelled "Pour Mr Charles" (CNAM, Inventory no. 4182). This probably dates from about 1817.

[22] Siber, *Schweigger's J.*, Vol. 20 (1817), pp. 465–66.

[23] Prony, *Instruction sur le thermomètre métallique de MM. Breguet père et fils* (pamphlet) (Paris, 1821), ii + 24 pp.

[24] Crichton, *Phil. Mag.*, Vol. 15 (1803), pp. 147–48.

similar instrument, but without extra pointers, in the CNAM,[25] made in 1833 by A. Janvier.

There were numerous other thermometers of the same general sort, usually with the bimetal bent into a ring[26] or a helix.[27] An especially strong and durable instrument of the latter kind was made by the firm of Hermann & Pfister of Berne.[28] Its construction will be clear from Fig. 7.4; it should be noted that it indicates only the maximum and minimum, not the current temperature. Opinions differed on this instrument, R. Wolf reporting some rather large disagreements with the usual liquid-in-glass thermometers.[29] But A. Hirsch,[30] after lengthy tests, decided that it was very suitable for meteorological stations, adding the sensible recommendation that the bimetallic strip should be protected from rusting by a coat of paint. A surviving example in the collection of the Meteorological Office, Bracknell, shows how wise this would have been.

Though they are scarcely meteorological instruments, I cannot avoid referring to the many beautiful bimetallic thermometers made in the shape of pocket watches. Just because they were never exposed out of doors, there are many of them in museums. Particularly elegant ones were made by the royal clockmaker at Copenhagen, Urban Jürgensen,[31] and by J. T. Winnerl.

The earliest description of one of these pocket instruments that I have come across is accompanied by elaborate calculations of its performance.[32] The theory of the bimetal is not at all simple, for the elasticity of the materials has to be considered. This was not recognized by Neumann,[33] but Jüllig[34] and Maurer[35] took it into account. There are several other treatments; a very clear one is by S. Timoshenko.[36]

[25] Inventory no. 10,622¹.

[26] For example Blatter, British patent 778 of 1854, April 5; Munn, British Patent 2551 of 1860, October 19.

[27] E.g., J. T. Winnerl, *Astron. Nachr.*, Vol. 7 (1829), col. 217–20.

[28] Hermann and Pfister, *Schweiz. meteorol. Beobb. für 1867*, pp. XV–XVIII; *Repert. f. phys. Techn.*, Vol. 5 (1869), pp. 314–19.

[29] Wolf, *Repert. f. phys. Techn.*, Vol. 5 (1869), pp. 314–17.

[30] Hirsch, *Bull. Soc. Sci. Nat. Neuchâtel*, Vol. 8 (1870), pp. 221–25.

[31] Jürgensen, *K. Dansk Vid. Selsk., nat. og math. Afh.*, Vol. 2 (1826), pp. 281–88.

[32] Argand, *Gergonne's Annales de Math.*, Vol. 4 (1813–14), pp. 29–41. This cannot be the famous Aimé Argand, who died in 1803.

[33] August Neumann, *Zeits. für Phys. und Math.*, Vol. 10 (1832), pp. 284–94.

[34] Max Jüllig, *Sitzb. Akad. Wien, 2 Abt.*, Vol. 79 (1879), pp. 349–74.

[35] J. Maurer, *Zeits. für Instr.*, Vol. 3 (1883), pp. 308–16.

[36] Timoshenko, *J. Opt. Soc. Amer. & Rev. Sci. Instr.*, Vol. 11 (1925), pp. 233–55. A summary is given in Middleton and Spilhaus, *Meteorological Instruments* (3rd ed.; Toronto, 1953), pp. 75–78.

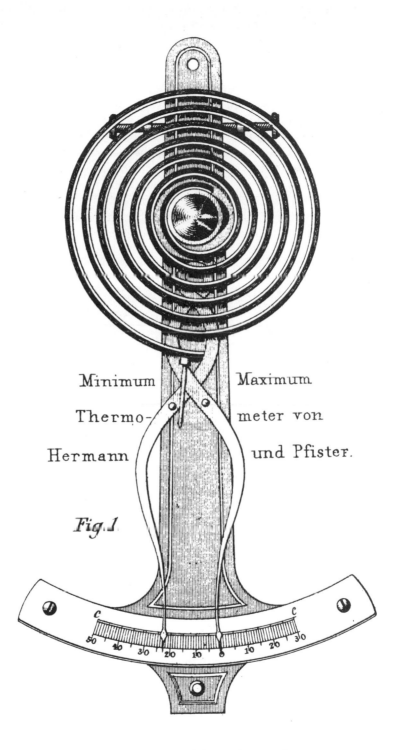

Fig. 7.4   *Hermann & Pfister's metallic maximum-and-minimum thermometer.*

4. A Thermometer Using Slightly Curved Bars. A metallic thermometer that seems to belong to a class of its own was invented by the Paris instrumentmaker Edme Regnier at the end of the eighteenth century and reported on by Leroy and Brisson at a meeting of the Institut.[37] It was made of two strips of brass in an iron frame. The strips were slightly curved and had their concave sides facing each other. One carried a pinion, on the axis of which was a pointer; the other had a rack. He had presented a small model to the Institut. His large model, obviously intended for a public place, was to have strips about 95 cm. long and a dial 1.3 meters in diameter. Its frame was to be of stone, and the rack and pinion were to be gilt or made of platinum, the pointer moving on agate bearings. The project was approved.

There is a thermometer by Regnier at the CNAM,[38] but this has a curved iron bar and a straight brass one.

5. Liquid-in-Metal Thermometers. In this section I have in mind thermometers in which the expansion of a liquid causes the deformation of some metallic system, thus giving an indication of the temperature. A way of arranging this extremely simply was discovered in 1846 by a German railway engineer named Schinz,[39] who found that a curved tube of elliptical cross-section will change its curvature when subjected to internal pressure. Schinz was interested in pressure gauges for locomotives. The principle was patented in 1849 by the Paris instrumentmaker Bourdon,[40] an energetic man who made a fortune out of it. The "Bourdon tube" is well known, but more as a pressure gauge than as a thermometer, though it held its own for many years in the construction of thermographs,[41] especially in France. Indicating thermometers on this principle are not common. There is an elegant one in the Museo Copernicano[42] in which the Bourdon tube, about 15 cm. in diameter, is arranged in a nearly complete circle around a flat, glass-sided cylindrical box. The essential requirement in the construction of such a thermometer is that the tube should be completely filled with some liquid that is entirely free from air. Absolute alcohol is commonly used.

[37] *Mém. de l'Institut,* Vol. 2 (1796), *Histoire,* pp. 18–22.
[38] Inv. no. 3427.
[39] *Eisenbahn-Zeitung,* Vol. 7 (1849), March 5 and April 2.
[40] French Patent 4408, June 19, 1849. British patent 12,889, Dec. 15, 1849.
[41] See Chapter 9.
[42] Inventory no. 2921.

It is possible to imagine other configurations that will act as a liquid-in-metal thermometer, such as a metal box with elastic sides, filled with alcohol,[43] but difficult to imagine one simpler than the Bourdon tube.

6. *Thermometers Giving the Mean Temperature.* In the first half of the nineteenth century a number of instruments were constructed for indicating the mean temperature over any desired interval. All these were simply clocks or watches designed so that their going rate varied with temperature. To give a true mean, the rate of such a clock must vary linearly with the temperature, which is not easy to arrange.[44] Attempts were made by J. G. Grassmann in 1835,[45] Jürgensen in 1836 and 1841,[46] and Edmond Becquerel in 1852.[47] Jürgensen used a watch with a bimetallic balance wheel. Becquerel's pendulum clock is at the CNAM in Paris.[48] Such instruments would give fairly good results in a room.

[43] Chadburn, British patent 732 of 1858, April 6.
[44] The period of a pendulum is proportional to the square root of its length.
[45] Grassmann, *Ann. der Phys.,* Vol. 4 (1825), pp. 419–42.
[46] Jürgensen, *Compt. Rend.,* Vol. 3 (1836), pp. 143–45; Vol. 13 (1841), pp. 304–5.
[47] Becquerel, *Compt. Rend.,* Vol. 35 (1852), p. 754.
[48] Inventory no. 8306.

175

VIII

Electrical Thermometers

1. Introduction. If this were a history of industrial thermometry, the present chapter might well be the longest in the book, in view of the number and diversity of the technical applications of electrical thermometers. In meteorology, however, thermometers of this sort have had only a limited application (as for instance, to earth thermometry and to the measurement of temperature gradients in the lowest layers of the atmosphere), if we except the measurement of radiation and the use of special resistance thermometers in radiosondes and aircraft, which are outside the scope of this work. I shall therefore confine myself to a brief account of some of the early papers on electrical thermometers in the century before 1914.

2. Thermoelectric Thermometry. In 1822 T. J. Seebeck described to the Berlin Academy the production of an electric current in a circuit made of two dissimilar metals when the temperature of one junction was raised.[1] It was only after extensive experiments that he convinced himself that it was actually the difference in temperature that was producing the electric current that moved the magnetized needle placed within the circuit. He was finally able to arrange the common metals in what is now called the thermo-electromotive series.[2]

The effect was soon applied to the measurement of small tem-

---

[1] Seebeck, "Magnetische Polarization der Metalle und Erze durch Temperatur-Differenzen," *Akad. Berlin, Abh.* (1822–23), pp. 265–374. The peculiar title of this paper is explainable by the fact that Oersted's experiment was not then properly understood.

[2] For an excellent, brief summary of Seebeck's paper, see E. Gerland and F. Traumüller, *Geschichte der physikalischen Experimentierkunst* (Leipzig, 1899), pp. 387–89. (Reprinted, Hildesheim, Georg Olms, 1965.)

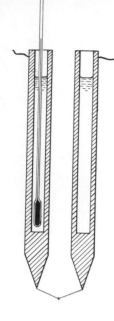

Fig. 8.1 Czermak's mounting for a fine thermocouple.

perature differences, using a number of thermocouples in series and the more sensitive galvanometers that were becoming available.[3] Before it could be seriously used its linearity had to be investigated, and in 1837 C. S. M. Pouillet found that a bismuth-copper thermocouple gave an electromotive force that was sensibly linear in comparison with the air thermometer between about 0° and −80° or −100°C.[4] It is interesting that he referred to the assembly of couple and galvanometer as a "pyromètre magnétique." At about this time A. C. Becquerel used an iron-copper circuit to measure the temperature of the Lake of Geneva to a depth of 104 meters, and suggested its use for earth temperatures.[5]

The great Regnault experimented with this sort of thermometry[6] and of course discovered some of the difficulties. In view of Regnault's experiments, Becquerel, who was evidently a great believer in thermocouples and had been using them for measuring temperatures in inaccessible places, adopted a null method.[7] In this, one of the junctions was heated or cooled in a liquid until zero deflection of the galvanometer was obtained. The temperature of the liquid was then measured with a mercury thermometer. In 1863 Becquerel was still measuring earth temperatures by this cumbersome method,[8] and even in 1876 it was in use for gradient measurements at the Observatory of Montsouris in Paris.[9]

Meanwhile, J. Pernet had described a method of interpolation with which he was measuring earth temperatures.[10] He used steel (piano wire) and German silver (*Neusilber*). He had two baths at different known temperatures and measured the deflections of the galvanometer when a thermojunction in either one is connected, in turn, in the circuit with the buried junction and the galvanometer. In view of the nonlinearity, he was obliged to develop a formula for interpolation.

After this time the thermocouple seems to have gone to its rightful place as far as meteorology is concerned, namely, in researches where the possibility of measuring rapidly fluctuating temperatures is important. By making a junction between fine wires of different metals thermometers of extremely small lag can

[3] Léopold Nobili, *Bibl. Univ., Geneva,* Vol. 44 (1830), pp. 225–34.

[4] Pouillet, *Compt. Rend.,* Vol. 4 (1837), pp. 513–19.

[5] Becquerel and Breschet, *Compt. Rend.,* Vol. 3 (1846), pp. 778–79.

[6] Regnault, *Mém. Acad. r. Sci. Paris,* Vol. 21 (1847), pp. 240 ff.

[7] Becquerel, *Compt. Rend.,* Vol. 46 (1858), pp. 1185–86.

[8] *Compt. Rend.,* Vol. 56 (1863), pp. 1057–62.

[9] *Zeits. österr. Ges. Meteorol.,* Vol. 11 (1876), pp. 305–7.

[10] *Repert. für Meteorol.,* Vol. 2 (1872), pp. 85–108.

easily be made, as was pointed out by Paul Czermak in 1895.[11] His manner of mounting a very fine junction is ingenious (Fig. 8.1), though the Dewar (or "Thermos") flask, which became availabl at about this time, provides a simpler solution to the prc m.[12]

3. *Electrical Resistance Thermometry.* The dependence of the electrical resistance of metals on temperature was discovered by Sir Humphry Davy,[13] but as far as I am aware, the first proposal to use this phenomenon for the purposes of thermometry was made by the distinguished engineer Carl Wilhelm Siemens, later Sir William, some forty years later.[14] The title of Siemens' paper is "On an electric resistance thermometer for observing temperatures at inaccessible locations," and while it was the measurement of industrial temperatures that interested him most, he did suggest that there might be meteorological applications for the resistance thermometer. The firm of Siemens & Halske began to make pyrometers of this sort, and in 1871 Siemens gave the Bakerian Lecture to the Royal Society on the subject of the change of resistance with temperature.[15] In this he proposed the use of resistance thermometers for the routine measurement of temperature, preferring platinum for the variable resistor. The interpolation formula that he derived from his experiments did not stand the test of time, and there was criticism of his pyrometers on the grounds of instability. With the immense range of his interests he was unable to give the subject the attention it deserved.

This attention was provided by the English physicist Hugh Longbourne Callendar, who made elaborate experiments and described them in a tremendous paper in the *Philosophical Transactions.*[16] From his comparisons with the air thermometer he deduced that the resistance of a properly made platinum thermometer can be related to the readings of the air thermometer by a parabolic formula, and that very close agreement can

[11] Czermak, *Ann. der Phys.*, Vol. 56 (1895), pp. 353–59. (Summary in *Meteorol. Zeits.*, Vol. 13 (1896), pp. 190–91).

[12] For a review of the fairly recent history of precision thermoelectric thermometry, see William F. Roeser, "Thermoelectric thermometry," in *Temperature, Its Measurement and Control in Science and Industry* (New York, 1941), pp. 180–205.

[13] Davy, *Phil. Trans.* (1821), p. 431.

[14] C. W. Siemens, *B.A.A.S. Report, Manchester, 1861*, Sections, pp. 44–45.

[15] Siemens, *Proc. Royal Society*, Vol. 19 (1871), pp. 443–45.

[16] Callendar, *Phil. Trans. A*, Vol. 178 (1887), pp. 161–230.

be obtained at temperatures up to about 600°C. The accuracy of such comparisons depends mainly on that of the air thermometer.

In a later paper[17] it appears that his statements about the stability of the platinum thermometer had been badly received, largely because of experience with the early Siemens pyrometers. He gave practical suggestions for the construction of stable thermometers with mica insulation, wound so as to avoid strains in the platinum wire. In this paper he seriously criticized Siemens' experiments, especially the use of high-range mercury thermometers without correction.

Meteorological applications began to be made at Kew Observatory, and in 1896 E. H. Griffiths, with the consent of the Kew Committee, made an unofficial but detailed report on the elaborate installation at Kew for platinum resistance thermometry,[18] in which he strongly urged its suitability for the calibration of liquid-in-glass thermometers at ordinary temperatures. As far as ground-based meteorological observations are directly concerned, the main use of resistance thermometers has been for earth temperatures and measurements on masts to determine the gradient of temperature in the lower atmosphere.

As a laboratory instrument, the platinum resistance thermometer has fully justified Callendar's hopes for it. In 1899 a Committee on Electrical Standards, headed by Lord Rayleigh, accepted Callendar's proposals for interpolation formulas at temperatures above −100°C.[19] The gas thermometer was to be the ultimate standard, but at that time the difference between it and the "platinum scale" was less than the probable errors of gas thermometry. The platinum thermometer is now the internationally recognized means of interpolation between points fixed by definition, all the way from the boiling point of liquid oxygen (−182.97°C.) to the freezing point of antimony (630.5°C.).[20] Above the latter temperature a thermocouple is employed.

Returning to meteorological matters, there has been a certain demand for the instant availability of outdoor temperatures in a distant place, especially at airports. This was pioneered by C. F. Marvin in the United States as long ago as 1911.[21] Marvin

[17] Callendar, *Phil. Mag.*, Vol. 32 (1891), pp. 104–13.

[18] Griffiths, *Nature*, Vol. 53 (1896), pp. 39–46.

[19] Callendar, *Phil. Mag.*, Vol. 48 (1899), pp. 519–46.

[20] For the details see *Comm. Int. Poids et Mesures, Compt. Rend. 11th Int. Conference*, October, 1960. For a historical review of precision resistance thermometry, see Mueller in *Temperature, Its Measurement and Control*, pp. 162–79.

[21] Marvin, *Franklin Inst. J.*, Vol. 171 (1911), pp. 439–55.

found that for the moderate range of temperatures involved, pure nickel was a suitable material for the temperature-sensitive resistor, with a rather larger change of resistance than platinum. He also found that a parabolic interpolation formula is satisfactory for nickel. Various ways of measuring the resistance of the coil and compensating for changes in the temperature of the leads were also devised by Marvin. Later improvements have mainly been the work of ingenious manufacturers.[22]

I shall close this section with a mention of another way of producing an almost linear variation of electrical resistance with temperature.[23] In the distant-reading thermometer patented by Berthold in 1889, the transmitter is a mercury thermometer with a fine platinum wire down the tube. The resistance of that part of the wire that is not shorted by the mercury was really what was measured, plus of course that of the mercury column, which could be arranged to be much less. The platinum wire was connected in a Wheatstone bridge with a compensating wire at the transmitter, three connecting wires being required. There was an interrupter in the battery circuit, and a telephone receiver was used as a detector.

A slightly different arrangement was proposed by M. Eschenhagen,[24] but as soon as the excellent properties of the resistance thermometer came to be recognized such devices ceased to be of interest.

4. *Wheatstone's Tele-Thermometers.* At Cork in 1843 Professor Charles Wheatstone, one of the inventors of the electric telegraph, described to the British Association an "electro-magnetic meteorological register."[25] This was intended to be carried up in a kite, and the thermometer in it was a mercury-in-glass one with the end open. Down the bore ran a platinum wire, moved up and down by a clock in a cycle of six minutes. The breaking of the circuit as the wire came out of the mercury was observed on the ground by means of a galvanometer and timed by means of another clock.

In 1867 he described another "telegraphic thermometer," more suitable for continuous use at, for instance, a mountain station.[26] In this the thermometric element is a bimetallic spiral,

---

22 See for example Morris E. Leeds, U.S. patent 1,097,651, May 26, 1914.
23 M. Berthold, D. R. P. 51775, September 6, 1889.
24 Eschenhagen, *Zeits. für Instrum.*, Vol. 14 (1894), pp. 398–404.
25 Wheatstone, *B.A.A.S. Report, Cork, 1843*, pp. xl–xlii.
26 Wheatstone, *B.A.A.S. Report, Dundee, 1867*, Sections, pp. 11–13.

the pointer of which carries a contact. A hand-driven magneto at the place where the information is required causes an electro-magnet and ratchet to revolve a contact at the thermometer, and also a reading index near the magneto, in synchronism. When the contact touches the pointer at the thermometer, the move-ment of the reading index is stopped by a relay and the moving contact is returned to zero, ready for the next inquiry, before which the reading index is restored manually to its original position. The two "stations" of this instrument may be seen at the Science Museum, London.[27]

The files of the Patent Office contain many other rather similar servo systems.[28] They have found little use in meteorology, and I shall not deal with them further.

[27] Inv. no. 1950–197.
[28] Two examples: R. Howett and C. L. Clarke, British patent 454 of 1883, January 27; C. L. Clarke, British patent 11,898 of 1885, October 6.

IX

Recording Thermometers

1. Introduction. The first recording thermometer, as I have noted in Chapter 3, was invented by Sir Christopher Wren and was part of a "weather-clock" or meteorograph. Since that time a large number of different recording thermometers have been devised, of such various designs that it is not easy to provide a simple classification. The most obvious demarcation is between those making use of air, liquid-in-glass, metallic, and electrical thermometers respectively, and it is thus that I shall classify them for the purposes of this account; but in each class there is a good deal of choice in the way a record is made and a clear division between those in which the record is continuous and those in which it consists of a series of points, usually at equal intervals of time.

There are three distinct periods in the history of thermographs. In the first, extending up to about 1790, they were simply occasional scientific curiosities, few in number, and indeed (apart from those of Wren and of Hooke) it is doubtful whether any were actually built. The second period covers most of the nineteenth century; this is the era when the useful accuracy of meteorological observations was thought to be limited by the properties of instruments, rather than by those of the atmosphere itself,[1] and heroic efforts were made to refine the recording instruments. The third period began about 1880 with the production of large numbers of simple, light, and relatively inexpensive recording instruments of sufficient accuracy for nearly all meteorological purposes, assuming adequate control by observations with good nonrecording instruments. This revolution began in France, and as far as the thermograph is concerned can be credited to the Paris firm of Richard Frères. But

[1] Cf. W. E. K. Middleton, *Quart. J. Roy. Meteorol. Soc.*, Vol. 72 (1946), pp. 32–50.

this is nearly the end of the story; I must go back to the seventeenth century, and to the recording air thermometer designed by Wren.

2. Thermographs Based on the Air Thermometer.

I have already described the recording air thermometer devised by Wren about 1663.[2] With the minimum of mechanical complication, this instrument recorded the motion of a float on the mercury in one arm of a U-tube; its limitations were certainly the presence of a good deal of friction, and also, of course, the sensitiveness of the air thermometer to the changes in atmospheric pressure. The same defect—more pronounced as far as friction is concerned—would be found in the complicated designs of Jacob Leupold, who published a huge illustrated textbook of mechanical devices called the *Theatrum machinarum,* suggesting a thermograph in Part III of this work.[3] This was an air thermometer of the so-called "Galilean" form, using mercury as the liquid, the bulb and tube being hung on a sector of a wheel, and counterpoised by an arrangement involving a weight hung on a spiral cam. I agree with Hoff and Geddes in doubting whether it was ever built; at any rate it seems to have had no influence.

To make an air thermometer practically useful as a recording instrument, it needs to be freed from the influence of the atmospheric pressure, or compensated for the variations of the pressure. The latter alternative was chosen in an instrument described in 1832, apparently by a scientific popularizer, T. S. Traill.[4] In this instrument an air thermometer and a barometer tube, both dipping into the same U-shaped cistern of mercury, counterpoise each other by being attached to a cord passing over a wheel, to which an index or pen may be fastened. The barometer tube is dimensioned so as to compensate the air thermometer for pressure changes. I cannot find out whether such an instrument was built at this time, and the same remark applies to an almost exactly equivalent instrument (Fig. 9.1) described in 1865

[2] See p. 41 above.

[3] Jacob Leupold, *Theatrum machinarum Pars III. Theatri statici universalis, sive theatrum aërostaticum, Oder: Schau-Platz der Machinen zu Abwiegung und Beobachtung aller vornehmsten Eigenschafften der Lufft* [etc.] (Leipzig, 1726), plate XXIII. This has been dealt with by H. E. Hoff and L. A. Geddes, *Isis,* Vol. 53 (1962), pp. 307–9.

[4] [T. S.] Traill, "The thermometer and pyrometer," *in* Society for the Diffusion of Useful Knowledge, *Library of Useful Knowledge, Natural Philosophy, II* (London, 1832), Sec. IV, p. 47.

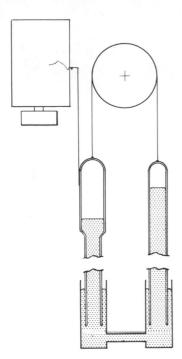

Fig. 9.1 Compensated air thermograph, 1865, derived from King's barograph.

by G. Hamilton of Queen's College, Liverpool.[5] In the interval a successful barograph had been built at Liverpool by the engineer Alfred King,[6] and Hamilton freely acknowledged that his idea was simply a modification of this, with the vessel of air substituted for the dead weight in the barograph.

Also derived from a successful barograph—of his own design[7] —were the thermographs of Adolf Sprung.[8] The barograph was the famous rolling-weight instrument that has given service at one or two stations for more than sixty years.[9] In this instrument a servo mechanism, operated by electric contacts at the end of a balance beam, causes a weight to roll along the beam and restore the balance, the record being made by a pen attached to this rolling weight. Actually, the weight oscillates continuously about the position of balance, for when the contacts are open it is moved at a constant speed to the left by a clockwork, acting through friction wheels. This motion soon tips the beam and

[5] Hamilton, *Proc. British Meteorol. Soc.*, Vol. 2 (1865), pp. 367–69; *Astr. Soc. Monthly Notices*, Vol. 25 (1865), pp. 29–31.

[6] *Report of the Astronomer to the Marine Committee, Mersey Docks and Harbour Board* (Liverpool, 1863), pp. 14–15. See also Middleton, *The History of the Barometer* (Baltimore, 1964), pp. 307–8.

[7] A. Sprung, in L. Löwenherz, *Bericht über die wissenschaftliche Instrumente auf der Berliner Gewerbeausstellung im Jahre 1879* (Berlin, 1880), pp. 234–42.

[8] Sprung, *Zeits. für Instrum.*, Vol. 1 (1881), pp. 357–66. A brief indication is also to be found in *Zeits. österr. Ges. Meteorol.*, Vol. 13 (1878), 299–300.

[9] See Middleton, *The History of the Barometer*, pp. 311–15.

Fig. 9.2 Sprung's rolling-weight thermograph, 1881, diagram.

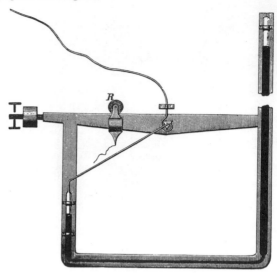

closes the circuit, when an electromagnet reverses the direction of motion and again separates the contacts. One of the ways in which this principle was applied to a thermograph is shown in Fig. 9.2. A siphon barometer with its two arms separated by a fairly long horizontal tube has its shorter arm connected by a capillary tube to a vessel of air placed in a suitable position out of doors. Any change in the temperature of this vessel will disturb the equilibrium of the beam by shifting mercury from one arm of the siphon to the other.

This idea does not seem to have met with much success; nor does the combination barograph and thermograph that Sprung devised a few years later,[10] which had two beams, each with its rolling weight. Nevertheless, in 1893 he still recommended the instrument described in 1881, with some improvements that he had made to the contact mechanism.[11]

Another instrument making use of an air vessel and a siphon barometer was described by the Berlin instrumentmaker R. Fuess in 1883,[12] also as a modification of a barograph. The recording part of this is shown in Fig. 9.3. In the vacuum space floated a magnet enclosed in a rubber cylinder and weighted with a small platinum ball to keep it horizontal. A larger U-shaped magnet *b* was supported on the left-hand knife-edge of an unequal-arm balance of 2 to 1 ratio, and on the right-hand knife-edge was hung a curved tube *r*, about half as long as the barometric col-

[10] Sprung, *Zeits. für Instrum.*, Vol. 6 (1886), pp. 189–98, 232–37.
[11] Sprung, in *Report of the International Meteorological Congress, Chicago, 1893* (U.S. Weather Bureau, *Bulletin* no. 11) (Washington, 1894), pp. 718–20.
[12] Fuess, *Zeits. für Instrum.*, Vol. 3 (1883), pp. 197–98.

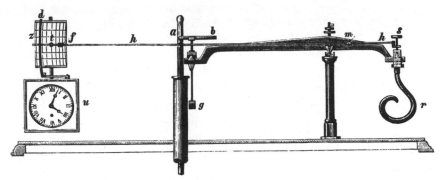

umn, which provided compensation for the temperature of the instrument itself in the following very ingenious way: a second, lighter beam *hh* was supported on knife-edges collinear with those of the main beam, and its right-hand end was fitted with a hardened screw *s* which rested on the hardened point *q* of a float that swam on the mercury in the tube *r*. If the temperature of the instrument rose, *q* was raised, and the pencil *t* correspondingly fell. The screw *s* also acted as a fine adjustment for the pen.

One would expect such air thermographs to be sluggish, but in fact this was not found to be so, especially if the air-vessel was made of a metal such as copper.

Fig. 9.3   (a) above, (b) below, Fuess's "magnetic" thermograph, recording parts.

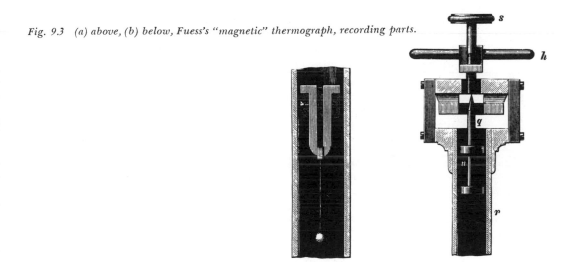

3. *Thermographs Based on the Spirit-in-Glass Thermometer.* Christopher Wren's idea for a thermograph, presented by Robert Hooke to the Royal Society on January 4, 1664/5, has already been de-

scribed.[13] It is not known whether the thermometer of Hooke's later "weather clock" functioned in this way, or whether it was more like the wheel barometer that he had invented, with a large bulb full of spirit, the expansion of which caused the rise of a surface of mercury in an attached U-tube.

At all events, the latter scheme was adopted about 1795 by Alexander Keith,[14] who built the indicating thermometer shown in Fig. 9.4 and projected a thermograph. The indicating thermometer needs no further description, except to note that the index could push two tiny pieces of oiled silk up and down a fine gold wire to indicate the extremes of temperature. In the design for a thermograph the bulb was to be about forty inches long, and the float was to raise and lower a rod carrying a pencil, which was to be made to press lightly against a revolving drum by the clever use of an offset weight. The drum was to revolve once a month, and it was suggested that the charts should be engravings made from a copper plate.

Another thermograph with a large bulb filled with spirit was that of the astronomer Johann von Lamont, the director of the Munich Observatory, who had a passion for constructing large meteorological instruments.[15] One of his three thermographs had a large serpentine glass tube mainly filled with alcohol, ending in a vertical tube filled with mercury and dipping into a thimble-shaped pot of mercury hung on a balance.

In the same decade G. W. Hough of the Dudley Observatory, Albany, N.Y., made a complicated thermograph which not only gave a graph of the temperature but also printed hourly values in figures.[16] In the use of a float this was similar to Keith's instrument, but the float was made to make and break electrical contacts controlling an elaborate electromechanical servo system, essentially the same as that of Hough's printing barograph of 1871.[17] It may be significant that this complicated thermograph is not even mentioned in another publication of the Signal Service in the next decade, Cleveland Abbe's great *Treatise on Meteorological Apparatus and Methods*.[18]

[13] See p. 43 above.
[14] Keith, *Trans. R. Soc. Edinb.*, Vol. 4, part II (1798), pp. 203–8.
[15] Lamont, *Repertorium für phys. Techn.*, Vol. 6 (1870), pp. 1–4; also *Zeits. österr. Ges. Meteorol.*, Vol. 5 (1870), pp. 129–32.
[16] It was devised for the Signal Service of the U.S. Army, and is briefly described in U.S. War Dept., *Annual Report of the Chief Signal Officer for 1877*, pp. 510–11.
[17] *Annals of the Dudley Observatory*, Vol. 2 (1871), xxiv; or see Middleton, *The History of the Barometer*, p. 325.
[18] This important work (392 pp. + 35 plates) is Appendix 46 of the *Annual Report of the Chief Signal Officer . . . for 1887* (Washington, 1888). It is of much value to the historian of meteorological instruments.

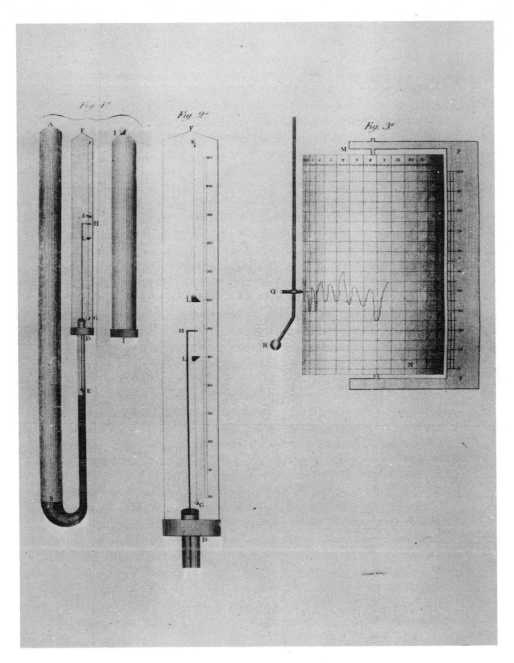

Fig. 9.4 Keith's project for a thermograph.

The principle of Lamont's balance thermograph was used again by A. Mallock ten years later, but with the important modification that the bulb, which contained about half a pint of spirit, could be at some distance from the rest of the apparatus, being connected to it by a capillary tube.[19] This instrument is interesting in that time marks were made on the recording drum by a pen that was jogged by an electromagnet controlled by the driving clock. But the sluggishness of a bulb containing half a pint of spirit can be imagined.

4. *Thermographs Based on the Mercury-in-Glass Thermometer.* The relative sluggishness of the spirit thermometer, which was known to the Accademia del Cimento,[20] was a real disadvantage when it came to designing thermographs. This, and the general preference for mercury as a thermometric liquid that developed during the late eighteenth century, seems to have led most of the designers of liquid-in-glass thermographs to use mercury.

The same elementary solution to the problem that occurred to Wren was repeated several times. Since the center of gravity of a thermometer moves as the temperature changes, why not merely balance a thermometer on a knife-edge and watch it tilt? The "Thermometrograph" of L. A. von Arnim was on this principle;[21] the balanced thermometer carries a stylus that moves across a smoked disk revolved by clockwork (Fig. 9.5). One cannot imagine this instrument withstanding much exposure.

A similar thermometer formed part of a barograph designed by Karl Kreil of Prague and described in 1843[22] (Fig. 9.6), with the difference that the index was separate from the thermometer —the well-designed bearings are shown in the smaller figures— and that the record was made eleven times in the hour at intervals of five minutes, the thermometer being otherwise free. This thermograph was really intended to measure the temperature of the barograph with a view to correcting its readings.[23]

Leonhard Wollheim was an engineer at Trieste, and it is doubtful whether he had ever heard of Wren's thermometer with the two bulbs and the curved tube;[24] but he invented a

[19] Mallock, *B.A.A.S. Report, Southampton, 1882,* pp. 477–78.
[20] See p. 36 above.
[21] Von Arnim, *Ann. der Phys.,* Vol. 2 (1799), pp. 289–96.
[22] Kreil, *Magn. und meteorol. Beobb. zu Prag,* Vol. 3 (1843), pp. 131–33.
[23] One of these barographs was bought for the Kew Observatory, and is now at the Science Museum, London (inv. no. 1876–793).
[24] See p. 42 above.

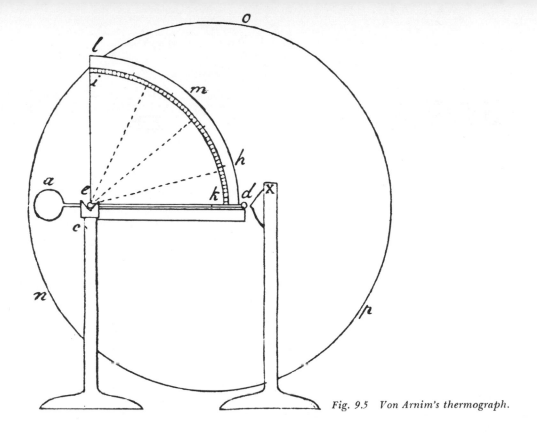

Fig. 9.5   *Von Arnim's thermograph.*

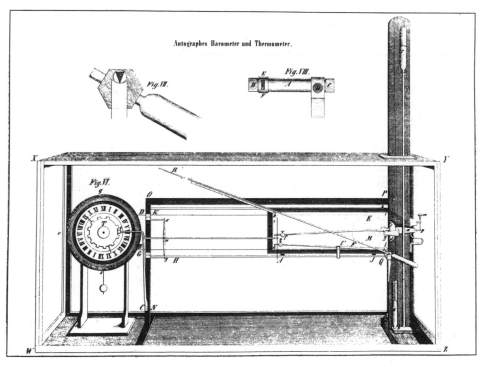

Fig. 9.6   *Kreil's barograph with recording thermometer.*

Fig. 9.7   The thermometer of Wollheim's thermograph, 1858.

thermograph on similar principles except that the tube was straightened out (Fig. 9.7). This was described in 1858.[25] The large bulb *A*, the tube, and part of the bulb *B*, are filled with mercury, and the fulcrum is at *C*. The deflection would be more nearly linear in temperature than, for example, in Kreil's instrument, though the recording was done pointwise in precisely the same manner.

All such instruments were necessarily delicate; indeed, one may wonder about the effect of even a moderate wind. There were other solutions to the problem, the simplest being just like the one suggested by Keith, but with mercury substituted for spirit. A year after Keith's paper appeared A. M. Vassalli-Eandi reported on just such an instrument.[26] That of Morstadt, exhibited at Prague in 1837,[27] differed mainly in having a flat rectangular iron box in place of a glass bulb, presumably to make it respond more quickly to changes of temperature. That of Osnaghi,[28] built to record the temperature of a barograph, made no such concessions, having a glass tube 54 inches long and 2½ inches in bore, bent 6 times and with the last bend open at the top. I doubt whether anyone in our twentieth-century affluent society would devote about 125 lb. of mercury to such a purpose.

Mercury thermographs with servosystems were much less common than barographs on this principle. Those that were made seem to have incorporated a large mercury thermometer, open at the top, into which a platinum wire is introduced and withdrawn on a time schedule, as in the remarkable printing meteorograph of Theorell,[29] or else caused to remain in intermittent contact with the mercury surface. This scheme was suggested by Johann Lamont in 1870[30] and constructed by G. Morgan Eldridge a decade later.[31] In the latter instrument a stylus pricked a chart whenever the wire touched the mercury surface, the motion of the wire being effected by clockwork through an

[25] By F. Stach in *Dingler's Journal*, Vol. 144 (1858), pp. 176–77.

[26] Vassalli-Eandi, *Mem. Soc. Ital. Sci.*, Vol. 8 (1799), pp. 518–19.

[27] G. W. Muncke in *Gehlers phys. Wörterbuch*, 2nd. ed., Vol. 9 (Leipzig, 1839), p. 986.

[28] Ferdinand Osnaghi, *Zeits. österr. Ges. Meteorol.*, Vol. 5 (1870), pp. 269–70.

[29] A. G. Theorell, *Kongl. Svenska Vetenskap-Akad. Handlingar*, Vol. 10 (1871), pp. 3–10.

[30] Lamont, *Repert. für phys. Techn.*, Vol. 6 (1870), pp. 1–4.

[31] Eldridge, *J. Franklin Inst.*, Vol. 113 (1882), pp. 438–42.

electrically-operated reversing gear. Eldridge covered the mercury with glycerine or a suitable oil to prevent oxidation.

Such elaborate instruments were quite unsuitable for installation out of doors, and have vanished without trace, while barographs from the nineteenth century—used indoors—abound in museums,[32] and a few are still giving good service. We must now consider the only type of liquid-in-glass thermograph of which this can be said. It uses photography as a means of registration.

It is remarkable that photography was actually used in a recording meteorological instrument—a barograph—within a few months of the announcement of its invention in 1839.[33] This instrument, which used daylight as an illuminant and so could not operate at night, was due to the energetic secretary of the Royal Cornwall Polytechnic Society, T. B. Jordan,[34] who simply mounted a drum on a vertical axis so that it revolved as close as possible to a barometer tube. The drum was covered with the "Calotype" paper invented by H. Fox Talbot.[35] Jordan seems to have built only a barograph, though he saw that other instruments could be used. The first photographic thermograph was described six years later by Mungo Ponton,[36] and made use of a gas lamp, which was turned up for five minutes every half hour. Meanwhile, a fresh portion of the sensitive paper had been moved into place, so that what was obtained was a record of the temperature at half-hourly intervals. There was no optical system, merely the shadow of the mercury thread on the photographic paper.

This did not satisfy Francis Ronalds, the Director of Kew Observatory, who suggested to Henry Collen, an instrument-maker of Somerset Street, London, that the thermometer should be imaged on the sensitive surface. So a Ross lens was used to do this.[37] The source of light was an Argand lamp, and the Calotype paper was moved by clockwork at a speed of one inch per hour. The mercury thermometer had "a broad flat bore," and light that would otherwise have been refracted round the mercury was intercepted by a slit between the thermometer and the lamp. Shortly afterward Ronalds built a thermograph as part of a collection of recording "meteorological and magnetical

[32] See my The History of the Barometer, appendix.

[33] For an account of the beginnings of photography, see H. and A. Gernsheim, A Concise History of Photography (London, 1965), pp. 20–30.

[34] Jordan, Royal Cornwall Polytech. Soc., Annual Report for 1838, pp. 184–89. The Society's year seems to have extended well into 1839, and the "1838" has caused some confusion.

[35] Talbot, Proc. Roy. Soc., Vol. 4 (1839), pp. 120–21, 124–26.

[36] Ponton, Trans. Scottish Soc. of Arts, Vol. 3 (1845), pp. 45–52.

[37] Collen, Phil. Mag., Vol. 28 (1846), pp. 73–75.

instruments" at Kew, similar to that of Collen except that the tube of the thermometer was horizontal and the photographic paper moved vertically.[38]

Similar activity went on at Greenwich, the thermograph—not fully described—being admittedly the same in principle.[39]

The meteorological instruments at Kew were constantly improved. The Observatory had the good fortune to have a mechanical assistant, R. Beckley, who had a remarkable flair for instrument design, apparently encouraged by his superiors. The result was an excellent group of recording instruments, of which the photographic barograph and the wet-and-dry-bulb thermograph have proved the most successful.[40] In 1867 copies of both instruments, as well as of Beckley's anemograph, were being set up at Kew, Falmouth, Stonyhurst, Glasgow, Aberdeen, Armagh, and Valentia. By 1885 twenty observatories throughout the world had been supplied.[41] Observations with the thermograph at Kew began in October, 1867,[42] and it was still in service in December, 1965.

The Kew thermograph as finally built was a great advance on previous instruments of this sort. In the first place, it was possible to have the bulbs of the thermometers in a louvered screen outside the building, while the remainder of the apparatus (Fig. 9.8) was protected from the weather. In the second place, the optical system was much improved by designing it on the principle of the lantern-slide projector, with each thermometer stem, in close contact with a narrow slit, acting as a lantern slide which is imaged on the photographic paper.

The thermometers have cylindrical bulbs. A few inches above the bulb, the stem is bent through a right angle and extends horizontally for about two feet through an opening in the wall, and this is followed by a further vertical section encompassing the useful range of the thermometer. Near the top of the mercury thread there is a small air bubble.

The arrangement of the optical system will be made clearer by reference to Fig. 9.9, in which it is represented in plan. The condensers B,B image the gas flames F,F on the photographic objectives L,L by way of the mirrors M,M. In the vertical planes containing the axes of the objectives are the stems of the ther-

[38] Ronalds, *Phil. Trans.*, Vol. 137 (1847), p. 113.

[39] Charles Brooke, *Phil. Trans.*, Vol. 137 (1847), p. 71.

[40] Both are described in Royal Society of London, *Report of the Meteorological Committee* for 1867, pp. 27–54.

[41] R. H. Scott, *Proc. Roy. Soc.*, Vol. 39 (1885), pp. 37–86.

[42] Personal communication from Mr. R. J. Collingbourne, the present superintendent.

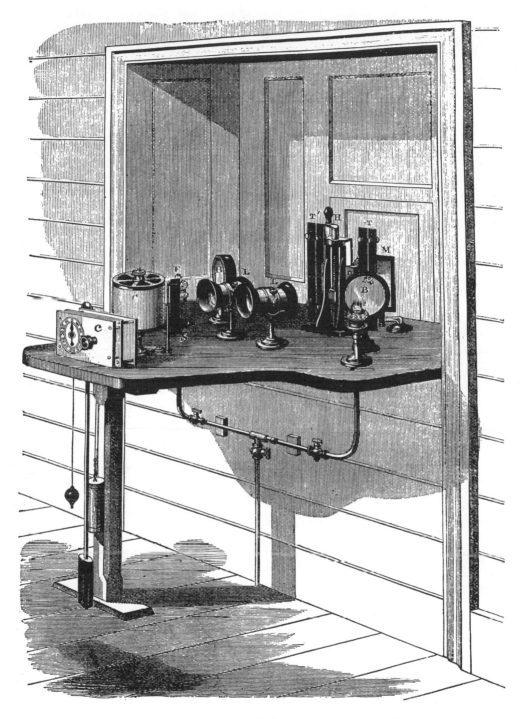

Fig. 9.8 *The Kew photographic thermograph, indoor part.*

Fig. 9.9   The Kew photographic thermograph, plan of optical system.

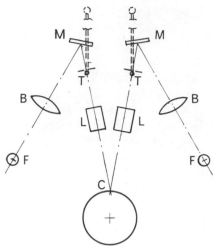

mometers *T,T*, each just behind a narrow slit, and the objectives image these slits on the same portion of the photographic paper on the drum *C*. Since the only light that can get through the slits is that traversing the air bubbles, two small spots of light appear at *C*, each producing a record of the position of one of the air bubbles as the drum revolves.

In recent years small electric lamps have replaced the gas flames, and of course very little light is now required with modern photographic paper. Naturally, the mechanism shown in Fig. 9.8 is covered by a light-tight box. One of these instruments has recently been set up at the Science Museum, London,[43] just as it would be installed at an observatory, with the bulbs of the thermometers in a louvered screen, and the recording mechanism —without its cover—on the other side of a "wall," the whole forming one of the most interesting exhibits in the newly enlarged meteorological collection, which has been beautifully arranged by Lieut. Cmdr. A. G. Thoday.

5. *Thermographs Based on Deformation Thermometers.* As we saw in Chapter 7, a thermograph that made use of a spiral bimetallic strip was at least projected by J. H. Magellan in 1782.[44] More than half a century later three such instruments were actually constructed in France, the earliest being due to one Calland, the royal clock-

[43] Inv. no. 1926–938.
[44] See p. 170 above. I doubt whether it was ever made.

maker, who worked at 6 rue Montesquieu in Paris. There is a reference to it, with no details, in the *Comptes Rendus;*[45] but the actual instrument is preserved.[46] It is plainly intended to be used indoors. A clock in the lower part of the instrument moves a flat chart, over which swings a lever actuated by a curved bimetal. The clock also operates a cam which at regular intervals pushes into the chart a point on the end of the lever.

At about the same time the Breguets made several thermographs, modifications of their extremely sensitive metallic thermometer[47] with its pendent helical trimetal and circular scale. The earliest was described briefly in 1840.[48] Every hour the pointer, terminated by a stylus, is pressed down by clockwork on to a paper chart. The chart is moved sideways so that a different circular scale on the paper is concentric with the axis of the bimetal at each successive hour. This was described again in 1844,[49] and also another instrument that used a moving band of paper. One of these instruments, we are informed, was tested by Regnault at the Collège de France and found "very comparable." In another pamphlet we read that one had been used by Knorr at Kazan during the entire year 1842, in temperatures going down to $-42°C$.[50] Certainly it must have been kept under the bell glass with which Breguet's delicate instruments were provided, and this must have made nonsense of its extreme quickness of response.

There were other slightly more practical solutions, such as that proposed by Veladini, a professor at Brescia,[51] who inverted Breguet's arrangement by having a rotating circular chart and making the stylus move along a radius, with continuous registration. This was an isolated example, because no one seemed aware of the very considerable stiffness that could be combined with a time of response more than adequate for most meteorological purposes. Therefore, bimetallic thermographs almost all used discontinuous recording. Among the most successful constructors were Hasler & Escher of Berne, who had adopted this procedure by 1860,[52] and in the succeeding decade made thermographs in

[45] *Compt. Rend.,* Vol. 7 (1839), p. 739.

[46] CNAM, inv. no. 12,327.

[47] See p. 171 above.

[48] *Compt. Rend.,* Vol. 11 (1840), p. 24.

[49] Breguet, Neveu & Cie, *Exposition de 1844, Produits de la Maison Breguet, Neveu & Cie.* (Lithographed from handwriting, 7 pp.). M. François J. Breguet informs me that Louis Breguet's nephew was named Lessieur.

[50] Louis F[rançois] C[lément] Breguet, *Notice sur les travaux de M. L. Breguet* (Paris, 1847), pp. 3–4.

[51] G. Veladini, *Giornale dell' I. R. Ist. Lomb. di Scienze, Lettere ed Arte,* Vol. 3 (1842), pp. 19–29.

[52] Cf. H. Wild, *Repert. für phys. Techn.,* Vol. 2 (1867), p. 163.

which an electromagnet, energized every ten minutes, presses a stylus into a chart, releases it, and then advances the paper. There is a similar instrument at the CNAM[53] in which the sensitive element is a bimetal in the form of a large conical helix, about 10 cm. in diameter and 10 cm. high, which looks as if it would have been stiff enough for continuous recording.

With such a construction, of course, it was necessary to expose the entire mechanism to the weather. To avoid this, Hipp of Neuchâtel designed an instrument[54] in which the spiral bimetal of brass and steel is supported outside a building on a long horizontal tube that comes through a hole in the wall. The outer end of the spiral is fastened rigidly to the tube, and its inner end to a rod concentric with the tube. Through a system of levers, the rotation of this rod is communicated to the stylus.

In 1873 F. Osnaghi of Trieste suggested a worthwhile modification, pointing out that if the magnets fail to work even once the time scale becomes erroneous, without it being possible to tell when this occurred.[55] The remedy was to leave out one recording in each hour.

At this period there was some disinclination to use electrical means of registration because of the nuisance of maintaining the wet batteries that were the only source of current generally available. This led the firm of Hottinger & Cie at Zurich to develop a line of meteorological instruments recording once an hour by purely mechanical means. One of these was the combination thermograph and hair hygrograph shown in Fig. 9.10.[56] In this the paper was moved continuously by a clockwork, which also rotated a saw-tooth cam. Each hour a follower fell off the point of a tooth of this cam, allowing a bar to strike the pointers of the two instruments and also a fixed pointer between them which provided a baseline.

In the following year they designed a special thermograph for the Zentralanstalt für Meteorologie und Geodynamik at Vienna, on similar principles, except that the bimetal was on the end of a long tube so that it could be installed in a louvered screen outside the building.[57] The motion of the free end of the bimetallic spiral was communicated to the recording mechanism by a fine steel wire within the tube. This instrument has vanished, but a large drawing is preserved at the Zentralanstalt.

[53] Inv. no. 17,420.
[54] M. Hipp, *Zeits. österr. Ges. Meteorol.*, Vol. 6 (1871), p. 104.
[55] Osnaghi, *Zeits. öterr. Ges. Meteorol.*, Vol. 8 (1873), pp. 119–21.
[56] Hottinger & Cie, *Zeits. österr. Ges. Meteorol.*, Vol. 16 (1881), pp. 281–83.
[57] *Ibid.*, Vol. 17 (1882), pp. 471–72.

Fig. 9.10 *Hottinger's combination thermograph and hygrograph.*

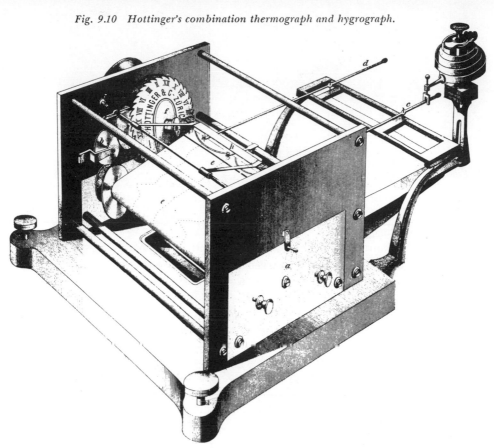

Corrosion and troubles with lubrication have always hounded the designers of instruments for outdoor use. In 1884 Hasler of Berne reported on such difficulties with a thermograph that he had designed for use at an unattended station on the Faulhorn, in which the clock was to be kept wound by a cup anemometer.[58] It was not successful.

One gets the impression when looking at instruments of this period that the designing of them sometimes became a pure intellectual exercise, practicality taking second place. An example is the extremely clever bimetallic thermograph in the CNAM at Paris,[59] made by the firm of Redier about 1885. The mechanical servosystem with two clockwork motors is similar to that used in their second barograph,[60] and while this beautiful machine may have been all right for a barograph, it could not have been durable when installed out of doors.

Thermographs were also being made that used the differential expansion of metal in other ingenious ways. The most ingenious

[58] Hasler, *Zeits. österr. Ges. Meteorol.,* Vol. 19 (1884), p. 312.
[59] Inv. no. 9048.
[60] Middleton, *The History of the Barometer,* p. 325.

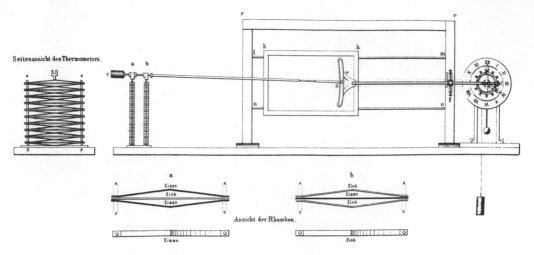

Fig. 9.11 Pfeiffer's thermograph, 1867.

was that of F. Pfeiffer,[61] in which the active element consists
of two piles of iron and zinc bars, bent in such a way that the
top of one pile rises while the top of the other falls, and vice
versa (Fig. 9.11). The recording was intermittent on a flat chart,
obviously reminiscent of Kreil.[62] This thermograph was praised
by the important meteorologist and astronomer Karl Jelinek of
Prague,[63] but Franz Karlinski of Cracow complained[64] of the
friction between the active strips and the posts that supported
them, causing Pfeiffer to abandon his ingenious metallic sand-
wiches and to adopt the more conventional solution of three
concentric perforated zinc tubes, the outermost rising solidly
from a base, the second and third supported by iron strips hanging from the tops of the first and second, respectively.[65]

Essentially the same conventional solution was adopted by
numerous other designers,[66] and there is no need to describe
their thermographs in detail. What was not generally recognized
was the necessity of having both the members, on the differential
expansion of which the instrument depended, equally rapidly
affected by changes in the temperature of the air. For example,
in the thermograph of Russell[67] these were a zinc tube and a
piece of plate glass. Russell claimed that his instrument would

[61] E. Mayer and J. Rund, *Zeits. österr. Ges. Meteorol.*, Vol. 2 (1867), pp.
567–71.
[62] See p. 190 above.
[63] Jelinek, *Zeits. österr. Ges. Meteorol.*, Vol. 1 (1866), pp. 382–84.
[64] Karlinski, *Zeits. österr. Ges. Meteorol.*, Vol. 3 (1868), p. 269.
[65] [Pfeiffer], *Zeits. österr. Ges. Meteorol.*, Vol. 3 (1868), pp. 409–12.
[66] Mansfield Harrison, *B.A.A.S. Report, Swansea, 1848*, Part 2, pp. 14–16;
F. W. C. Krecke, see E. H. von Baumhauer, *Ann. der Phys.*, Vol 154 (1875),
pp. 61–62; James Lewis, *Proc. A.A.A.S.* (1860), pp. 21–33; H. C. Russell,
J. Roy. Soc. New South Wales, Vol. 22 (1889), pp. 335–38; Johann von
Lamont, *Repert. für phys. Techn.*, Vol. 6 (1870), pp. 1–4.
[67] *Op. cit.*, note 66 above.

respond more quickly than an ordinary mercury thermometer and did not see that the glass plate would alter its temperature, and its length, very slowly.

In the 1880's the entire situation, as far as thermographs for meteorological stations are concerned, was changed by the activities of the Paris firm of Richard Frères.[68] Breaking away entirely from the large and costly instruments then in vogue, they manufactured barographs, thermographs, hygrographs, and other instruments that were light, self-contained, and relatively inexpensive. The essential feature of these instruments, designed about 1880, was the standardized clock, protected from the weather to a great extent by being inside the drum that was turned by it. Colonel Sébert, whose report of November, 1882, was so proudly reprinted by the makers, was especially impressed by these clocks, and also by the bold use of curved hour-lines on the charts, by the pens in the shape of a small triangular pyramid—split at the end like an ordinary pen nib—and by the aniline ink containing glycerine to prevent evaporation. Indeed, all these features have persisted with little change until the present day.

For their thermograph they decided on a Bourdon tube in an arc 100 mm. long. It was 18 mm. wide and held 2 cc. of alcohol. At first this was inside the glazed metal box that gave protection to the drum, but about 1885 they made a thermograph with the sensitive element outside the box (Fig. 9.12)[69]

They also designed thermographs of two other types.[70] One used a pile of metal capsules in a cylinder, the space between them being filled with liquid, but nothing further seems to have been heard of this. The other permitted the recording mechanism to be indoors and consisted of a bulb connected by a capillary tube to a Bourdon tube, the whole system being completely filled with alcohol. The readings of this instrument were made independent of the temperature of the Bourdon tube by providing a second tube (C in Fig. 9.13) giving half the deflection of the tube A that was connected to the bulb and arranging them in the ingenious way shown in the figure. Suppose that the temperature of the recording part of the instrument changes, that of the distant bulb remaining the same. Make $ab=bc$. Then

[68] *Notice sur les instruments construits par Richard Frères, comprenant le rapport de M. le Colonel Sébert à la Société d'Encouragement pour l'Industrie Nationale, et l'exposé des perfectionnements et applications nouvelles* (Paris, 1889). I am obliged to Mr. A. L. Maidens for drawing my attention to this document.

[69] *Ibid.*, p. 117.

[70] *Ibid.*, pp. 116–20.

Fig. 9.12   Richard thermograph with Bourdon tube.

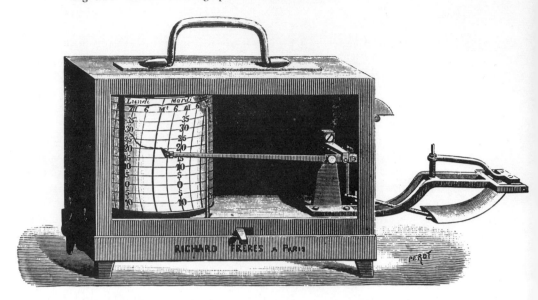

since the deflection oo' $[=bb']=\frac{1}{2}aa'$, $aa'c$ and $bb'c$ are similar triangles, so that the point c does not move; nor does the pen. The idea was patented.[71]

This was not, however, the first distantly recording liquid-in-metal thermometer. The earliest that has come to my attention was installed by H. Marie-Davy at the Observatory in Paris as one of a set of recording instruments.[72] In this, a U-shaped copper tube 8 mm. in diameter by 3 m. long was connected by

Fig. 9.13   Thermograph with remote bulb; principle of correction for the temperature of the recording part.

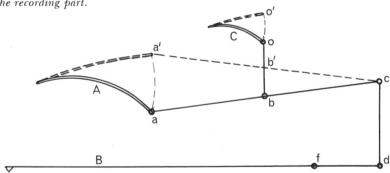

a capillary tube to a metal chamber like that of an aneroid barometer, but of the smallest possible internal volume. The whole was completely filled with absolute alcohol. The motion

[71] French Patent 156210, June 23, 1883.
[72] See *Zeits. österr. Ges. Meteorol.*, Vol. 11 (1876), pp. 294–95.

202

of the upper surface of the capsule was magnified by levers, and the recording was made on smoked paper carried by a drum.

Another liquid-in-metal thermograph for recording at a distance, and a very successful one, was developed in 1920 by Negretti & Zambra. The bulb, capillary, and Bourdon tube were made of steel and filled with mercury. For this instrument a special Bourdon tube was designed and patented.[73] It was a flat tube with a very small internal volume, wound into two coaxial spirals side by side, the inside of one being fixed, the outer ends of the two joined, and the pen-arm attached to the inside of the other. The temperature of the capillary was rendered of no consequence by enclosing within it a wire of Invar, a nickel steel with a very low coefficient of expansion, so proportioned that the expansion of the mercury in the annular space between the wire and the tube was exactly compensated by that of the tube itself.

For the ordinary station thermograph, most makers other than Richard Frères came to prefer the bimetal, usually wound into a helix. The ancestor of these instruments dates from as long ago as 1837, when a bimetallic thermograph, now in the possession of the Science Museum, London,[74] was built by N. S. Heineken, as is indicated by an inscription on a brass plate. It is of relatively crude construction, and consists, as shown in Fig. 9.14, of a thick bimetal in a roughly spiral curve, moving a pencil by way of a sector, two gear wheels, and a rack. A small drum is revolved by a decorative watch movement concealed in the base of the instrument.

I have not been able to trace the development of this instrument into the mechanically simple and durable modern form, one example of which is shown in Fig. 9.15. Its helical bimetal of several turns, fixed at one end and attached at the other to the axis of the pen arm, appeared in several variations before 1920.

6. *Recorders for the Electrical Thermometers.* While recording electrical thermometers are extremely common in industry, they are not very much used in meteorological practice, except at some airport stations where standard industrial instruments are frequently applied. I shall therefore confine myself to a reference to two

[73] British Patent 171217, November 17, 1921.
[74] Inventory no. 1915–419. It is referred to, but not described, in *Quart. J. Roy. Meteorol. Soc.*, Vol. 10 (1884), p. 198.

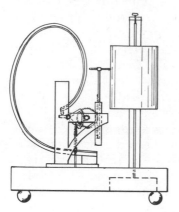

Fig. 9.14 *Heineken's thermograph, 1837.*

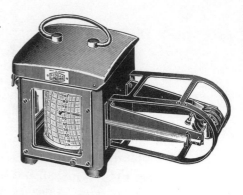

Fig. 9.15 *Bimetallic thermograph.*
(Courtesy of C. F. Casella & Co., Ltd.)

recorders that appeared almost simultaneously at the end of the nineteenth century—the "Callendar recorder"[75] and the "Cambridge thread recorder."[76] These two instruments used different mechanical means to achieve similar results. The first was essentially a self-balancing slide-wire that could be introduced into any Wheatstone bridge or potentiometer circuit, so that it could be used with either resistance thermometers or thermocouples. In the Callendar recorder (Fig. 9.16) the output of the bridge, or potentiometer, is connected to the moving-coil galvanometer near the top of the instrument. Instead of a pointer this has two contacts forming a fork which embraces a disk turned by a clock. This prevents sticking. The contacts are connected to electromagnets that release either of two clockwork motors to move a contact along a' slide-wire and restore the electrical balance, centering the galvanometer contacts. The recording pen is attached to the contact that moves along the slide-wire.

The "thread recorder" was so called because the actual record is made by forcing a pointer down onto an inked thread stretched just above the chart paper. Since 1940 both these instruments have been entirely superseded by self-balancing potentiometers using electronic circuits.

[75] *Engineering*, Vol. 67 (1899), pp. 675–76.
[76] H. Darwin, E. H. Griffiths, and W. C. D. Whetham, British Patent 16,926 of 1899, August 21.

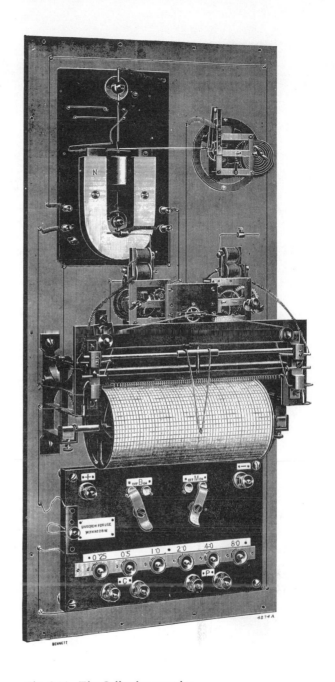

Fig. 9.16 *The Callendar recorder.*

X

The Exposure of Thermometers

1. General Considerations. Partly because of the properties of the atmosphere, and partly on account of the laws of the transmission of heat, the use of the thermometer in meteorology presents problems that do not arise in such disciplines as chemistry and medicine. When a chemist places a thermometer in a liquid and leaves it for an adequate length of time, the temperature of the liquid, or at least that part of the liquid near the bulb of the thermometer, can be derived from the reading of the instrument by applying small corrections that can be specified as exactly as desirable. If the same thermometer is left in the air, no similar conclusions can be drawn, for various reasons which I shall now enumerate.

Heat is exchanged between the thermometer and the liquid until an equilibrium is reached. This exchange proceeds by conduction, convection, and radiation. The same processes operate when the thermometer is in the air; but not only is their relative contribution entirely different, but the factors governing the exchange of heat by radiation are completely dissimilar. In a liquid, convection, natural or forced (stirring), is usually by far the most important of the three processes; conduction the second in importance, and radiation usually negligible, the more so because most liquids are highly opaque to the invisible infrared radiation of bodies at ordinary temperatures. In air, conduction is negligible, leaving convection and radiation to share the task of bringing about equilibrium; but now another very important property of the air complicates matters. Air is remarkably transparent to temperature-radiation, so that the radiative exchange is scarcely at all between the thermometer and the air around it, but rather between the instrument and whatever solid or liquid bodies can be seen from the position of the thermometer—of course including any source of heat, such as the sun, or heat-sink, such as the sky. Thus if all the exchange were by radiation, the final temperature of the thermometer would be equal to some sort of mean between the temperatures of all the surroundings. The matter is actually further complicated in the daytime by the reflection of the solar radiation to the thermometer from terrestrial objects.

But what is presumably required is "the temperature of the air." There are two ways in which, in theory, the temperature of the thermometer can be made equal to the temperature of the air: (1) by ensuring that every surface that can be seen from the thermometer is at that temperature; (2) by increasing the exchange of heat by convection to such a degree that radiation becomes negligible. It ought perhaps to be noted that each of these devices must be applied without changing the temperature of the air surrounding the thermometer.

In practice some combination of the two methods, or rather of attempts to approach the two conditions, is usually employed. The various devices that have been proposed are not easy to classify, but I shall divide them into those that make use of artificial ventilation, and those that do not.

Although this book is not the place to deal with the matter, a further difficulty in meteorological thermometry, and indeed in other measurements in meteorology, must be referred to. It has been found that the atmosphere, especially near the ground, is astonishingly variable both in space and in time.[1] Instrumentally, this raises the question of the necessary or desirable precision of meteorological instruments.

2. *Early Ideas on the Exposure of Thermometers.* The first users of thermometers did not need to use them to know that it is warmer in the sun than in the shade, but they were interested in knowing how much. We have seen that in December, 1654, Antonio Terillo fastened one instrument outside a south window, one outside a north window;[2] and Antinori notes[3] that this was the practice at all the stations of the world's first meteorological network, established by order of the Grand Duke Ferdinand. But by 1657 "thermometers out of doors and indoors had been substituted

[1] See for example W. E. K. Middleton and F. G. Millar, *J. Roy. Astron. Soc. Canada,* Vol. 30 (1936), pp. 265–72.

[2] See p. 30 above.

[3] In his introduction to the 1841 edition of the *Saggi di naturali esperienze,* p. 44.

for the northern and southern thermometers."[4] In a manuscript dating from about this time we are told that the "50-degree" thermometer,[5] "exposed in the free air without protection, and without any close reflection of the rays of the midsummer sun, here in Florence, went up to about 43 degrees at the most, and in the shade, in the same season, to 34 . . ."[6] which is the first indication I have found that the reflection from nearby objects was a matter of concern.

The distinction between indoors and outdoors was less noticeable than it would be today, but when Des Noyers sent a Florentine thermometer to Ismael Boulliau[7] he thought it necessary to warn him that "the thermometer is hung up by a small ribbon, not in the room, where the air is more temperate, but outside a window, so that it may be in the open air."[8] This seems to have been done fairly generally except by the English, whose idea of comfort has always, or until recently, been idiosyncratic, so that in 1666 we find John Wallis putting his thermometer "in a room that has a window only to the north." We cannot share his surprise that it sometimes read lower when there was no frost than at other times "when the frost hath been considerably hard."[9] Even in 1723 James Jurin, in his appeal for meteorological observations, advised that the thermometer be put "in a room facing north, where a fire is never or only very rarely kindled."[10]

Professor Johann Friedrich Weidler of Wittenberg disagreed heartily with this. Weidler has the distinction of having gone to some trouble to provide what he believed to be a suitable exposure for a group of instruments.[11] He put his barometer, two thermometers, and a hygrometer in the center of a space twenty feet square, more than thirty feet to the north of his house. The square plot was surrounded by a wooden fence, and there was a roof over his instruments to keep off the sun and rain. He found that a thermometer exposed in this way can sometimes give temperatures as much as twenty-five degrees[12] lower than one

[4] *Ibid.*
[5] See p. 30 above.
[6] Florence, Bibl. Naz., ms. Gal. 269, fol. 230r.
[7] See p. 38 above.
[8] BN, fonds fr. 13020, fol. 9r–9v.
[9] Wallis, *Phil. Trans.*, Vol. 1 (1666), p. 169.
[10] Jurin, *Phil. Trans.*, Vol. 32 (1723), p. 425.
[11] J. F. Weidler, *Observationes meteorologicae atque astronomicae ann. MDCCXXIIX. et MDCCXXIX. illustratae dissertationibus binis de observatorio meteorologico et de hiemis a. MDCCXXIX. asperitate* (Wittenburg, 1729).
[12] His "English thermometers" probably had Hauksbee's scale, so that this might be about 12°C.

"near an open window in a north room that was never heated."[13]

The following year Réaumur ended his first long paper on the thermometer[14] with some remarks on exposure. It is essential, he wrote, that the thermometer be exposed out of doors, to the north of a building, in a position where the sun cannot shine upon it at any time of day; and reflected heat from nearby walls must be avoided.

Before long even the English were putting the thermometer out of doors, but usually where it could be read from inside a room. In 1744 Roger Pickering described his meteorological instruments,[15] putting a special emphasis on one point.

> Note, all the machines, except the barometer, are exposed to the open air. The thermometer and hygrometer are placed in a little shed, made for their reception, against my study-window, where I can see the graduation thro' the glass; and by lifting up the sash, can take them in, as occasion requires.[16]

Three years later the Reverend Henry Miles of Tooting wrote a paper with the express intention of showing the inadequacy of an indoors exposure.[17] On December 1, 1747, a very considerable cold front (as we now say) passed Tooting, the thermometer outside his window falling from 19 degrees (presumably Fahrenheit) above the freezing point at 8 A.M. to freezing point at 9 P.M. During the same period a similar thermometer in his unheated bedroom fell from 14 to 12 degrees above freezing point, although the two thermometers were only three feet apart. A convincing demonstration, one would think; and indeed, not much more was heard about indoor exposures in serious meteorological circles after this date. In the year of his death, the influential Pieter van Musschenbroek described an exposure for his thermometer that was very similar to Weidler's.[18] In future the argument was to be between those who believed in an exposure at some distance from any building and those who favored hanging the thermometer near the north wall of a house. The latter alternative had the powerful support of Henry Cavendish[19] and the pervasive example of the Mannheim Meteorological Society,

[13] Weidler, *Observationes,* p. 6.

[14] Réaumur, *Mém. Acad. Sci. Paris* (1730), pp. 452–507.

[15] Pickering, *Phil. Trans.,* Vol. 43 (1744), no. 473, pp. 1-17 (no. 473 is erroneously numbered from page 1).

[16] *Ibid.,* p. 5.

[17] Miles, "Concerning the difference of the degrees of cold marked by a thermometer kept within doors, or without in the open air." *Phil. Trans.,* Vol. 44 (1747), pp. 613–16.

[18] Musschenbroek, *Novi Comment, Acad. Imp. Sci. Petrop.,* Vol. 8 (1760–61), p. 377.

[19] Cavendish, *Phil. Trans.,* Vol. 66 (1776), p. 375.

or Societas meteorologica Palatina, founded by the Elector Karl Theodor in 1780, which sent instruments to many stations in us parts of Europe and even to some in North America, including Cambridge, Massachusetts.[20] The moving spirit of this remarkable effort was J. J. Hemmer, the Elector's chaplain, and he described the instruments and their use in an appendix to the first volume of the published observations.[21]

Both Cavendish and Hemmer emphasize that the thermometer should be a few inches from the north wall, and Hemmer described the wooden brackets that hold it so. The sun must be prevented from shining on it at any time. They are both concerned with sunlight reflected from buildings opposite, and Hemmer gives useful warnings against breathing on the thermometer while reading it, or holding a candle too close at night.

At about this time there was a lively controversy about the exposure of thermometers, set in motion by a passage in the *Recherches sur les modifications de l'atmosphère* of Jean André Deluc.[22] That remarkable man, on the basis of some mountain observations, probably in a strong wind, maintained that a mercury thermometer with a small *isolated* bulb gives the true temperature of the air whether it is in the sun or in the shade; but there must be no material other than glass near the bulb. Horace Benedict de Saussure, who was much less given to speculation than Deluc, decided to test this idea on the Col du Géant in July, 1788,[23] of course finding that it was not true. He used thermometers with bulbs only 2¼ lines (about 5 mm.) in diameter, hanging one in the sun at a distance of 4 inches from a thin cylindrical stake, and the other at the same distance but in the shade of the stake. The difference between them was as much as 4°R. near sunrise and sunset, decreasing to nearly zero about noon. De Saussure adduced two reasons for this: in the first

[20] For the Mannheim Society, the only account I know of is Friedrich Traumüller, *Die Mannheimer meteorologische Gesellschaft (1780–1795). Ein Beitrag zur Geschichte der Meteorologie* (Leipzig, 1885). This is unfortunately rare; I have seen only the copy at Offenbach-am-Main.

[21] *Ephemerides societatis meteorologicae Palatinae. Historia et observationes anni 1781. Accedit descriptio instrumentorum meteorologicorum, tam eorum, quae Societas per Europam distribuit, quam quibus praeter haec Manheimii utitur* (Mannheim, 1783). The appendix was separately printed in 1782 as *Descriptio instrumentorum societatis meteorologicae Palatinae* [etc.], paged from p. 1. A German translation of Hemmer's instructions to the observers is readily available in K. Schneider-Carius, *Wetterkunde, Wetterforschung* (Freiburg and Munich, 1955), pp. 127–29.

[22] (Geneva, 1772), ¶ 536.

[23] De Saussure, *J. de Phys.*, Vol. 33 (1788), pp. 401–12. See also *Voyages dans les Alpes* [etc.] (4 vols., 4°, and also 8 vols., 8°, Neuchâtel, 1779–96), ¶¶ 2052–53.

place there was more wind in the middle of the day, and in the second place, when the sun was high in the heavens, the small bulb of the thermometer was largely shaded by the tube.

Deluc was not at all nonplussed. He noticed that in De Saussure's observations, the temperature in the sun remained nearly the same all day; it was the temperature in the shade that varied. He explained this by a strange theory that the sunlight, as soon as it reaches the air on the mountain, "begins to act on the fire distributed in the air, . . . increases its expansive force, and thus gives it a greater power of penetrating bodies."[24] It is probable that Deluc was especially concerned to uphold his peculiar technique because his measurements of heights with the barometer disagreed with those of several of his contemporaries,[25] and it was suspected[26] that his insistence in measuring temperatures in the sun may have been the cause of this disagreement.

The shading of a thermometer with a narrow lath was investigated again quite independently by James Six, who hung two mercury thermometers in an open pasture, about seven feet from the ground, on a hot summer day, and found that when he shaded one of them with a narrow lath it fell about 4°F. He was aware that a mercury thermometer was not as much affected by the sun's radiation as some other bodies, because "of its spherical figure and polished surface."[27] The relations between radiation and the surfaces of solids were beginning to be grasped intuitively before they were codified in the early years of the nineteenth century.

The idea that a thermometer made entirely of glass and mercury is a complete reflector, not affected by the rays of the sun, cropped up again twenty years later.[28] But Jean Baptiste Joseph Fourier, the great theorist of heat, knew better, and in 1817 gave a detailed exposition[29] of the effect of radiating surroundings on a thermometer, showing how it could be either warmed or

[24] Deluc, *J. de Phys.*, Vol. 37 (1790), p. 68. Deluc made wild speculations about heat, light, and electricity in the atmosphere, as well as about chemical processes that were supposed to go on in the air. I have dealt with these in *A History of the Theories of Rain* [etc.] (London, 1965), Chap. 6. See also W. E. K. Middleton, *Annals of Science,* Vol. 20 (1964), pp. 125–41.

[25] Such as De Saussure, William Roy, and George Shuckburgh.

[26] E.g., by De Saussure, *Voyages dans les Alpes* ¶ 2052.

[27] James Six, *The Construction and Use of a Thermometer for Shewing the Extremes of Temperature in the Atmosphere, during the Observer's Absence. Together with Experiments on the Variations of Local Heat; and Other Meteorological Observations* (Maidstone, 1794 [posthumous]), p. 52.

[28] Placidus Heinrich, *Schweigger's Journal,* Vol. 2 (1811), pp. 509–27. He was insistent that there should be no brass or wood near the bulb.

[29] Fourier, *Ann. de Chim.*, Vol. 6 (1817), pp. 259–303.

cooled, depending on the temperature of its environment. Near the end of his paper he came to the question of how to measure the true temperature of the air under any conditions; and his solution was to have two similar thermometers, the bulb of one blackened, that of the other covered with polished metal. Then "in general, the temperature of the air is equal to that of the metallized thermometer, plus the difference of the temperatures of the two thermometers divided by a constant number."[30] If the blackened thermometer is lower, this difference will be taken as positive, and vice versa. Several decades later it was realized that things are not quite as simple as this, because of the variation of reflectance with wavelength, and for some other reasons that will appear below.

3. Shelters, Stands, and Screens. Shortly after the time of Fourier's paper, though certainly not because of it, more thought began to be given to the protection of thermometers from radiation. This led to the design of a large number of different protective structures variously known as thermometer shelters and thermometer screens. There is a question of nomenclature here which deserves a remark. In England and the countries of the British Commonwealth the word *screen* seemed usually to be reserved for structures intended to give the thermometer protection from radiation in all directions, except perhaps from directly below;[31] those giving protection mainly from rain and direct solar radiation were called *shelters* or *stands*. In the United States the former class are also called shelters, as in France (*abri*). In Germany the general word is *Hütte;* this corresponds to the Italian *capanna,* meaning a shed or hut. I shall adopt the English usage, as it makes distinctions that seem necessary.

Somewhat similar to those of Weidler and Musschenbroek, the first stand of which I have found a fairly complete description was that designed and erected by Dr. George A. Martin at Ventnor on the Isle of Wight, about 1838,[32] and used for ten years after that date. Martin gives no illustration, and our Fig. 10.1 is a reconstruction by Frederick Gaster, who reproduced it, with slight variations, for comparative tests in 1869.[33] It had a

[30] *Ibid.,* p. 301.

[31] But sometimes these were called stands in the nineteenth century.

[32] Martin, *The "Undercliff" of the Isle of Wight: Its Climate, History and Natural Productions* (London, 1849), pp. vii–viii.

[33] Gaster, *Great Britain, M.O., Quarterly Weather Report for 1879,* Appendix II.

213

Fig. 10.1   Martin's stand, 1837.

A A A.   **Rafters.**   P. **Chimney.**   C C. **Thatch.**   D D. **Thermometer Board.**   E E E. **Posts.**

stout timber frame supported on posts and roofed with thatch, with a small chimney to prevent the accumulation of heated air under the roof. It will be noticed that the bulbs of the thermometers are level with the lowest part of the roof, so that radiation from the ground has free access to them. Large shelters of this general type became almost ubiquitous in tropical countries, though probably designed quite independently of Martin.

There were other ways of sheltering the thermometers from rain and sunshine. One of the best known is generally ascribed to James Glaisher[34] and called the Glaisher stand (Fig. 10.2), but it ought to be called the Greenwich stand, for it was brought into use at the Royal Observatory on March 23, 1841, and is said[35]

34 [G. J. Symons], *Meteorol. Mag.,* Vol. 3 (1868), pp. 155–57. There is a ⅓ scale model in the Science Museum, London, Inv. no. 1926–153.

35 By William Ellis, in the discussion of a paper by H. S. Eaton, *Quart. J. Meteorol. Soc.,* Vol. 14 (1888), p. 38.

214

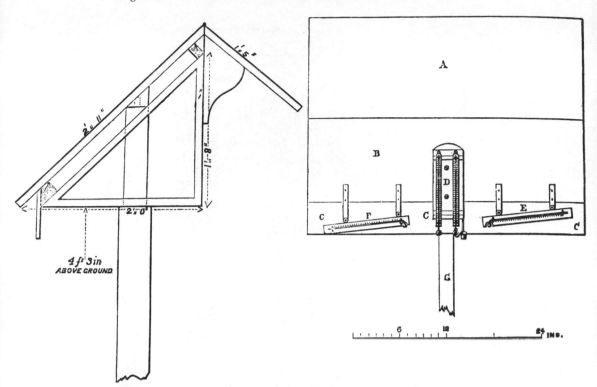

Fig. 10.2   The Greenwich stand, called Glaisher's (side view, front view).

to have been designed by Sir George Airy, the Astronomer Royal. To call it the Airy stand is descriptive if considered as a pun, for its distinguishing characteristic is that it exposes the thermometers very freely to the air. The figure is description enough, if it is explained that the stand can revolve around its post, and is supposed to be reoriented during the day to keep the thermometers in the shade, a requirement that would seem to render it unsuitable for small stations where only the extremes of temperature are observed. A variant, not very different, was described in 1851 by Sir Henry James of the Royal Engineers.[36]

Glaisher thought highly of the Greenwich stand, and as one result of an enormous series of observations of thermometers placed in the shade, and also laid on surfaces of a large number of different materials,[37] felt able to derive formulas for calculating "the true temperature of the air" from the reading of a thermometer on the stand or even completely exposed to the sky.[38] He made

36 James, *Instructions for Taking Meteorological Observations* [etc.] (London, 1851), p. 8.
37 Glaisher, *Phil. Trans.*, Vol. 137 (1847), pp. 119–216.
38 *Ibid.*, p. 152.

215

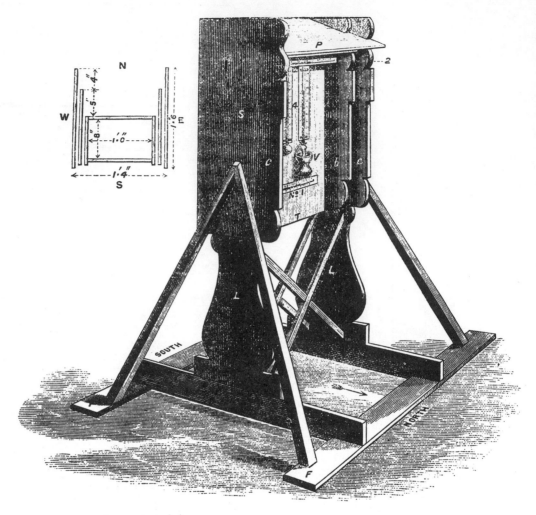

Fig. 10.3 Lawson's stand.

extravagant claims:

> If attention be paid to the placing of thermometers, so that their bulbs be in the shade, protected from rain and from the effects of radiation from walls (by placing their bulbs at least six inches from them), but in other respects freely exposed to the air, and correcting their readings by the preceding formulae, it will ensure the obtaining the true temperature of the air from them at night. To avoid the effects of reflected heat during the day, the thermometers should be placed at a greater distance than six inches from walls, &c., and their readings corrected as before by the preceding formulae. No simple rules have heretofore been given for placing a thermometer so that from its readings the true temperature of the air could be deduced.[39]

[39] *Ibid.*, p. 153.

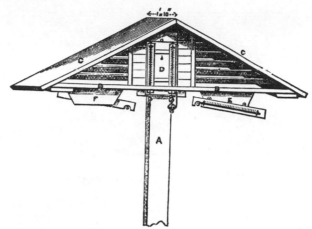

Fig. 10.4   Stow's stand.

The idea that thermometers are affected by radiation from terrestrial objects only if they are close to them is a strange one that keeps cropping up throughout the nineteenth century. A reference to Fourier would have shown its falsity. It is doubly strange that Glaisher should have been confused in this way, because the formulas to which he refers contain the number of tenths of clear sky and the number of tenths of sky from which the bulb of the thermometer is protected. We may speculate that the idea arose because a thermometer very near a radiating or reflecting surface is likely to be in an ascending or descending current of air warmed or cooled by contact with the surface.

Several other stands were designed which gave exposures similar to the Greenwich stand. Lawson's[40] is shown in Fig. 10.3, the diagram at the left being a horizontal section indicating the double walls. Lawson's stand is fixed in position, and so is the one designed by the Rev. F. W. Stow in 1867[41] (Fig. 10.4). This had a short innings, for Stow's own experiments at Harpenden soon led him to favor the louvered screen.[42]

On the other hand the French continued to prefer the open *abri*. It seems not to have been standardized until about 1873, when H. Marie-Davy left the Observatoire de Paris to become Director of the new meteorological observatory in the Montsouris

[40] Henry Lawson, *Observations on the Placing of Thermometers, with the Plan of a Stand, by which Many of the Errors Arising from Want of Uniformity Will Be Avoided* (London, n.d. [1846]), broadsheet. See also *Meteorol. Mag.*, Vol. 3 (1868), pp. 137–38; and *Quarterly Weather Report for 1879*, p. 16, from which Fig. 10.3 is taken. The Science Museum has a model (no. 1925–975).

[41] [G. J. Symons], *Meteorol. Mag.*, Vol. 4 (1869), pp. 3–5; *Quarterly Weather Report for 1879*, p. 17. Again the Science Museum has a model, scale ⅓ (no. 1926–152).

[42] Stow, *Quart. J. Meteorol. Soc.*, Vol. 2 (1873), pp. 49–52.

Fig. 10.5 The Montsouris stand.

Park. At the old observatory the thermometers had for a long time been "placed side by side on one of the lateral faces of a sort of revolving lantern destined to shelter them from rain and shade them from the rays of the rising sun."[43] All this was 7 m.

[43] [Marie-Davy], *Annuaire de l'Observatoire municipal de Montsouris*, 1873, p. 80.

above ground, on a swinging bracket so that it could be moved in front of a window for observation, but normally it was pushed out to about 2 m. from the north wall. When he was at the Observatoire de Paris, Marie-Davy had started comparative observations in a shelter on the lawn, in which four posts 3 m. high at the corners of a one-meter square supported a wooden roof 1.24 m. × 1.24 m., sloping down a little toward the south. A green-painted cloth covered the roof and hung down 25 cm. on the east and west sides. Parallel to the roof, and 10 cm. below it, another cloth was stretched and the thermometers were exposed just below this.

The shelter at the Montsouris Observatory (Fig. 10.5) was a development of this, made of iron, including, apparently, the steps,[44] and having "wings" to the east and west to shade the thermometers from the morning and evening sun, though it was also thought essential to plant evergreen shrubs around the east, south, and west sides. If it is quite in the open, Renou says, the temperatures will be "a little too high" in hot, calm weather. This shelter was designed by Charles Saint-Claire Deville, the Director of the new Montsouris Observatory from 1871 to 1873, when he became Inspector-General of Meteorological Stations and gave it a wide distribution. In 1875 Marie-Davy was making comparisons between this shelter, the Kew screen, and the sling thermometer.[45]

We now come to the use of screens, more or less closed, in which the necessary circulation of air is allowed for by constructing the walls of louvers. The idea behind this is centuries old, being embodied in the Venetian blind, of which the oriental origin is suggested by the French equivalent *persienne* and the German *Jalousie*.[46] I should not like to be dogmatic about the first use of a louvered enclosure for thermometers; but the earliest printed account that I have seen dates from 1835,[47] and it is illustrated by our Fig. 10.6. This seems to me as if it might have been designed by some mariner who had made voyages to the East, especially as it was set up at Plymouth Dockyard. It is not a complete surround, but is open to the north to some extent.

The next that has come to my notice is by way of improving

44 *Ibid.*, p. 84. But E. Renou, *Annuaire Soc. météorol. France*, Vol. 22 (1874), pp. 139–40, says the roofs were of zinc.

45 See below, p. 225. In the twentieth century the French turned increasingly to closed screens. See E. Delcambre, *La Météorologie* (1926), pp. 73–76, for a description of an excellent large screen derived from English models.

46 The louvered thermometer screen is called a *Jalousie-Hütte* in German.

47 W. Snow-Harris, *B.A.A.S. Report, Dublin, 1835*, p. 182.

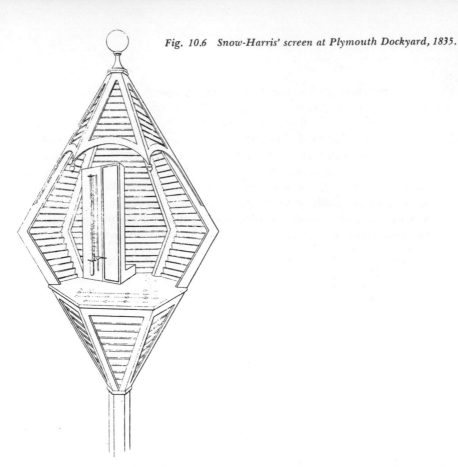

Fig. 10.6   Snow-Harris' screen at Plymouth Dockyard, 1835.

a north-wall exposure, and I should not be entirely surprised if this procedure had become fairly common by about 1840. First a fragment of Canadian meteorological history: the Toronto Magnetic and Meteorological Observatory was established by the British government in 1839, the first Director being Lieut. Riddel of the Royal Artillery.[48] In 1841 Lieut. Younghusband succeeded him, and in the autumn of 1844 Lieut. John Henry Lefroy, who became a General and has nearly five pages in the *Dictionary of National Biography*, took over. From the beginning, the thermometers had been "exposed on the north wall of the Observatory, in a shed formed of Venetian slats which extended [down?] to a distance from the ground of three to four feet."[49] This was apparently not good enough for Lieut. Lefroy, for we read on:

> From January, 1945, to December, 1852, the shed had a second roof, and a second enclosure of Venetian slats eighteen inches exterior to the first.
>
> In no case was any screen interposed between the thermometers

[48] *Abstracts and Results of Magnetical & Meteorological Observations, at the Magnetic Observatory, Toronto, Canada, from 1841 to 1871 inclusive* (Toronto, 1875). [Part I] "Magnetical observations," p. ix.
[49] *Ibid*. [Part II], "Meteorological observations," p. 1.

220

and the ground, or between the thermometers and the wall of the Observatory; this mode of exposure, though to some extent faulty, being retained to avoid a breach of continuity in the series.[50]

We are also informed that the bulbs of the thermometers were 4½ feet above the ground.

Now a double screen of this kind, but larger and free-standing, became known as the Kew screen (or stand). There seems to have been some doubt about its origin, and in 1873, Robert H. Scott offered the Meteorological Society in London the following fantastic account:

> I do not know whether any of you are aware of the origin of the Kew Stand; I have heard that it was simply, that Gen. Lefroy copied a meat safe, when he wanted a stand for use at Toronto, and used it for a Thermometer Stand, and hence we have the origin of the "Kew" Stand.[51]

If this were so, it took a long time for the meteorological meat safe to get from Toronto to the famous Observatory at Kew, for until 1849 the thermometers were merely placed "at the north window of the quadrant room."[52] In October of that year they were removed to "a revolving stand, on the Greenwich plan," newly erected on the balustrade near the north door of the Observatory.[53] Only in 1853 was a louvered screen erected, just outside the balustrade. Observations were begun with it on January 1, 1854.[54]

The Kew stand—it was so called in the 1870's—is shown in Fig. 10.7.[55] It is a large double structure, two louvered boxes, one inside the other, each with louvered doors; but the bottom is quite open. The outer box is 6 × 6 × 5 feet in size, and there is an 18-inch space between the boxes.

Returning to Toronto for a moment, I detect the hand of Professor G. T. Kingston in the strictures on Lefroy's screen. Indeed, in a very cold climate radiation from the wall of a heated building cannot be neglected. Kingston's solution was to put the thermometers in a louvered screen, 24 × 18 × 8 inches in size, made of sheet iron, enclose this in a wooden louvered "shed," 37 × 30 × 18 inches in size, having a double wooden roof, and then mount the whole thing on the north side of a "fence,"

---

[50] *Ibid.*

[51] *Quart. J. Meteorol. Soc.*, Vol. 2 (1873), p. 41.

[52] Ronalds, *B.A.A.S. Report, Edinburgh, 1850*, p. 178.

[53] *Ibid.*, p. 181.

[54] Kew Committee (J. P. Gassiot, Chairman), *B.A.A.S. Report, Liverpool, 1854*, pp. xxxiii–xxxiv.

[55] The figure is from *Quarterly Weather Report for 1879*, Appendix II, p. [21].

Fig. 10.7   The Kew screen.

actually a double wooden wall 6 feet long and 7 feet high, with a 4-inch space between the boards. This was to be well away from all other structures.[56] He must have sacrificed a good deal of ventilation.

The name of Stevenson is associated in the minds of many people with the louvered screen, which is called the Stevenson screen in most countries of the British Commonwealth. Thomas Stevenson, one of the famous family of lighthouse engineers,[57] and the father of Robert Louis Stevenson, did not invent the louvered screen—indeed he was rather late in this field—but he seems to have been the first to adopt double louvers, sloping in opposite directions,[58] as shown in the small diagram in Fig. 10.8. This screen had a pyramidal roof with a ventilator, probably of little use; it was rather small, and a larger pattern with a double

[56] Kingston, *Meteorological Service, Dominion of Canada. Instructions to Observers at Ordinary Stations of the Second Class* (Toronto, 1878), pp. 11–12.

[57] Not to be confused with the Stephensons, the railway engineers.

[58] *J. Scottish Meteorol. Soc.*, Vol. 1 (1864), p. 122. The illustration in this paper is not very informative, and I have reproduced one from the *Quarterly Weather Report for 1879*, Appendix II, p. [19].

222

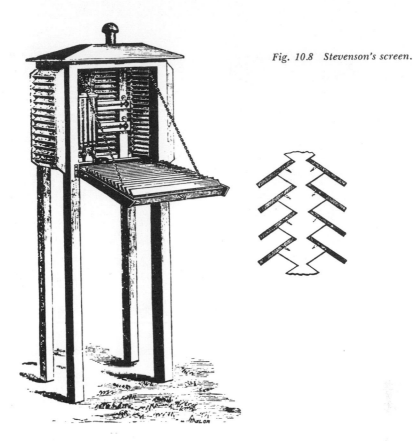

Fig. 10.8   Stevenson's screen.

roof was later recommended by the Royal Meteorological Society[59] (Fig. 10.9). This had a floor made of boards alternately over and under the lower sills, with an overlap, to prevent radiation to or from the ground. It was to be painted with two coats of white lead, and one of zinc white enamel. The tendency has been to make such screens larger, as room for a thermograph and a hygrograph is frequently required. It has also been found more economical to unite each pair of louvers into an L-section machined out of a single stick of wood.

Although such louvers make it impossible for radiation to get into or out of the screen without encountering solid matter, this advantage is undoubtedly purchased at the cost of reducing the flow of air past the thermometers, which has appeared to some people as an insuperable disadvantage, especially in hot climates. I shall return to this later, but now I must refer briefly to the various attempts made, particularly in England, to assess the relative merit of screens and stands of different types.

[59] "Report of the Thermometer Screen Committee," *Quart. J. Roy. Meteorol. Soc.,* Vol. 10 (1884), pp. 92–94.

Fig. 10.9 Stevenson screen, Royal Meteorological Society's pattern.

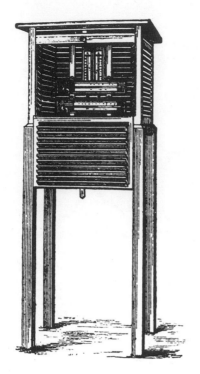 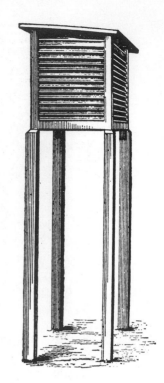

The difficulty in comparing exposures is to decide which of them, if any, gives "the true temperature of the air." One popular approach was based on the assumption that the net effect of radiation will be to increase the reading of the thermometer in the daytime, and to reduce it at night. Thus, the argument runs, the best exposure will be the one giving the lowest maximum temperatures, especially in summer, and the highest minimum temperatures, especially on clear nights. This is valid, with one caveat: it must be demonstrated that the surroundings so carefully provided for the thermometer do not retain some air around it with a temperature different from that of the air outside at the same height above the ground. This height should presumably be standardized, and this seems to have been recognized in England from the first, though not always elsewhere.

The elaborate series of investigations conducted by Frederic Gaster at Strathfield Turgiss in 1869, but not published till a decade later,[60] is in a class by itself.[61] All the stands and screens

[60] *Great Britain, Meteorological Office, Quarterly Weather Report for 1879,* Appendix II, pp. [13]–[39].

[61] Some others: J. J. Plummer, *Quart. J. Meteorol. Soc.,* Vol. 1 (1872), pp. 241–46 (Discussion, p. 264); F. W. Stow, *ibid.,* Vol. 1 (1872), pp. 146–54; *ibid.,* Vol. 2 (1873), pp. 49–52; David Gill (at the Cape of Good Hope), *ibid.,* Vol. 8 (1882), pp. 238–43.

I have mentioned so far—except the Montsouris stand and that of Harris—and also several other patterns, were carefully compared. The results may be summarized by the statement that the closed screens were found to be preferable to the open stands, such as the Greenwich stand, on the criteria discussed above. The large double Kew screen seemed marginally better than the Stevenson; but the latter came out well enough to ensure its general acceptance in the British Isles from that day to this.

4. The Sling Thermometer. On the Continent, however, the Stevenson screen had to wait a long time for acceptance, and in the nineteenth century other exposures, such as the Montsouris stand already described, were in vogue. In France, particularly, a completely different approach to the measurement of the temperature of the air had powerful support; this depended not so much on reducing radiation as on increasing convection. I refer to the *thermomètre fronde,* or sling thermometer, an instrument now little used for the measurement of temperature alone, but familiar in its duplex form as the sling psychrometer, for the measurement of humidity.

As far as I know, the first to describe the whirling of a thermometer on the end of a string to ventilate it was H. B. de Saussure,[62] in 1788; but his thermometer had its bulb covered with a wet sponge, for he was studying the cold produced by evaporation. He bequeathed his successors one lesson: after losing a thermometer by the fraying of the string, he used a swivel.

For measuring temperature the sling thermometer was apparently used to some extent in France in the 1840's, for in 1848 we find J. Haeghens mentioning it, though without enthusiasm, in an official handbook.[63] I should like to digress long enough to commend Haeghens' realistic view of the necessary accuracy of meteorological thermometry, in view of the rapid fluctuations of temperature in the open air. Meteorologists are advised "to consider as exact, observations made to the nearest *two or three* tenths of a degree [centigrade]."[64] He was half a century ahead of his time; in 1879 we have J. Pernet demanding that ther-

---

62 De Saussure, *Voyages dans les Alpes,* ¶ 2064.

63 Haeghens, "Instructions sur la construction, la vérification et l'observation des thermomètres," *Annuaire météorol. de la France pour 1849* [etc.] (Paris, 1848), pp. 175–204.

64 *Ibid.,* p. 198. The italics are from the original.

b ··· a

c
e
d ··
d
f
g   k
h i

Fig. 10.10   Sling psychrometer, 1896.

mometers for first-class stations should be calibrated to ±0.01°C.,[65] while Cleveland Abbe spent thirty-six pages of his great treatise[66] on the corrections to the mercury thermometer.

The sling thermometer was strongly advocated by the well-known astronomer Auguste Bravais in 1853.[67] Bravais had made many comparisons, both on land and at sea, between the readings of a thermometer hung in the shade and those of the same thermometer whirled round. He recommended a relative air speed of 8 or 9 m. per second, the process being continued until successive readings show no difference. "This definitive reading was considered as representing the true temperature of the air."[68] To make sure that the centrifugal force had no effect on the thermometer he provided a whirling machine and made observations in a cellar, the temperature of which was very nearly constant. His results showed that neither the centrifugal force nor the friction of the air were important at a speed of 10 m. per second. In the open air he found that the sling thermometer gave lower temperatures by day and higher by night, than a fixed one.

Two years later the meteorologist Émilien Renou suggested a superior sort of sling thermometer in which the thermometer is surrounded by three tin cylinders 12, 8, and 5 cm. in diameter and 30 to 40 cm. long, terminating in elbows facing in opposite directions.[69] This was to keep radiation from the thermometer, the bulb of which was at the center of the screen. It all sounds rather heroic, and a decade later he was back to the simple sling thermometer, making careful comparative observations in the sun and in the shade of a large tree trunk.[70] The mean monthly differences varied from 0.06°C. at 7 A.M. in winter to 0.86°C. (mean of seven observations) at midday in July, and Renou thought that the smallness of these differences showed that the sling thermometer *in the shade* must give a reading very close to the temperature of the air. It would not do to whirl it in the sun, as Heinrich Wild found in 1879.[71] John Aitken also came to this conclusion,[72] but Richard Assmann,[73] in the same year,

[65] Pernet, *Zeits. österr. Ges. Meteorol.*, Vol. 14 (1879), p. 137.

[66] Abbe, "Treatise on meteorological apparatus and methods." U.S. War Dept., *Annual Report of the Chief Signal Officer . . . for 1887*, Appendix 46 (Washington, 1888), pp. 41–77.

[67] Bravais, *Annuaire Soc. météorol. France*, Vol. 1 (1853), pp. 127–35. See also *Compt. Rend.*, Vol. 38 (1854), pp. 1077–78.

[68] Bravais (1853), p. 128.

[69] Renou, *Compt. Rend.*, Vol. 40 (1855), pp. 1083–85.

[70] Renou, *Annuaire Soc. météorol. France*, Vol. 12 (1864), pp. 237–39.

[71] Wild, *Repert. für Meteorol.*, Vol. 6 (1879), No. 9, p. 14.

[72] Aitken, *Trans. Roy. Soc. Edinb.*, Vol. 12 (1884), p. 677.

[73] Assmann, *Zeits. österr. Ges. Meteorol.*, Vol. 19 (1884), pp. 154–62.

thought extremely highly of the sling thermometer, even in the sun. As we shall see, he modified his ideas later.

Thermometers slung on a string are vulnerable to the slightest carelessness, and the string or chain came to be replaced by a frame and a handle. The frame always held two thermometers—one with a wet bulb—and some attempt was made at radiation shielding, as in the fairly early example shown in Fig. 10.10.[74] The radius from the axis of rotation to the thermometer bulbs was much reduced by this construction, and more revolutions per minute were necessary.

In the following year B. Sresnewsky reported on a sling thermometer in which the bulb is between two rather flat cones of nickel-plated and polished metal, arranged so that when it is swung, the cones go through the air edgewise.[75]

5. *More Screens.* In 1860 air temperatures were often measured with unprotected thermometers hung outside north windows, even at some official meteorological stations. Heinrich Wild, a supremely energetic young man who had just become Director of the Berne Observatory, knew that this was totally inadequate, and in 1860 devised a sheet metal screen for such locations.[76] This is shown in Fig. 10.11, and consisted of segments of two cylinders in sheet zinc, 30 cm. and 34 cm. in diameter, respectively, with a conical roof separated from the outer cylinder by a space 2 cm. wide. A door was provided on one side so that the thermometers could be read, and the whole thing was hung on a hinged bracket, so that it could be well away from the wall most of the time, but be swung in front of the window for observations. It was to be installed on a north wall at least 3 m. above the ground. This screen was adopted throughout Switzerland and Bavaria.[77]

In 1868 Wild became Director of the Central Physical Observatory at St. Petersburg, and thus of the huge Russian weather service which he developed with indefatigable zeal. In 1869 he designed a louvered screen of zinc (Fig. 10.12) to be put outside a north window. The bottom of this was wire netting.

A free-standing screen was felt to be desirable, and about 1870 he produced an enormous one, 1.5 m. square, with the bottom 3 m. up, as he had convinced himself that "thermometers that

[74] Schubert, *Zeits. für Instrum.*, Vol. 16 (1896), pp. 329–31.
[75] Sresnewsky, *Zeits. für Instrum.*, Vol. 17 (1897), pp. 114–15.
[76] Wild, *Mittheilungen naturf. Ges. in Bern*, (1860), pp. 91–119.
[77] Wild, *Repert. für Meteorol.*, Vol. 6 (1879), No. 9, p. 4.

Fig. 10.11   Wild's screen of 1860.

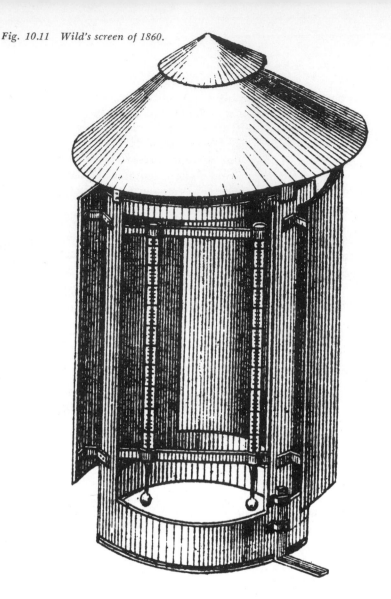

are to serve to determine the true air temperature should not be placed less than 2 meters above the ground."[78] This screen (Fig. 10.13) was to contain his cylindrical zinc one, and its north side and its bottom were entirely open. The south side had a double wall of close boards, and the observer climbed up into the screen on a ladder to make the readings. This arrangement became standard at the more important Russian stations. Just how large it was is shown in Fig. 10.14, which shows a Stevenson screen beside it.[79]

[78] Wild, *Zeits. österr. Ges. Meteorol.,* Vol. 11 (1876), p. 207.
[79] *M. O. Quarterly Weather Report for 1880,* Appendix, p. [16]. The drawing obviously does not agree with Wild's, but the dimensions are about right.

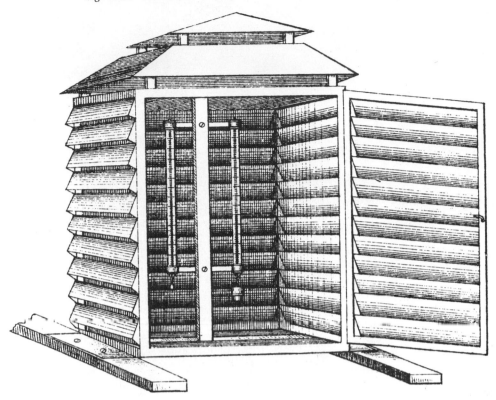

Fig. 10.12   Wild's screen of 1869.

Wild then improved his sheet-zinc shelter (*Blechgehaus*) for use either at a window or in his big screen.[80] Our Fig. 10.15 shows how its two coaxial segmental cylinders could be over-lapped, or lined up for observation and brought in front of the window, without opening the latter. For experimental purposes one of two such shelters was provided with a hand-operated fan, the other not. The differences were negligible, and Wild came to the unshakeable conclusion that the screen used at St. Petersburg would get the true air temperature to ±0.05°C.

This obviously assumes without proof that the air in the big screen is at the same temperature as that outside it. Henry A. Hazen of the U.S. Signal Service did not believe that it was, and in the course of a long paper entitled "Thermometer exposure,"[81] claimed that unless it is artificially ventilated, "the Wild 'shelter' will tend to assume the temperature of a black bulb thermometer."[82] This led to a violent controversy between Wild

[80] *Zeits. österr. Ges. Meteorol.*, Vol. 11 (1876), pp. 25–27. (Abstracted from *Jahresber. des phys. Central Obs. zu St. Petersburg für 1873/74.*)
[81] Hazen, *Professional Papers of the Signal Service*, no. 18 (Washington, 1885).
[82] *Ibid.*, p. 26.

Fig. 10.13   Wild's screen of 1870.

Fig. 10.14   Wild's screen and the Stevenson screen.

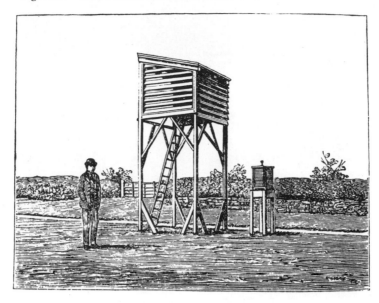

and Hazen in which neither was very logical, Wild's experiments to confute Hazen apparently losing sight of the vertical lapse-rate of temperature near the ground, as the great climatologist W. Köppen pointed out in a critical review[83] of a paper by Wild.[84] I shall not go into details about this very acrimonious argument, which was carried on in the *Zeitschrift der österreichischen Gesellschaft für Meteorologie* and the *Meteorologische Zeitschrift* in 1885 and 1886, as well as in Wild's own *Repertorium*. A contributing factor in the controversy was certainly the very different latitudes of Washington and St. Petersburg.

Hazen's experiments led to the design of the Signal Service "thermometer shelter," which became the basis of the one long used by the United States Weather Bureau. It was 3½ feet long, 3 feet wide, and 3 feet high, with single louvers on all sides, the bottom solid pine, and the roof double, solid, and sloping, with 6 inches between the two boards. Hazen held, probably with reason, that the Stevenson screen was much too small. He also believed in exposures on roofs, in the interests of better ventilation, and set a pattern which resulted in meteorological stations in the United States being different from all others for many years.

The controversy between Wild and Hazen may have inspired Köppen to write an excellent 54-page paper on the subject, based on experiments and observations in the German Coast-

83 Köppen, *Meteorol. Zeits.,* Vol. 3 (1886), pp. 375–77.
84 Wild, *Repert. für Meteorol.,* Vol. 10 (1885), No. 4.

231

Fig. 10.15   Wild's screen of 1874.

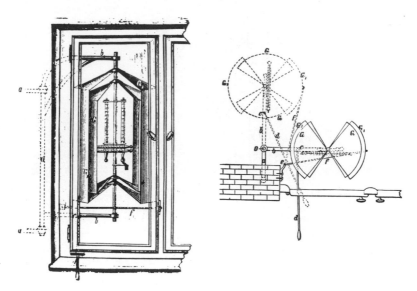

guard (Deutsche Seewarte),[85] filtered through his systematic mind. His worry about screens of all sorts is less that they radiate to the thermometer than that they change the temperature of the air passing through them; and for this and other reasons he does not think that free-standing screens are to be unconditionally preferred to north-wall exposures, and he seems inclined to favor the arrangement shown in our Fig. 10.15.

While this had been going on, the Scottish natural philosopher John Aitken, famous for his work on the nuclei of condensation in the atmosphere, had been thinking with his habitual independence about the exposure of thermometers. In his first paper on the subject[86] he pointed out the unsuitability of the Stevenson screen for warm climates, and designed various screens, of which Fig. 10.16 is one, incorporating a chimney to produce a draft. This was intended for a maximum thermometer; for a minimum thermometer it would be inverted, the draught-tube underneath, so that the air would not be cooled by nocturnal radiation before it passed the thermometer. Nobody seems to have paid much attention to screens of this kind, possibly because minimum and maximum thermometers are generally horizontal.[87] Aitken did say that ventilation with a suction fan is better than any other method, and we shall deal with this later.

[85] W. Köppen, "Studien über die Bestimmung der Lufttemperatur und des Luftdrucks," *Aus dem Archiv der deutschen Seewarte,* Vol. 10 (1887), no. 2.
[86] Aitken, *Proc. Roy. Soc. Edinb.,* Vol. 12 (1883–84), pp. 661–76.
[87] In 1929 the firm of Fuess patented (D.R.P. 572,451, Jan. 25) this use of a chimney, with a cowl, rotated by the wind, at the top.

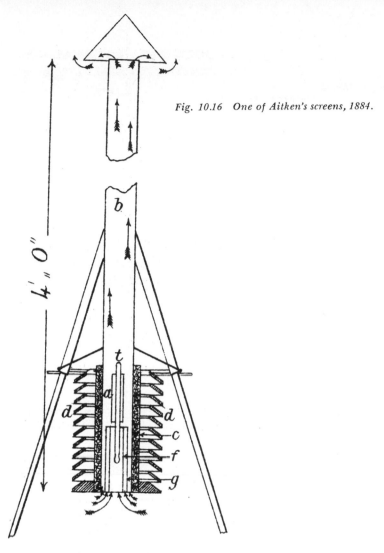

Fig. 10.16   One of Aitken's screens, 1884.

4' 0"

He returned to the subject at the very end of his life,[88] noting
that nothing had been done about the screens in use all over
the country. He believed that the major defect of the Stevenson
screen is its great thermal inertia, as he called it, and designed
several simple screens (Fig. 10.17) in which the thermal inertia
was much lower. In these the upper board was 48 cm. in diameter, the next one 36 cm., and the small boards in the second
and third designs 11.6 cm. in diameter. The small boards, as the
figure shows, greatly reduce the solid angle visible from the bulb
of the thermometer. From August 17 until November 8, 1921—
six days before Aitken's death—the maximum temperatures were
nearly always higher in the Stevenson screen, the greatest difference, on a calm October day, being 4.6°F.

[88] Aitken, *Proc. Roy. Soc. Edinb.*, Vol. 40 (1921), pp. 172–81 (*Collected
Works* [Cambridge, 1923], pp. 580–88). This paper was posthumous.

233

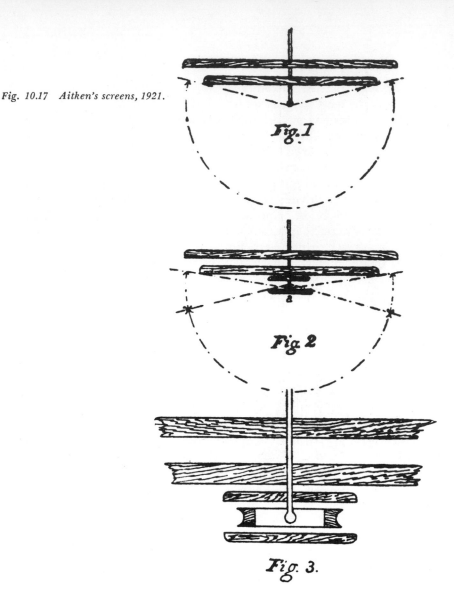

Fig. 10.17   Aitken's screens, 1921.

This paper seems to have attracted no more attention than his earlier ones, and the louvered screens continued in use almost everywhere.

6. *The Aspirated Thermometer.* As I said at the beginning of this chapter, there are two approaches to the perfect exposure: to ensure that the surroundings of the thermometer are at air temperature, and to increase the transfer of heat by convection. Drawing a current of air through a tube surrounding the bulb of the thermometer attacks the problem in both ways at once. Its role in increasing convective transfer is obvious, but with careful design it may

also ensure that the surroundings of the thermometer are very nearly at the temperature that it is desired to measure.

While it was not an aspirated thermometer, an idea of Honoré Flaugergues' should be mentioned in this connection.[89] Not believing that Fourier's technique[90] will work because of the uncertainty of the constant factor, he simply surrounds his thermometer with a shiny tube 2½ inches in diameter and 8 inches long, open at both ends. The tube is made to have a very small capacity for heat by being rolled up from a sandwich of two pieces of silvered paper, stuck together after coating the back with lampblack, which he believed to be an insulator. He laid stress on the small heat capacity of such a tube as well as its power of stopping radiation.

François Arago recommended "several" vertical polished concentric tin tubes surrounding a thermometer for balloon ascents.[91] This would be aspirated while the balloon was in vertical movement, but John Welsh of Kew Observatory decided that this was not enough, and on four balloon flights in 1859 drew air up past the bulb of a dry thermometer and then down past that of a wet one, each in a silvered tube 0.4 inch in diameter protected by an external silvered conical frustum.[92] The suction was provided nearly continuously by a long "concertina" bellows pulled open gradually by a weight, and an air speed of 12 to 14 feet per second was maintained past the bulbs. This technique seems justified by many comparisons with another pair of thermometers protected by double conical shields but without aspiration, differences of 2° or 3°F. being common, especially at the greater heights.

John Aitken made some remarkable experiments with an aspirated thermometer, coming early to the conclusion that ventilation by a suction fan was better than any other method, even the sling thermometer,[93] and much better than the Stevenson screen in calm, sunny weather.[94] Two years later he experimented with coaxial screens of muslin or wire cloth between the thermometer and the metal duct; and he even built an apparatus for raising the temperature of the wall of the duct to 100°C. to demonstrate the almost complete success of this scheme.[95]

[89] Flaugergues, *Correspondance Astronomique*, Vol. 2 (1819), pp. 434–35.
[90] See p. 212 above.
[91] Arago, *Oeuvres* (16 vols.; Paris, 1854–57), Vol. XI, pp. 600–1.
[92] Welsh, *Phil. Trans.*, Vol. 143 (1853), pp. 311–46.
[93] Aitken, *Proc. Roy. Soc. Edinb.*, Vol. 12 (1883–84), p. 667.
[94] *Ibid.*, p. 681.
[95] Aitken, *Proc. Roy. Soc. Edinb.*, Vol. 13 (1886), pp. 632–42.

A year later Richard Assmann reported on his first experiments with aspirated thermometers.[96] He provided the bulbs of two thermometers (constituting a psychrometer) with separate ducts of nickel-plated brass, through which air was drawn by a specially-constructed bellows that moved 600 cm.[3] of air in 4 seconds, giving an air-speed of 1.2 m. per second past the bulbs. He carefully measured the fall of pressure in the ducts to be sure that the adiabatic fall in temperature would be negligible. Experimenting with this in full September sunshine, he could detect no effect of the radiation.

Heinrich Wild, whose big screen the younger man had dared to criticize, constructed what he believed to be a replica of Assmann's apparatus and made experiments,[97] getting enormous differences in radiation weather, often several degrees centigrade, the aspiration thermometer being too high. Wild concluded that "the true temperature of the air in full sunshine cannot be obtained in this way, for *the principle of Mr. Assmann's method is contrary to experience.*"[98]

It is impossible to believe that Wild conducted his experiments with complete openness of mind, apart from the fundamental point that the thermometer in the screen was much farther from the ground (about 3.7 m.) than the aspirated one (1.5 m.), a factor of which Wild seems to have taken little notice. Assmann, who felt that he had been treated very unjustly, pointed out many of the defects of Wild's experiments in the tremendously thorough paper in which he described his final instrument and the experiments that led up to it.[99] Perhaps we may be grateful to Wild for goading Assmann into developing his very elegant and useful instrument (Fig. 10.18).[100]

It is unnecessary to insist on the details, which will be clear enough. The important features are: the provision of a double radiation shield, the inner plated tube *b* thermally insulated from the outer one *c* by an ebonite ring *d*, and the possibility of continuous ventilation for several minutes by a clockwork fan. An essential point is that the air is drawn between the concentric tubes, as well as through the inner one. The purpose of the accessories should perhaps be mentioned. The shield *k* clips

[96] Assmann, *Sitzungsber. preuss. Akad. Wiss., Berlin* (1887), pp. 935–45.

[97] Wild, *Repert. für Meteorol.*, Vol. 12 (1889), no. 11.

[98] *Ibid.*, p. 18. The italics are after Wild.

[99] Richard Assmann, "Das Aspirations-Psychrometer. Ein Apparat zur Bestimmung der wahren Temperatur und Feuchtigkeit der Luft," *Abh. des K. preuss. Meteorol. Insts.*, Vol. 1 (1892), pp. 115–270.

[100] Also described by Assmann in *Zeits. für Instrum.*, Vol. 12 (1892), pp. 1–12.

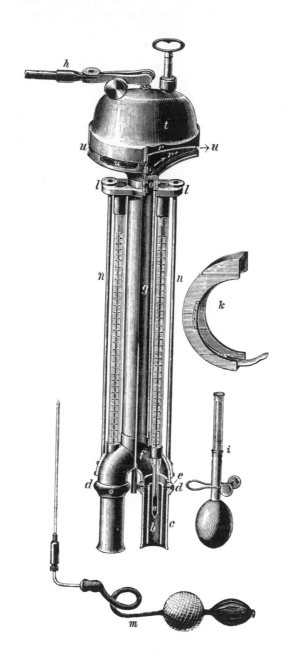

Fig. 10.18 *The Assmann psychrometer, 1892.*

round the fan at u and shields half the exit port from the wind. The syringe i is for moistening the wet bulb. Finally the injector m is to be inserted into the central duct g and worked as an emergency measure if the clockwork motor should fail; or alternatively it could supplement the fan to produce a more rapid ventilation.

Assmann's aspirated psychrometer came to be considered as a standard instrument, especially for calibrating other hygrometers in the measurement of the water vapor in the air. Various manufacturers have made modifications in detail, such as the provision of a smaller version. I remember climbing the shrouds of a ship in Arctic waters in the summer of 1933 with such an instrument, trying to relate the gradient of temperature above the calm sea to the complicated and beautiful mirage phenomena that were visible in every direction.

Index

Berthold, M., 181
Berthoud, Ferdinand (1727–1807), 137–38
Bessel, Friedrich Wilhelm (1784–1846), 129
Biancani, Giuseppe (1566–1624), 20
—*Sphaera mundi,* 10
Bianchi, Giovanni, 95
Bianchy, Jacob, 116, 139
Bianchy, R., 116n
Bianchy & Co., 116n, 139
Bibliothèque Universelle, 144
Bimetal: 169–70; theory of, 172
Bimetallic thermograph, 196–99
Bimetallic thermometer, 169–74
Bird, John (*ca.* 1709–76), 119n, 124, 127
Birembaut, Arthur, 121
Black, Joseph (1728–99), 123
Black-bulb thermometer: 162–64; Hicks, 163; Negretti & Zambra, 163; vacuum, 163
Blagden, Charles (1748–1820), 123
Blancanus. *See* Biancani
Bodeur, 136
Boerhaave, Herman (1668–1738), 71, 76
Boffito, Giuseppe, 30
Boiling point: constancy of, 82, 83–84; at Royal Society, 127
Boissier de la Croix de Sauvages, François (1706–76): 86; and Linnaeus, 100
Borde, 101
Borelli, Gianalfonso (1608–79), 32
Bossier, Joseph Louis: 104, 129; reform of thermometer, 120
Boulliau, Ismael (1605–94): 35–36, 209; first observations in Paris, 37
Bourdon thermometer, 174–75
Bourdon tube, 201
Boyle, Robert (1627–91): 38, 46, 47; makes thermometers in England, 38–39
—*New Experiments and Observations Touching Cold,* 38, 41
Boyle's law, 105
Bracknell, Meteorological Office, 135, 172
Braun, Joseph Adam (1712–68): 111; froze mercury, 121–22
Bravais, Auguste (1811–63), 226
Breguet, Abraham Louis (1747–1823): dilatation of metals, 171; trimetallic thermometer, 171
Breguet, firm of, 197
Breguet, François J., 171, 197n
Brisson, Mathurin Jacques (1723–1806): 117, 119, 174; deformation thermometer, 169
British Association, 146, 155, 159
Brouncker, Lord (1620–84), 42
Bulb, thermometer: expansion of, 36; shapes of, 137
Burattini, Tito Livio (d. 1682), 38

Bureau International des Poids et Mesures, 109, 131n, 147

C

Calender, 17
Calibration of thermometer, 127–30
Calland, 196
Callendar, Hugh Longbourne (1863–1930): thermodynamic scale, 113n; resistance thermometer, 179
Callendar recorder, 204
Cambridge thread recorder, 204
Cappy, 119
Carnot, Sadi (1796–1832), 113–14
Casati, Pierre, 104
Casbois, Nicholas, 143
Casella, Louis, 155, 159
Casella, Louis Marino, 159n
Casella, Louis P., 162
Casella & Co.: 136; porcelain support, 135
Cassini, Jacques Dominic (1748–1845): Observatory cellars, 119; on changes in zero, 142
Castelli, Benedetto (1577–1644), 6, 8, 22
Caus, Salomon de: 22; air thermometer, 18–19
Cavendish, Charles, 150–52
Cavendish, Henry (1731–1810): and freezing of mercury, 123; calibration of thermometers, 127–28; stem correction, 131; dial thermometer, 138–39; on exposure of thermometers, 210–11
Cecchi, Filipo, 169
Celsius, Anders (1701–44): 65, 78, 91, 104, 105; centigrade scale, 95–98, 101; calibration procedure, 97; thermometer replaced by Strömer's, 98; dies, 101
Centigrade scale: 89–105; adopted in France, 121
Cesarini, Ferdinando (1595–1624), 6, 8
Chaldecott, J. A., 11, 12, 171n
Chamaraud, Marcel, 101n, 103n
Chappuis, P.: 126; steam point apparatus, 129n
Charles, Jacques André César (1746–1823): 86, 108, 171; inventory, 132n
Charles II, King of England (1630–85), 42
Charles's law, 108
Chilton, D., 18n
Christin, Jean Pierre (1683–1755): 91, 109, 121; and centigrade scale, 101–5; favors mercury, 102
Clifford, G., 99
Cohen, Ernst, 71
Cohen, I. Bernard, 73
Collen, Henry, 193
Collingbourne, R. J., 194n
Compass, use of, 9, 10

L

La Condamine. *See* De la Condamine

La Hire. *See* De la Hire

La Lande, J. J. le François de (1732–1807), 116n

Lallemand, A., 156

Lambert, Johann Heinrich (1728–77): 117, 123n, 124; nonlinear dilatation of spirit of wine, 86; air thermometer, 108, 126; discussed the air thermometer, 110; absolute zero, 111; criticized Deluc, 126; earth thermometer, 139; bimetal, 170

—*Pyrometrie*, 139

Lamont, Johann von (1805–79): 188, 192; thermograph, 192

Lana-Terzi, Francesco (1631–87), 56

Landriani, Marsiglio, 153–54

Lapland, expedition to, 85

La Rive. *See* Delarive

Lavoisier, Antoine Laurant de (1743–94): 124, 133; compared thermometers, 119; thermometers of, 119

Lawson, Henry (1774–1855), 217

Leach, G., 136

Leeds, Morris E., 181n

Lefroy, John Henry (1817–1900), 220

Legrand, J. N., 145

Leibnitz, Gottfried Wilhelm (1646–1716), 149

Leiden, History of Science Museum, 78, 132

Leopold, Prince of Tuscany, 28, 38

Leroy, Charles (1726–79), 120, 174

Le Sage, George Louis the younger (1724–1803), 125

Leslie, John (1766–1832), 140n, 163

Lessieur, 197n

Leupold, Jacob (1674–1727): thermograph, 184

—*Theatrum machinarum*, 184

Leurechon, Jean (1591–1670): *Récréation mathématique*, 20

Leyst, Ernst, 131

Libri, G. (1803–69): on Telioux, 12; Florentine thermometers, 34

Liljequist, G. H., 78n, 96n

Linnaeus (1707–78): 91, 105; and centigrade scale, 98–101

—*Hortus Cliffortianus*, 99, 101

Linné, Carl von. *See* Linnaeus

Linseed oil, 57

Liquid-in-glass thermometer: invention of, 27–39

Locke, John (1632–1704), 46

Lomonosov, M. W. (1711–65), 122

London, Great Exhibition of 1851, 157

—International Exhibition of 1862, 136, 157

—Meteorological Society, 155, 156

—Royal Institution, 139

—Science Museum: Guericke's thermometer, 23; "Thermomètre de Lyon," 105; tele-thermometer, 182; Kreil's barograph, 190n; photographic thermograph, 196; thermograph, 203; Lawson's stand, 217n; Stow's stand, 217n

Löser, Hans von (1704–63), 167

Louis XIV, King of France (1638–1715), 51

Louvered screens, 219–25, 227–34

Lyon: Académie des Sciences, Belles-Lettres et Arts, 101, 103; Observatory, 101

M

Mach, Ernst (1838–1916): 49, 109

—*Die Prinzipien der Wärmelehre*, 4n

Machin, John, 87n

McLeod, Herbert, 164

Macquer, Pierre Joseph (1718–84), 120

Macvicar, John G., 153

Maddison, F. R., 170n

Magalhaens. *See* Magellan

Magalotti, Lorenzo (1637–1712), 34

Magellan, Jean Hyacinthe de (1722–90): bimetal, 170; thermograph, 196

Maidens, A. L., 201n

Mairan, J. J. d'Ortous de (1678–1771), 84, 87, 108, 111

Mallock, A., 190

Manley, Gordon, 47

Mannheim, Meteorological Society of: 133; on exposure of thermometer, 210

Marcet, François (1803–83), 145

Marchis, L., 147

Mariani, 33n, 35

Marie-Davy, Edme Hippolyte (1820–93): 217, 219; thermograph, 202

Mariotte, Edme (*ca.* 1620–84), 51, 52

Mariotte's law, 105

Martin, George A., 213

Martine, George (1702–41): 59n, 97; criticized Réaumur, 115–16; favored mercury, 116, 124

Marvin, C. F. (1858–1943), 180–81

Maskelyne, Nevil (1732–1811), 127

Maupertuis, Pierre Louis Moreau de (1698–1759), 85n, 121

Maurer, J., 172

Maximum and minimum thermometer: 149–64; classification of, 149–50; Six's, 159–61, 162; Hicks's, 162

Maximum thermometer: 149–57; Rutherford's, 153, 162; Negretti & Zambra's,

W

Walferdin, François Hippolyte (1795–1880), 155
Waller, Richard, 32
Wallis, John (1616–1703), 209
Washington, D.C., Smithsonian Institution, 136
Water, minimum volume of, 36, 49
Watson, Richard (1737–1816), 162
"Weather clock," 41, 183, 188
Weather-glass, 17, 18, 19
Weidler, Johann Friedrich (1691–1755): 210, 213; exposure of thermometer, 209
Weights and Measures, Ninth general conference of, 91
Weitbrecht, Josias (1702–47): 115; ice point on Delisle's scale, 88; on calibration, 88
Welsh, John (1824–59): 155; aspirated thermometer, 235
Wentz, Ludwig (1695–1772), 129
Wheatstone, Charles (1802–75), 181 82
Wheatstone bridge, 181
Whipple, G. M. (1842–93), 146
Wild, Heinrich (1833–1902): sling thermometer, 226; thermometer screens, 227–31; controversy with Hazen, 229–32; shelter, 229; criticized Assmann, 236
Wildt, Johann Christian Daniel (1770–1844), 124
Window exposure, 210, 227

Winnerl, J. T., 172
Wolf, R., 172
Wolff, Christian von (1679–1754), 71, 74, 79
Wollaston, Francis Hyde (1762–1823), 129, 137n
Wollheim, Leonhard, 190–92
Wollny, Ewald, 141
Woodcroft, Bennet (1803–79), 5n
Wren, Christopher (1632–1723): 183; drum thermometer, 26; thermometers of, 41; meteorograph, 183; recording thermometer, 184; thermograph, 187
Wren, Christopher the younger (1695–1747); *Parentalia,* 41

Y

Younghusband, Lieutenant, 220

Z

Zambra, J. W., 161
Zeiher, Johann Ernst (1720–84): 122; deformation thermometer, 167
Zeitschrift der österreichischen Gesellschaft für Meteorologie, 231
Zero: absolute, 109–12; changes of, 142–47; temporary depression of, 142, 143
Zimmer, J. G., 167
Zink, 143

A History of the Thermometer and Its Use in Meteorology

by W. E. Knowles Middleton

designer: Gerard A. Valerio
typesetter: Monotype Composition Co.
typeface: Baskerville
printer: Universal Lithographers
paper: 60 lb. P&S RR B-10
binder: Moore and Company
cover material: Interlaken AV3-485 and Fabriano text